CLASSICAL ALGEBRA

FOURTH EDITION

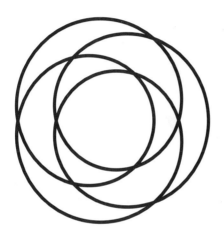

William J. Gilbert
Scott A. Vanstone

University of Waterloo

Centre for Education in Mathematics and Computing

First Edition . . . . August 1975
Second Edition . . . . June 1988
Third Edition . . . . July 1993
Fourth Edition . . . . June 2000

Published by the
Centre for Education in Mathematics and Computing
University of Waterloo
Waterloo, Ontario, Canada, N2L 3G1

Telephone: 519-885-1211, extension 3030
Fax: 519-746-6592

Canadian Cataloguing in Publication Data

Gilbert, William J., 1941–
Classical algebra

4th ed.
ISBN 0-921418-94-9

1. Algebra.   2. Algebra — Problems, exercises, etc.
I. Vanstone, S. A. (Scott Alexander), 1947–
II. University of Waterloo. Centre for Education in
Mathematics and Computing. III. Title.

QA154.2.G55 2000   512   C00-931679-5

Printed by Graphic Services, University of Waterloo
Cover by David Bartholomew

Preface

This book is designed for a first algebra course for university students who wish to major in mathematics or computer science. The idea behind this book is that all the useful topics in a College Algebra course will follow from the quest to solve polynomial equations over various number systems. This motivation to solve equations is precisely the same as that of most of the classical algebraists, and indeed, most of the material in the book was known prior to 1800. Besides giving the reader the techniques for solving polynomial equations and congruences, this book will prepare the student for more advanced courses in Linear and Modern Algebra, as well as the Calculus.

The book starts with the integers, and works its way up the number systems until the complex numbers and the solutions of complex polynomials is reached. We begin by attacking the solution of Diophantine equations, using greatest common divisors, as this topic gives the students something to get their teeth into that they have not tasted at high school. Diophantine equations naturally lead to congruences modulo an integer. We then discuss mathematical induction and give a brief chapter on rational and real numbers. Functions are introduced so we can talk about inverses. We then give a current application to cryptography; the RSA scheme for encrypting and decrypting messages relies on Classical Algebra, even though its use is so new that it was not discovered when the first edition of this book was written. This topic ties together many of the ideas from the initial chapters.

It is assumed that the reader has some knowledge of Trigonometry; a brief summary is provided in the Appendix. While a knowledge of Calculus is not necessary for this book, many students learn a little in high school, so we occasionally use the derivative of a polynomial to help us sketch a graph.

There are ample questions for the student to tackle at the end of each chapter. They are divided into two types; the Exercises are routine applications of the material in the chapter, while the Problems usually require more ingenuity, and range from easy to nearly impossible. Answers to the odd numbered questions are given at the back of the book.

Changes in the Fourth Edition

Chapter 0 on Logic and Proofs has been added, and Section 3.2 has been changed from the Well Ordering Property to Recursion. The definition of the GCD has been rewritten and it is now defined to be nonnegative. Various theorems and algorithms have been rewritten to make them clearer. We would especially like to thank Jim Geelen, Alfred Menezes, and Paul Schellenberg for their comments and suggestions on the revision.

Acknowledgments

We are grateful for all the assistance we received from our colleagues and students in the first year algebra course at the University of Waterloo, and especially from Edward Moskal, who edited an earlier set of notes for the course.

Finally we would like to thank Andrea Vanstone for typing the third edition, and Ruth Gilbert for typing the original edition. The book was typeset using LATEX with the Times Roman font, on a NeXT computer running OPENSTEP, and all the figures are in Encapsulated PostScript.

Contents

Introduction

The most basic problem in mathematics is the solution of equations. Attempts at solving various types, such as algebraic equations, differential equations and integral equations, lead to different branches of mathematics.

The endeavour to solve the general algebraic or polynomial equation lies at the heart of the branch of mathematics called Classical Algebra. Classical Algebra encompasses most of the algebra discovered before 1800. Around that time it was proved that a precise solution to the general polynomial equation was impossible, and this work lead to the development of what is known as Modern Algebra.

A polynomial equation in the variable x is an equation of the form

$$a_n x^n + a_{n-1} x^{n-1} + \cdots + a_1 x + a_0 = 0.$$

The numbers $a_n, a_{n-1}, \ldots, a_1, a_0$ are called the coefficients of the equation.

Mathematicians originally searched for an algorithm that would lead to all the numbers that would satisfy such an equation. It soon became clear that some of the number systems, such as the rational numbers, were not broad enough to always give a solution, and various number systems were developed to solve wider classes of polynomial equations.

In this book we initially consider equations with integer coefficients and integer solutions; these are called Diophantine equations. We then extend the integers to include the rational and real numbers. Our development of the number systems finally culminates in the complex number system. The Fundamental Theorem of Algebra states that every polynomial equation with complex coefficients has a solution in the complex numbers, though it gives no algorithm for finding such a solution. However we demonstrate many methods for solving particular equations in the various number systems. Those solutions that cannot be found precisely can always be approximated to any desired degree of accuracy.

Although most of the material in this book, except the cryptography, has been known since 1800, it is presented in a contemporary manner using the hindsight of two centuries of Modern Algebra.

Chapter 0

Logic and Proofs

Mathematics makes precise use of language in stating and proving its results. We use the English language to express our ideas and arguments, though we give some common English words a more precise meaning so as to make them unambiguous. Good mathematical writing consists of complete sentences, allowing for the fact that symbols stand for words. For example, '$A = B$.' is a sentence in which the subject is 'A', the verb is 'equals' and the object is 'B'.

In mathematics, we tend to use more complicated and compound expressions than we do in everyday language, so this chapter explains some methods for dealing with these expressions. We also introduce the more common types of mathematical reasoning we use in proofs.

0.1 PROPOSITIONAL LOGIC

Logic is the study of correct reasoning. The rules of logic give precise meaning to mathematical statements, and allow us to make correct arguments about these statements.

0.1.1 Definition.   In mathematics, a *statement*, or *proposition*, is a sentence which is either TRUE or FALSE.

For example,

- The year 2000 is a leap year.
- $3 + 2 = 6$.
- $\pi^2 < 10$.
- The decimal expansion of π contains one hundred consecutive 3's.

are statements, since they are sentences which are either TRUE or FALSE, though you most probably do not know the truth value of the last statement.

However the following sentences are not statements.

- Let $x = 4$.

- Find the nearest integer to $\sqrt{5}^{13}$.

- Is it Friday today?

Questions are never statements. If we changed the last sentence to "It is Friday today." it would be a statement.

Propositional logic is that part of logic that deals with combining statements using connectives such as AND, OR, NOT, or implies. We use these connectives in everyday English, but in mathematics and computer science we tend to use them in more complex combinations. We (and the computers) need to know precisely what these combinations mean. For example, the Principle of Mathematical Induction says that: If $P(1)$ is true and $P(k + 1)$ is true whenever $P(k)$ is true, then $P(n)$ is true for all positive integers n.

We can always combine any two statements using AND to form a third statement. For example

- Ottawa is the capital of Canada and New York is the capital of the United States.

If P denotes the statement 'Ottawa is the capital of Canada.' and Q denotes the statement 'New York is the capital of the United States.' then the above statement will be denoted by P AND Q.

0.1.2 Definition. P AND Q is called the *conjunction* of P and Q. The statement P AND Q will be TRUE if P is TRUE and Q is TRUE, but will be FALSE otherwise.

P OR Q is called the *disjunction* of P and Q. The statement P OR Q will be TRUE if either P is TRUE or Q is TRUE, or both are TRUE.

We can define these relationships in the following *truth tables*, in which T stands for TRUE and F stands for FALSE.

P	Q	P AND Q
T	T	T
T	F	F
F	T	F
F	F	F

P	Q	P OR Q
T	T	T
T	F	T
F	T	T
F	F	F

In everyday English, the word 'or' can be used in two different ways. Consider the meaning of 'or' in the following two sentences.

- The prerequisite for this course is algebra or trigonometry.

- You will be served tea or coffee.

Mathematics always uses the 'inclusive OR' which means that P OR Q is true even if both P and Q are true. This is the use of 'or' in the first sentence; you can still take the course if you have both algebra and trigonometry. However in the second sentence, 'or' is used in an exclusive way; you should not expect tea *and* coffee.

Every statement has a negation. For example, if P is the statement '$3 + 2 = 6$.' then its negation is 'It is not true that $3 + 2 = 6$.' or more simply '$3 + 2 \neq 6$.' In mathematics, we are always using conditional statements such as 'If $x > 2$ then $x^2 > 4$.' or biconditional statements such as '$xy = 0$ if and only if $x = 0$ or $y = 0$.'

0.1.3 Definition.

P	NOT P
T	F
F	T

P	Q	$P \Longrightarrow Q$
T	T	T
T	F	F
F	T	T
F	F	T

P	Q	$P \Longleftrightarrow Q$
T	T	T
T	F	F
F	T	F
F	F	T

The *negation* of the statement P is denoted by NOT P.

If P and Q are two statements, the *conditional statement* 'If P then Q' is denoted by $P \Longrightarrow Q$ and is defined by the truth table above. The following are alternative ways of expressing this conditional statement.

- $P \Longrightarrow Q$.
- If P then Q.
- If P, Q.
- Q if P.
- P only if Q.
- P is sufficient for Q.
- Q is necessary for P.

The *biconditional statement* 'P if and only if Q' is denoted by $P \Longleftrightarrow Q$. The expression "if and only if" is used so often in mathematics that it is often abbreviated as "iff". If $P \Longleftrightarrow Q$ is TRUE, then P and Q have the same truth values and we say that P and Q are *equivalent statements*.

The conditional is an extension of everyday English usage, but it has some unusual consequences because $P \Longrightarrow Q$ is always true, if P is false. For example, 'If $5 > 7$ then $2 + 2 = 3$.' is a true statement.

0.1.4 Example.
Show that the statement $P \Longleftrightarrow Q$ has the same truth table as the statement $(P \Longrightarrow Q)$ AND $(Q \Longrightarrow P)$.

This example shows that 'P if and only if Q' has the same meaning as the statement '(If P then Q) and (if Q then P).'

Solution.

P	Q	$P \implies Q$	$Q \implies P$	$(P \implies Q)$ AND $(Q \implies P)$	$P \iff Q$
T	T	T	T	T	T
T	F	F	T	F	F
F	T	T	F	F	F
F	F	T	T	T	T

The last two columns are the same, so the two statements have the same truth table.

□

The symbol □ denotes the end of a proof or solution.

0.1.5 Example.   Show that the statement NOT $(P$ AND $Q)$ has the same truth table as the statement (NOT P) OR (NOT Q).

Solution.

P	Q	P AND Q	NOT $(P$ AND $Q)$
T	T	T	F
T	F	F	T
F	T	F	T
F	F	F	T

P	Q	NOT P	NOT Q	(NOT P) OR (NOT Q)
T	T	F	F	F
T	F	F	T	T
F	T	T	F	T
F	F	T	T	T

The final two columns are the same, so the two statements have the same truth table.

□

0.1.6 Example.   Show that the statement $P \implies Q$ is equivalent to the statement Q OR NOT P.

Solution.

P	Q	$P \implies Q$	NOT P	Q OR NOT P
T	T	T	F	T
T	F	F	F	F
F	T	T	T	T
F	F	T	T	T

Since the statements $P \implies Q$ and Q OR NOT P have the same truth tables, they are equivalent.

□

Alternative Notations for Connectives		
Connective	Propositional Logic	C and Java syntax
AND	$\wedge$	&&
OR	$\vee$	||
NOT	$\neg$ or $\sim$	!
$\Longrightarrow$	$\longrightarrow$	
$\Longleftrightarrow$	$\longleftrightarrow$	

0.2 SETS

Mathematics not only deals with individual objects, such as the integer 2007 or the number $\sqrt{3}$, but also with collections of objects, such as all the real numbers, or all the solutions to an equation. In mathematics, such a collection is called a set.

A *set* is any well-defined collection of objects; the objects are called the *elements* of the set. If x is an element of the set S, we say x belongs to S and write

$$x \in S.$$

If y is not an element of S, we write $y \notin S$. The set of *real numbers* is denoted by the blackboard bold symbol $\mathbb{R}$, so '$\sqrt{3} \in \mathbb{R}$' is a true statement.

There are two basic ways of describing a set. One method is to list all its elements. For example, a set S whose elements are 2, 4, 6 and 8 can be written as

$$S = \{2, 4, 6, 8\}.$$

We might write the set of letters of the alphabet as $\{A, B, C, \ldots, X, Y, Z\}$, where the three dots indicate that all the letters between C and X are also to be included. By abusing this notation, we write the set of *positive integers* (or *natural numbers*) as

$$\mathbb{P} = \{1, 2, 3, 4, \ldots\}$$

and also the set of all *integers* as

$$\mathbb{Z} = \{\ldots, -2, -1, 0, 1, 2, 3, \ldots\}.$$

The set $\mathbb{Z}$ consists of the positive integers, zero and the negative integers.

The other basic method of describing a set is by means of a rule. For example,

$$S = \{x \mid x \in \mathbb{R} \text{ AND } 1 < x < 2\}$$

is read as "S is the set of all elements x, such that x is a real number and x is greater than 1 and less than 2"; in other words, S is the set of real numbers lying between 1 and 2.

The set with no elements is called the *empty set* or *null set* and is denoted by $\emptyset$.

If S and T are sets such that every element of S is also an element of T, then we say that S is *contained* in T, or that S is a *subset* of T and write $S \subseteq T$ or $T \supseteq S$. For example, $\{2, 7, 5\} \subseteq \mathbb{P}$ but $\{-1, 5, 8\}$ is not a subset of $\mathbb{P}$, because $-1 \notin \mathbb{P}$. Note that if S is any set then $S \subseteq S$ and also $\emptyset \subseteq S$.

The two sets S and T are *equal* if $S \subseteq T$ and $T \subseteq S$.

The *intersection* of two sets S and T is the set, $S \cap T$, of all elements that are in both S and T; hence

$$S \cap T \;=\; \{x \mid x \in S \text{ AND } x \in T\}.$$

If $S \cap T = \emptyset$, then S and T are said to be *disjoint*. The *union* of the sets S and T is the set, $S \cup T$, of all elements that are in either S or T (or both S and T). Hence

$$S \cup T \;=\; \{x \mid x \in S \text{ OR } x \in T\}.$$

The *Cartesian product* of two sets S and T is the set, $S \times T$, of all ordered pairs (x, y) where $x \in S$ and $y \in T$; hence

$$S \times T \;=\; \{(x, y) \mid x \in S \text{ AND } y \in T\}.$$

0.3   QUANTIFIERS

In mathematics we are always using sentences involving variables, such as '$x^2 > 0$.' However, until the value of x is specified, this sentence has no truth value. If we let $P(x)$ denote the sentence '$x^2 > 0$.' then $P(-3)$ is a true statement and $P(0)$ is a false statement.

If $P(x)$ is a sentence depending on the variable x, we often want to say that $P(x)$ is true for all values of x, or that it is true for at least one value of x. This can be done by adding quantifiers that convert the sentence $P(x)$ into a statement.

0.3.1 Definition.   The *universal quantification* of $P(x)$ is the statement

- $P(x)$ is true for all values of x.

and is denoted by

$$\forall x \quad P(x)$$

where the symbol $\forall$ is called the *universal quantifier.*

This statement $\forall x P(x)$ can also be expressed in any of the following ways.

- For all x, $P(x)$.
- For every x, $P(x)$.
- For each x, $P(x)$.

The values of x are assumed to lie in a particular set called the *universe of discourse*. For example, the universe of discourse may be the integers, or the real numbers, or the set of all people.

If we are dealing with the real numbers, the statement '$\forall x, x^2 > 0$.' means that 'For all real numbers x, $x^2 > 0$.' which is a false statement. However the statement '$\forall x, x^2 \geq 0$.' is true.

0.3.2 Definition. The *existential quantification* of $P(x)$ is the statement

- There exists an x for which $P(x)$ is true.

and is denoted by

$$\exists x \quad P(x)$$

where the symbol $\exists$ is called the *existential quantifier.*

Again this is interpreted to mean that 'There exists an x in the universe of discourse for which $P(x)$ is true.' This statement $\exists x P(x)$ could also be expressed in any of the following ways.

- There is an x for which $P(x)$.
- For some x, $P(x)$.

For example, if the universe of discourse is the set of real numbers, then the factorization $x^3 - 1 = (x - 1)(x^2 + x + 1)$ is true for all x. So

$$\forall x \quad x^3 - 1 \ = \ (x - 1)(x^2 + x + 1)$$

is a true statement. However the equation $x^2 + x - 6 = 0$ is true for only certain values of x, namely $x = 2$ and $x = -3$. So

$$\exists x \quad x^2 + x - 6 \ = \ 0$$

is a true statement.

0.3.3 Example. Express the statement 'Every real number has a real square root.' as a logical expression using quantifiers.

Solution. If we assume that the universe of discourse is the set of real numbers, we can express this statement as

$$\forall a \ \exists x \quad x^2 \ = \ a.$$

Note that this is just a statement. It does not have to be true; in fact it is not. $\square$

0.3.4 Example.   If A and B are sets, then $A \subseteq B$ means that A is a subset of B, and this can be defined using a quantifier as

$$\forall x \quad (x \in A \Longrightarrow x \in B).$$

If S is a set and $\emptyset$ denotes the empty set, show that $S \subseteq S$ and $\emptyset \subseteq S$.

Solution.   The statement $S \subseteq S$ is equivalent to $\forall x(x \in S \Longrightarrow x \in S)$. If $P(x)$ is the statement $x \in S$, then $P(x) \Longrightarrow P(x)$ is true for all x. Hence $S \subseteq S$ is true.

The statement $\emptyset \subseteq S$ is equivalent to $\forall x(x \in \emptyset \Longrightarrow x \in S)$. Now $x \in \emptyset$ is false for all x. However $P \Longrightarrow Q$ is always true if P is false, so that the statement $\emptyset \subseteq S$ is true. $\qquad\qquad\qquad\qquad\qquad\qquad\qquad\qquad\qquad\qquad\qquad\qquad\qquad\quad$ $\square$

0.3.5 Example.   In Definition 1.1.1 the *divisibility* relation $a|b$ is defined as

$$\exists q \quad b = qa$$

where the universe of discourse is the set of integers. Determine whether (i) $0|3$ and (ii) $0|0$.

Solution. (i). $0|3$ is equivalent to $\exists q \; 3 = q0$; that is, $\exists q \; 3 = 0$. Since $3 = 0$ is always false, $0|3$ is not true.

(ii). $0|0$ is equivalent to $\exists q \; 0 = q0$; that is, $\exists q \; 0 = 0$. Since $0 = 0$ is always true, we can choose q as any integer, and so $0|0$ is true. $\qquad\qquad\qquad\qquad\qquad\qquad\qquad\quad$ $\square$

How do we negate quantifiers? For example, the statement 'All Canadians speak French.' is not true. However we do not have to show that 'All Canadians do not speak French.' to show that the statement is false. We only have to show that 'There exists a Canadian who does not speak French.' Similarly, the statement 'There exists a real solution to the equation $x^2 = -1$.' is false. To show this, we have to show that 'For all real x, $x^2 \neq -1$.' We have the following rules for negating quantifiers.

0.3.6 Quantifier Negation Rules.

$$\text{NOT } (\forall x \quad P(x)) \quad \text{is equivalent to} \quad (\exists x \quad \text{NOT } P(x))$$
$$\text{NOT } (\exists x \quad P(x)) \quad \text{is equivalent to} \quad (\forall x \quad \text{NOT } P(x))$$

As an example of the first rule, "Not everyone has a calculator" has the same meaning as "Someone does not have a calculator." As an example of the second rule, "No one has a calculator" has the same meaning as "Everyone does not have a calculator."

In general, two statements involving quantifiers will be equivalent if they have the same meaning. We cannot always use truth tables to check for equivalence or implications involving quantifiers, so at this stage we have to reason informally to check the equivalence or implication.

0.3.7 Example. If the universe of discourse is the real numbers, what does the following statement mean in English? How would you prove it true or false?

$$\exists x \; \forall y \;\; (x \geq y).$$

Solution. The statement says that there is a real number x that is greater than or equal to all real numbers. That is, statement says that there is a largest real number.

This is false. To show that it is false, we have to prove that

$$\text{NOT} \; (\exists x \; \forall y \;\; (x \geq y))$$

is true. This is equivalent to the following statements.

$$\forall x \;\; \text{NOT} \; (\forall y \;\; (x \geq y)).$$
$$\forall x \; \exists y \;\;\; \text{NOT} \; (x \geq y).$$
$$\forall x \; \exists y \;\; (x < y).$$

This last statement is true because, for all x, we can take $y = x + 1$.

0.4 METHODS OF PROOF

Mathematicians use a variety of terms to label their results. We shall use the terms **Theorem**, **Proposition**, and **Lemma** in decreasing order of importance. These are all usually general statements that apply to a large number of cases; they will often be of the form $\forall x \; P(x) \implies Q(x)$. A Theorem will be a major landmark in the mathematical theory, a Proposition a lesser result, while a Lemma will usually be a result that is needed to prove a Theorem or Proposition, but is not very interesting on its own. A **Corollary** is a result that follows almost immediately from a Theorem. An **Example** is not usually a general result, but often a particular case of a Theorem or Proposition. An **Algorithm** is an explicit procedure for solving a problem in a finite number of steps.

There are many methods for proving Theorems, Propositions, and Lemmas, but there is no procedure that will apply to all proofs. It is extremely difficult to get a computer to write a good proof. Proof writing is an art that requires much practice. There is a delicate balance between writing down too many details, and leaving out logical steps that cannot easily be filled by the reader. However there are some standard strategies for attacking proofs, and we now introduce the most important of these. These methods of proof are not only important in mathematics, but also in computer science where, for example, they are used in software specification for verifying programs.

Many mathematical theorems can be expressed symbolically in the form $P \implies Q$. The statement P is called the *assumption* or *hypothesis* of the theorem and the statement Q is the *conclusion.* The assumption will consist of one or more statements, normally involving some variables. The theorem says that if the assumption is true, then the conclusion is true.

0.4.1 Direct Method of Proving $P \Longrightarrow Q$.

The direct method of proving $P \Longrightarrow Q$ is to assume that the hypothesis P is true, and use this to prove that the conclusion Q is true.

PROPOSITION. If $a > b$ and $c < 0$ then $ac < bc$.

Proof. If $a > b$ then $a - b > 0$. The positive number $a - b$ times the negative number c is negative so

$$(a - b)c \; < \; 0.$$

Hence $ac - bc < 0$ and $ac < bc$. $\qquad\qquad\qquad\qquad\qquad\qquad\square$

0.4.2 Proving $P \Longleftrightarrow Q$.

This type of result can usually be recognized by the phrase 'if and only if' or the phrase 'necessary and sufficient.' The result 'P if and only if Q' can be split up into the two cases, the 'only if' part $P \Longrightarrow Q$, and the 'if' part $Q \Longrightarrow P$, and then each case can be proved separately.

PROPOSITION. Let x be a real number. Then $x^2 + x < 0$ if and only if $-1 < x < 0$.

Proof. We first prove $x^2 + x < 0 \Longrightarrow -1 < x < 0$.
    We have

$$x(x + 1) \; < \; 0.$$

If the product of two numbers is negative then one number is positive and the other is negative. There are two cases to consider.
Case (i). If $x > 0$ and $x + 1 < 0$ then $x > 0$ and $x < -1$. This case is impossible.
Case (ii). If $x < 0$ and $x + 1 > 0$ then $x < 0$ and $x > -1$. Hence $-1 < x < 0$.
    We now prove $-1 < x < 0 \Longrightarrow x^2 + x < 0$.
    If $-1 < x < 0$ then $x + 1 > 0$. Since $x < 0$ and the product of a positive number and a negative number is negative, it follows that $x(x + 1) < 0$. That is, $x^2 + x < 0$. $\qquad\qquad\square$

0.4.3 Contrapositive Law. $P \implies Q$ is equivalent to NOT $Q \implies$ NOT P.

Proof.

P	Q	$P \implies Q$	NOT Q	NOT P	NOT $Q \implies$ NOT P
T	T	T	F	F	T
T	F	F	T	F	F
F	T	T	F	T	T
F	F	T	T	T	T

We see from the truth table that $P \implies Q$ is equivalent to NOT $Q \implies$ NOT P. ☐

For example, the contrapositive of the statement 'If it rained then I would be wet.' is the statement 'If I am not wet then it has not rained.' These statements mean the same thing.

0.4.4 Contrapositive Method of Proving $P \implies Q$.

This method uses the Contrapositive Law above. We assume that Q is false and use this to prove that P is false.

PROPOSITION. Let n be an integer. If n^3 is odd then n is odd.

Proof. Suppose that n is not odd; that is, suppose n is even. Then n^3 will also be even; that is n^3 is not odd. Hence we have shown

$$\text{NOT } (n \text{ is odd}) \implies \text{NOT } (n^3 \text{ is odd}).$$

The contrapositive is

$$n^3 \text{ is odd} \implies n \text{ is odd}$$

which is what we had to prove. ☐

0.4.5 Proof by Contradiction.

In the proof technique called *proof by contradiction* we assume that the statement we want to prove is false, and then show that this implies a contradiction.

For example, suppose we wanted to prove the statement Q. If we can show that NOT Q leads to a contradiction, then NOT Q must be false; that is, Q must be true.

PROPOSITION. There is no real solution to $x^2 - 6x + 10 = 0$.

Proof. This result can be stated symbolically as

$$\text{NOT } (\exists x \quad x^2 - 6x + 10 = 0)$$

where the universe of discourse is the set of real numbers.

Assume that the result is false; that is, assume that there is a real number x with $x^2 - 6x + 10 = 0$. Then, by completing the square, we can write this as

$$(x - 3)^2 + 1 \;=\; 0.$$

However $(x - 3)^2 \geq 0$, so the left side of this equation is greater than or equal to 1. This gives a contradiction. Hence the original statement is true.   □

Alternatively, suppose we wanted to prove the statement $P \implies Q$. If we assume P and NOT Q, and show that this leads to a contradiction, then P AND NOT Q is false. Hence NOT(P AND NOT Q) is true. This is equivalent to (NOT P) OR Q being true and, by Example 0.1.6, this is equivalent to $P \implies Q$ being true.

PROPOSITION.   If x is a real number such that $x^3 + 7x^2 < 9$ then show that $x < 1.1$.

Proof.   Suppose that x is a real number such that $x^3 + 7x^2 < 9$, but $x < 1.1$ is not true; that is $x \geq 1.1$. It follow that

$$x^3 + 7x^2 \;\geq\; 1.1^3 + 7(1.1)^2 \;=\; 1.331 + 8.47 \;=\; 9.801.$$

However this gives a contradiction to the assumption that $x^3 + 7x^2 < 9$. Hence the original result is true.   □

This example could also be proved by using the contrapositive law.

Other good examples of proof by contradiction are Proposition 1.5.2, Euclid's Theorem 1.5.3, and Theorem 4.2.1.

0.4.6 Proving $P \implies (Q$ OR $R)$.

The statement Q is either true or false. If Q is true then $P \implies (Q$ OR $R)$ is true, regardless of the truth values of P and R. We therefore only have to prove the result when Q is false. The method of proof therefore consists of assuming that P is true and NOT Q is true, and using these to prove that R is true. The theorem is equivalent to the statement

$$(P \text{ AND NOT } Q) \implies R.$$

PROPOSITION.   Let m and n be integers. If $m^3 + n^3$ is odd then m is odd or n is odd.

Proof.   Suppose that $m^3 + n^3$ is odd, and that m is not odd. Therefore m is even and so m^3 will also be even. Hence $m^3 + n^3 - m^3 = n^3$ will be odd. By the result in subsection 0.4.4 it follows that n is odd, and we have shown

$$(m^3 + n^3 \text{ is odd}) \text{ AND NOT } (m \text{ is odd}) \implies (n \text{ is odd}).$$

This is equivalent to the statement that was to be proved, namely $(m^3 + n^3 \text{ is odd}) \implies (m \text{ is odd})$ OR $(n \text{ is odd})$.   □

Another good example of this type of proof is in Theorem 1.5.4.

0.4.7 Proving $P \implies (Q$ AND $R)$.

The result can be split up into the two cases, $P \implies Q$, and $P \implies R$, and then each case can be proved separately.

0.5 COUNTEREXAMPLES

Sometimes a conjectured result in mathematics is not true. In that case, we would not be able to prove it. However, we could try to disprove it; that is, try to prove that its negation is true. If the conjectured result is of the form $\forall x \; P(x)$ then its negation is NOT $(\forall x \; P(x))$, which by the Quantifier Negation Rules 0.3.6, is equivalent to $\exists x$ NOT $P(x)$. Hence to disprove the statement $\forall x \; P(x)$ we only have to find *one* x_0 such that $P(x_0)$ is false. This x_0 is called a *counterexample* to the conjecture $\forall x \; P(x)$.

If the conjectured result is of the form $\forall x \; P(x) \implies Q(x)$ then its negation is $\exists x$ NOT $(P(x) \implies Q(x))$ which, by Example 0.1.6, is equivalent to the statement $\exists x \; (P(x)$ AND NOT $Q(x))$. Hence x_0 is a counterexample to the conjecture if $P(x_0)$ is true while $Q(x_0)$ is false.

EXAMPLE.   Let x be a real number. Disprove the statement:

$$\text{if } x^2 > 9 \text{ then } x > 3.$$

Solution.   One counterexample to the statement is obtained by taking $x_0 = -4$, since $x_0^2 = 16 > 9$ and $x_0 \le 3$. This counterexample disproves the statement. $\qquad\square$

Note that if we wanted to disprove an existence statement such as $\exists x \; P(x)$ then its negation is NOT $(\exists x \; P(x))$, which is equivalent to $\forall x$ NOT $P(x)$. In this case we cannot use a counterexample, because we have to show that $P(x)$ is false *for all* values of x.

Exercise Set 0

1 - 6. Determine which of the following sentences are statements. What are the truth values of those that are statements?

1. $7 > 5$.

2. $5 > 7$.

3. Is $5 > 7$?

4. $\sqrt{2}$ is an integer.

5. Show that $\sqrt{2}$ is not an integer.

6. If 5 is even then $6 = 7$.

7 - 12. Write down the truth tables for each expression.

7. NOT(NOT P)

8. NOT(P OR Q)

9. $P \implies (Q$ OR $R)$

10. $(P$ AND $Q) \implies R$

11. $(P$ OR NOT $Q) \implies R$

12. NOT $P \implies (Q \iff R)$

13. P UNLESS Q is defined as (NOT Q) $\implies P$. Show that this statement has the same truth table as P OR Q. Give an example in common English showing the equivalence of P UNLESS Q and P OR Q.

14. Write down the truth table for the *exclusive or* connective XOR.

15. Write down the truth table for the *not or* connective NOR.

16. Write down the truth table for the *not and* connective NAND.

17 - 21. Write each statement using P, Q, and connectives.

17. P whenever Q.

18. P is necessary for Q.

19. P is sufficient for Q.

20. P only if Q.

21. P is necessary and sufficient for Q.

22. Show that the statements P AND $(Q$ AND $R)$ and $(P$ AND $Q)$ AND R have the same truth tables. This is the *associative law* for AND.

23. Show that the statements P AND $(Q$ OR $R)$ and $(P$ AND $Q)$ OR $(P$ AND $R)$ have the same truth tables. This is a *distributive law*.

24. Is $(P$ AND $Q) \implies R$ equivalent to $P \implies (Q \implies R)$? Give reasons.

25 - 28. Let P be the statement 'It is snowing.' and let Q be the statement 'It is freezing.' Write each statement using P, Q, and connectives.

25. If it is snowing, then it is freezing.

26. It is freezing when it is snowing.

27. It is freezing but not snowing.

28. When it is not freezing it is not snowing.

29 - 32. *Let P be the statement* 'I can walk.' *Q be the statement* 'I have broken my leg.' *and R be the statement* 'I take the bus.' *Express each statement as an English sentence.*

29. $Q \Longrightarrow$ NOT P **30.** $P \Longleftrightarrow$ NOT Q
31. $R \Longrightarrow (Q$ OR NOT $P)$ **32.** $R \Longrightarrow (Q \Longleftrightarrow$ NOT $P)$

33 - 36. *Express each statement as a logical expression using quantifiers. State the universe of discourse.*

33. There is a smallest positive integer.
34. There is no smallest positive real number.
35. There exists an integer that is larger than the product of any two integers.
36. Every pair of integers has a common divisor.

37 - 40. *Negate and simplify each expression.*

37. $\forall x \ (P(x)$ OR $Q(x))$ **38.** $\forall x \ ((P(x)$ AND $Q(x)) \Longrightarrow R(x))$
39. $\exists x \ (P(x) \Longrightarrow Q(x))$ **40.** $\exists x \ \forall y \ (P(x)$ AND $Q(y))$

41 - 44. *If the universe of discourse is the real numbers, what does each statement mean in English? Are they true or false?*

41. $\forall x \ \forall y \ \ (x \geq y)$.   **42.** $\exists x \ \exists y \ \ (x \geq y)$.
43. $\exists y \ \forall x \ \ (x \geq y)$.   **44.** $\forall x \ \exists y \ \ (x \geq y)$.

45 - 48. *Determine whether each pair of statements is equivalent. Give reasons.*

45. $\exists x \ (P(x)$ OR $Q(x))$ $(\exists x \ P(x))$ OR $(\exists x \ Q(x))$
46. $\exists x \ (P(x)$ AND $Q(x))$ $(\exists x \ P(x))$ AND $(\exists x \ Q(x))$
47. $\forall x \ (P(x)$ OR $Q(x))$ $(\forall x \ P(x))$ OR $(\forall x \ Q(x))$
48. $\forall x \ (P(x)$ OR $Q(y))$ $(\forall x \ P(x))$ OR $Q(y)$

49. If A, B and C are sets, the statement $A \cap B \subseteq C$ can be expressed as

$$\forall x \ \ ((x \in A \text{ AND } x \in B) \Longrightarrow x \in C).$$

Express and simplify the negation of this expression, namely $A \cap B \not\subseteq C$, in terms of quantifiers.

50. If A and B are sets, the statement $A = B$ can be expressed as

$$\forall x \ \ (x \in A \Longleftrightarrow x \in B).$$

What does $A \neq B$ mean? Give different ways of expressing this using quantifiers. How would you go about showing that two sets are not the same?

51. The definition of the limit of a function, $\lim\limits_{x \to a} f(x) = L$, can be expressed using quantifiers as

$$\forall \epsilon > 0 \; \exists \delta > 0 \; \forall x \quad (0 < |x - a| < \delta \Longrightarrow |f(x) - L| < \epsilon).$$

Use quantifiers to express the negation of this statement, namely $\lim\limits_{x \to a} f(x) \neq L$.

52. Show that the statement $P \implies (Q \text{ OR } R)$ is equivalent to the statement $(P \text{ AND NOT } Q) \implies R$.
[This explains the proof method 0.4.6 for $P \implies (Q \text{ OR } R)$.]

53. Show that the statement $P \implies (Q \text{ AND } R)$ is equivalent to the statement $(P \implies Q) \text{ AND } (P \implies R)$.
[This explains the proof method 0.4.7 for $P \implies (Q \text{ AND } R)$.]

54. Is the statement $P \implies (Q \implies R)$ equivalent to $(P \implies Q) \implies R$? Give reasons.

55. Show that the statement $P \text{ AND } Q \text{ AND } R$ is equivalent to the statement $(\text{ NOT } P \text{ AND } \text{ NOT } Q) \implies R)$.

56 - 60. *Write the contrapositive of each statement.*

56. If I do my assignments then I will get a good mark in the course.
57. If $x > 3$ then $x^2 > 9$.
58. If $x < -3$ then $x^2 > 9$.
59. If a number is divisible by 2 then it is not prime.
60. If $x \geq 0$ and $y \geq 0$ then $xy \geq 0$.

61. Let a and b be real numbers. Prove that if $ab = 0$ then $a = 0$ or $b = 0$.

62. Let A and B be sets. Prove that if $x \notin A \cap B$ then $x \notin A$ or $x \notin B$.

Chapter 1

Integers and Diophantine Equations

Throughout this chapter, all the numbers that are used will be integers. The basic tool in this chapter is the Division Algorithm. We use it to demonstrate the Euclidean Algorithm, which in turn enables us to solve linear Diophantine equations. The Division Algorithm is also used to represent numbers to different bases. The Unique Factorization Theorem, which is also called the Fundamental Theorem of Arithmetic, states that any integer can be factored into primes in a unique way, and the proof of this result depends on the Division Algorithm.

1.1   THE DIVISION ALGORITHM

The set of integers, $\mathbb{Z}$, has the property that any two elements can be added, subtracted and multiplied together, and the result will still be an integer. However, division of one integer by another is not always possible, if the quotient is also to be an integer.

1.1.1 Definition.   If $a, b \in \mathbb{Z}$, we say that a *divides* b, and write this symbolically as $a|b$, if there exists $q \in \mathbb{Z}$ such that $b = qa$.

Alternative ways to express this are to say that a is a *factor* of b or that b is a *multiple* of a. If no integer q exists such that $b = qa$ we say that a *does not divide b* and write $a \nmid b$.

Hence $-3|12$ because $12 = (-4)(-3)$. Also $5|10$, $7|7$, $7|-7$ and $4|0$. It should be noted that with this definition $0|0$ because $0 = q0$, where q can be chosen to be any integer. However $0 \nmid 4$ because there is no integer q such that $4 = q0$.

We now prove some elementary properties of this divisibility relation.

1.1.2 Proposition. Let $a, b, c \in \mathbb{Z}$.

(i) If $a|b$ and $b|c$ then $a|c$.

(ii) If $a|b$ and $a|c$ then $a|(bx + cy)$ for any $x, y \in \mathbb{Z}$. In particular $a|(b + c)$ and $a|(b - c)$.

(iii) If $a|b$ and $b|a$ then $a = \pm b$.

(iv) If $a|b$, and a and b are positive integers, then $a \leq b$.

Proof. *(i).* If $a|b$ and $b|c$ then there exist $q, r \in \mathbb{Z}$ such that $b = qa$ and $c = rb$. Hence $c = rqa$ and, because $rq \in \mathbb{Z}$, it follows that $a|c$.

(ii). If $a|b$ and $a|c$ then there exist $q, r \in \mathbb{Z}$ such that $b = qa$ and $c = ra$. Now $bx + cy = (qx + ry)a$ and, since $qx + ry \in \mathbb{Z}$ for any $x, y \in \mathbb{Z}$, it follows that $a|(bx + cy)$.

(iii). If $a|b$ and $b|a$ then there exist $q, r \in \mathbb{Z}$ such that $b = qa$ and $a = rb$. Hence $a = rqa$ and $0 = a(rq - 1)$. If $a \neq 0$ then rq must be 1 and $r = q = \pm 1$. Therefore $a = \pm b$. On the other hand, if $a = 0$ then $b = q0 = 0$ and $a = b$.

(iv). If $a|b$ then there exists $q \in \mathbb{Z}$ such that $b = qa$. If a and b are positive integers, so is q. In particular $q \geq 1$ and hence $b = qa \geq a$. □

Even if the integer b cannot be exactly divided by the integer a, we can try to divide b by a and obtain a remainder. This familiar process is known as the Division Algorithm.

1.1.3 Division Algorithm. If $a, b \in \mathbb{Z}$ where $a > 0$, then there exist unique integers q and r such that

$$b = qa + r \quad \text{where} \quad 0 \leq r < a.$$

The integer q is called the *quotient* and the integer r is called the *remainder* when b is divided by a. The important part of the result is the fact that the remainder is always a positive or zero integer less than a, and that this remainder is unique. It is easily seen that $a|b$ if and only if the remainder is zero.

The following are examples of the Division Algorithm when $a = 6$.

$$
\begin{aligned}
15 &= 2 \cdot 6 + 3 \\
30 &= 5 \cdot 6 + 0 \\
-10 &= (-2) \cdot 6 + 2 \\
-2 &= (-1) \cdot 6 + 4
\end{aligned}
$$

Note that, even if b is negative, we can find a positive or zero remainder.

Proof. We wish to find a nonnegative remainder $r = b - qa$, which is as small as possible. The idea of the proof is to start with b and to subtract (or add) integer multiples of a until the desired remainder is obtained.

More formally, let $S = \{b - xa \mid x \in \mathbb{Z}\}$ and let S' be the nonnegative elements of S. The set S' is nonempty because, if $b \geq 0$, the element $b - 0a = b \in S'$ and, if $b < 0$, the element $b - ba = (-b)(a - 1) \geq 0$ and belongs to S'.

One of the properties of the integers is that every nonempty set of nonnegative numbers contains a smallest element. Let r be the smallest element of S' and let q be the integer such that $b - qa = r$. Since all the elements of S' are nonnegative, $r \geq 0$. Furthermore $r < a$, otherwise $r - a = (b - qa) - a = b - (q + 1)a$ would be a nonnegative integer smaller than r but in the set S'. We have therefore shown the existence of integers q and r with $b = qa + r$ and $0 \leq r < a$.

To show that these integers are unique, suppose that $b = q_1 a + r_1 = q_2 a + r_2$ where $0 \leq r_1 < a$ and $0 \leq r_2 < a$. Suppose $r_1 \neq r_2$ and say $r_1 < r_2$. Then $0 < r_2 - r_1 < a$ and $(q_1 - q_2)a = r_2 - r_1$. Hence $a | r_2 - r_1$ and, by Proposition 1.1.2 (iv), $a \leq r_2 - r_1$ which contradicts the fact that $r_2 - r_1 < a$. Therefore the supposition that $r_1 \neq r_2$ is false and r_1 must equal r_2. Furthermore $(q_1 - q_2)a = r_2 - r_1 = 0$ and, since $a \neq 0$, $q_1 = q_2$. This proves that the integers q and r are unique. □

The above proof does not give a method for finding the quotient and remainder in concrete examples. If $b > 0$, we can find these by ordinary long division with remainder. If $b < 0$, use long division to divide $-b$ by a to obtain

$$
\begin{aligned}
-b &= q'a + r' & \text{where} && 0 \leq r' < a \\
b &= (-q')a - r' & \text{where} && -a < -r' \leq 0.
\end{aligned}
$$

If $-r' < 0$, rewrite this as

$$
b = (-q' - 1)a + (a - r') \qquad \text{where} \quad 0 < a - r' < a.
$$

In the Division Algorithm it was assumed that $a > 0$. However, if $a < 0$, the Division Algorithm can be applied to $-a$ to obtain unique integers q' and r such that

$$
b = q'(-a) + r \qquad \text{where} \quad 0 \leq r < |a|.
$$

Rewriting this and putting $q = -q'$ we have

$$
b = qa + r \qquad \text{where} \quad 0 \leq r < |a|
$$

and this is the form of the Division Algorithm when $a < 0$.

1.2   THE EUCLIDEAN ALGORITHM

A *common divisor* of two integers is any integer that divides both. The *greatest common divisor* is the nonnegative common divisor that is divisible by all other common divisors. It is not obvious that there will be a common divisor that is a multiple of all the other common divisors. However the Euclidean Algorithm 1.2.3 will show that such a greatest common divisor does exist. Hence, for nonzero numbers, the greatest common divisor will be the largest of all the common divisors, and will be a multiple of each of them. The greatest common divisor is also called the highest common factor. Formally, we have the following definition.

1.2.1 Definition.   Let a and b be integers. The *greatest common divisor* of a and b is the nonnegative integer d such that

(i) d divides both a and b;

(ii) any divisor of both a and b also divides d.

We shall write the greatest common divisor as $d = \text{GCD}(a, b)$, or $d = \gcd(a, b)$.

For example, the common divisors of 12 and 18 are ± 1, ± 2, ± 3, ± 6, while 6 is the greatest common divisor. If $b = 0$, then d divides b for all integers d, and so $\text{GCD}(a, 0) = |a|$. If $a = b = 0$ then $\text{GCD}(0, 0) = 0$, as this is the only number that satisfies Definition 1.2.1 (though in this case it is not the largest divisor).

One crude way of finding the greatest common divisor of two integers is to look at all the common divisors of each of them. This method becomes impractical for large numbers, and we will now give an algorithm for finding the greatest common divisor in general. If $a \neq 0$, we can use the Division Algorithm to write $b = qa + r$ where $0 \leq r < |a|$. The next result will show that the problem of calculating $\text{GCD}(a, b)$ is reduced to the easier problem of calculating $\text{GCD}(a, r)$; it is easier because the numbers involved are smaller.

1.2.2 Proposition.   If $b = qa + r$ and $\text{GCD}(a, b)$ exists, then $\text{GCD}(r, a)$ exists and

$$\text{GCD}(a, b) = \text{GCD}(r, a).$$

Proof.   Denote $\text{GCD}(a, b)$ by d. We shall use Definition 1.2.1 to show that d is also the greatest common divisor of r and a. Since d divides both a and b, it follows from Proposition 1.1.2 (ii) that $d|(b - qa)$. Therefore $d|r$ and d divides both r and a.

Now suppose that c is any divisor of r and a. By Proposition 1.1.2 (ii) again, $c|(qa + r)$; that is, $c|b$. Since $c|a$ and $c|b$, it follows from the definition of $\text{GCD}(a, b)$ that $c|d$. Therefore $\text{GCD}(r, a)$ exists and is equal to d.   ☐

By repeated use of this result, we obtain the following algorithm for finding the greatest common divisor of two integers.

1.2.3 Euclidean Algorithm. If $a, b \in \mathbb{Z}$ where $a \neq 0$ and a does not divide b, then $\mathrm{GCD}(a, b)$ is the last nonzero remainder, r_n, in the following list of equations obtained from the Division Algorithm. If a does divide b then $\mathrm{GCD}(a, b) = |a|$.

$$
\begin{aligned}
b &= q_1 a + r_1 & \text{where} \quad 0 < r_1 < |a| \\
a &= q_2 r_1 + r_2 & \text{where} \quad 0 < r_2 < r_1 \\
r_1 &= q_3 r_2 + r_3 & \text{where} \quad 0 < r_3 < r_2 \\
&\;\;\vdots \\
r_{n-2} &= q_n r_{n-1} + r_n & \text{where} \quad 0 < r_n < r_{n-1} \\
r_{n-1} &= q_{n+1} r_n + 0.
\end{aligned}
$$

Proof. The remainders in the above list form a strictly decreasing set of nonnegative integers and hence must eventually reach zero. Therefore the algorithm terminates after a finite number of steps. If $a \nmid b$, then $r_1 \neq 0$ and so r_n is a nonnegative integer.

We know that $\mathrm{GCD}(0, r_n)$ exists and is r_n. By repeated use of Proposition 1.2.2 we have

$$
\begin{aligned}
r_n &= \mathrm{GCD}(0, r_n) &= \mathrm{GCD}(r_n, r_{n-1}) &= \mathrm{GCD}(r_{n-1}, r_{n-2}) &= \cdots \\
&= \mathrm{GCD}(r_2, r_1) &= \mathrm{GCD}(r_1, a) &= \mathrm{GCD}(a, b).
\end{aligned}
$$

Hence $\mathrm{GCD}(a, b)$ exists and is r_n.

If $a \mid b$ then $b = q_1 a + 0$ and there is no last nonzero remainder. In this case, it follows that $|a|$ is a common divisor of a and b. Moreover any common divisor of a and b must also divide $|a|$, so $|a|$ satisfies the definition of $\mathrm{GCD}(a, b)$. □

This algorithm shows the existence of the greatest common divisor of any two numbers, which are not both zero. Moreover this algorithm is very efficient, even for very large numbers.

1.2.4 Example. Find $\mathrm{GCD}(481, 1053)$.

Solution. Putting $a = 481$ and $b = 1053$ in the Euclidean Algorithm we have

$$
\begin{aligned}
1053 &= 2 \cdot 481 + 91 \\
481 &= 5 \cdot 91 + 26 \\
91 &= 3 \cdot 26 + 13 \\
26 &= 2 \cdot 13 + 0.
\end{aligned}
$$

Hence $\mathrm{GCD}(481, 1053) = 13$.

Check. Since the Euclidean Algorithm usually involves many operations it is good practice to check the answer for arithmetical mistakes. We can easily check whether 13 is a common divisor of 481 and 1053 or not. We have $481 = 37 \cdot 13$ and $1053 = 81 \cdot 13$ and so the answer is correct. □

The next theorem, which uses the Euclidean Algorithm, is very important in the theory of Diophantine equations. It also provides another good characterization of the greatest common divisor.

1.2.5 Theorem.   Let a and b be nonzero integers, and let d be a positive common divisor of a and b. Then $d = \text{GCD}(a, b)$ if and only if there exist $x, y \in \mathbb{Z}$ such that

$$ax + by \; = \; d.$$

Proof.   If $d = \text{GCD}(a, b)$, then it is the last nonzero remainder, r_n, in the Euclidean Algorithm. From the nth equation of the Euclidean Algorithm we can write r_n in terms of r_{n-1} and r_{n-2}.

$$d \; = \; \text{GCD}(a, b) \; = \; r_n \; = \; r_{n-2} - q_n r_{n-1}.$$

Solving the $(n-1)$st equation for the remainder r_{n-1} and substituting into the above equation we have

$$
\begin{aligned}
d \; = \; \text{GCD}(a, b) \; &= \; r_{n-2} - q_n(r_{n-3} - q_{n-1}r_{n-2}) \\
&= \; (1 + q_n q_{n-1})r_{n-2} - q_n r_{n-3}.
\end{aligned}
$$

This is an expression for $\text{GCD}(a, b)$ in terms of r_{n-2} and r_{n-3}. By continuing in this way, up the list of equations, we can eventually express $\text{GCD}(a, b)$ in terms of r_2 and r_1, then in terms of r_1 and a, and finally in terms of a and b.

Conversely, suppose d is a positive common divisor of a and b satisfying an equation $ax + by = d$ for some $x, y \in \mathbb{Z}$. Let e be any other common divisor, so that $e|a$ and $e|b$. Then, by Proposition 1.1.2 (ii), $e|ax + by$; that is $e|d$ and, by Definition 1.2.1, $d = \text{GCD}(a, b)$. $\qquad\square$

The above proof gives one practical method, using the Euclidean Algorithm, for finding one pair of integers x and y satisfying the equation $ax + by = \text{GCD}(a, b)$. However this pair of integers is by no means the only pair that will satisfy the equation. As Theorem 1.3.1 will show, there are infinitely many solutions.

1.2.6 Example.   Find integers x and y so that

$$481x + 1053y \; = \; 13$$

Solution.   Working our way up the equations in the Euclidean Algorithm in Example 1.2.4 we have

$$
\begin{aligned}
13 \; &= \; 91 - 3 \cdot 26 \; = \; 91 - 3(481 - 5 \cdot 91) \; = \; 16 \cdot 91 - 3 \cdot 481 \\
&= \; 16(1053 - 2 \cdot 481) - 3 \cdot 481 \; = \; 16 \cdot 1053 - 35 \cdot 481.
\end{aligned}
$$

Hence $x = -35$, $y = 16$ is one solution.

Check. $16 \cdot 1053 - 35 \cdot 481 = 16848 - 16835 = 13$. □

1.2.7 Example.
Find integers x and y so that $89x + 33y = 1$.

Solution. Even though we can see, by inspection, that $\text{GCD}(89, 33) = 1$ we will still apply the Euclidean Algorithm to 89 and 33 in order to find integers x and y. We have

$$
\begin{aligned}
89 &= 2 \cdot 33 + 23 & \text{or} && 23 &= 89 - 2 \cdot 33 \\
33 &= 1 \cdot 23 + 10 & \text{or} && 10 &= 33 - 23 \\
23 &= 2 \cdot 10 + 3 & \text{or} && 3 &= 23 - 2 \cdot 10 \\
10 &= 3 \cdot 3 + 1 & \text{or} && 1 &= 10 - 3 \cdot 3.
\end{aligned}
$$

$$
\begin{aligned}
\text{Hence} \quad 1 &= 10 - 3 \cdot 3 & \text{from the last equation} \\
&= 10 - 3(23 - 2 \cdot 10) & \text{from the third equation} \\
&= 7 \cdot 10 - 3 \cdot 23 \\
&= 7(33 - 23) - 3 \cdot 23 & \text{from the second equation} \\
&= 7 \cdot 33 - 10 \cdot 23 \\
&= 7 \cdot 33 - 10(89 - 2 \cdot 33) & \text{from the first equation} \\
&= 27 \cdot 33 - 10 \cdot 89.
\end{aligned}
$$

Therefore $x = -10$, $y = 27$ is one solution.

Check. $27 \cdot 33 - 10 \cdot 89 = 891 - 890 = 1$. □

If $\text{GCD}(a, b) = 1$ then a and b are said to be *relatively prime* or *coprime*.

1.2.8 Theorem.
If $a, b, c \in \mathbb{Z}$ with $c|ab$ and $\text{GCD}(a, c) = 1$ then $c|b$.

Proof. By Theorem 1.2.5 there exist integers x and y such that $ax + cy = 1$. Multiplying by b, we have $abx + cby = b$. Since $c|ab$ and $c|c$ it follows from Proposition 1.1.2 (ii) that $c|(abx + cby)$; that is, $c|b$. □

1.2.9 Proposition.
Let a and b be integers, not both zero, and $d = \text{GCD}(a, b)$, so that $\frac{a}{d}$ and $\frac{b}{d}$ are integers. Then, $\text{GCD}\left(\frac{a}{d}, \frac{b}{d}\right) = 1$.

Proof. By Theorem 1.2.5 there exist integers x and y such that $ax + by = d$. Therefore

$$
\frac{a}{d}x + \frac{b}{d}y = 1
$$

and, also by Theorem 1.2.5, it follows that $\text{GCD}\left(\frac{a}{d}, \frac{b}{d}\right) = 1$. □

1.3   LINEAR DIOPHANTINE EQUATIONS

Theorem 1.2.5 showed how to solve equations of the form

$$ax + by \;=\; c$$

for integers x and y, where a, b, c are given integers in which $c = \mathrm{GCD}(a, b)$. Such an equation is called a *linear Diophantine equation* or a *linear integer equation*. A Diophantine equation is an equation in one or more unknowns with integer coefficients for which integer solutions are sought. The word "Diophantine" refers to the Greek mathematician of the third century A.D., Diophantus of Alexandria, who made a study of such equations. He was also one of the first mathematicians to introduce symbolism into algebra. The significance of this can be appreciated if one tries to imagine doing algebraic manipulation without symbols. A "linear" equation is one in which the unknowns appear only to the first power.

The first problem, when confronted by any type of equation, is to discover whether any solution exists. If a solution does exist, we are then faced with the problem of determining how many solutions there are and how to find one or all of them explicitly.

Consider the simple linear Diophantine equation in one variable x

$$ax \;=\; b$$

where $a, b, x \in \mathbb{Z}$. We know that this equation has an integral solution for x if and only if $a|b$. Furthermore, if a solution exists, it is unique unless $a = b = 0$, in which case, every integer is a solution.

We shall now investigate Diophantine equations in two variables x and y, of the form $ax + by = c$, where $a, b, c \in \mathbb{Z}$, but c is not necessarily the greatest common divisor of a and b.

1.3.1 Linear Diophantine Equation Theorem.

(i) The linear Diophantine equation

$$ax + by \;=\; c$$

has a solution if and only if $\mathrm{GCD}(a, b)|c$.

(ii) If $\mathrm{GCD}(a, b) = d$ and $x = x_0, y = y_0$ is one particular solution, when a and b are not both zero, then the *complete* integer solution is

$$x \;=\; x_0 + n\frac{b}{d}, \qquad y \;=\; y_0 - n\frac{a}{d} \qquad \text{for all } n \in \mathbb{Z}.$$

Proof. (i).   Firstly, suppose that the equation does have an integer solution; that is, there are integers x and y for which $ax + by = c$. If $d = \mathrm{GCD}(a, b)$ then $d|a$ and $d|b$ and so, by Proposition 1.1.2 (ii), $d|(ax + by)$. Hence, if there is a solution, $d|c$.

Secondly, suppose that $d|c$; that is, $c = dc_1$ for some $c_1 \in \mathbb{Z}$. By Theorem 1.2.5 there exist integers, say x_1 and y_1, such that

$$ax_1 + by_1 = d.$$

Multiplying by c_1 we have

$$ac_1x_1 + bc_1y_1 = dc_1 = c$$

and we see that $x_0 = c_1x_1$ and $y_0 = c_1y_1$ is one particular solution to $ax + by = c$.

(ii). Let x, y be an arbitrary solution, and $x = x_0$, $y = y_0$ be a particular solution to the Diophantine equation. Then

$$ax + by = c$$
$$ax_0 + by_0 = c.$$

Subtracting, we have

$$a(x - x_0) = b(y_0 - y)$$

and dividing each side by $d = \text{GCD}(a, b)$

$$\frac{a}{d}(x - x_0) = \frac{b}{d}(y_0 - y).$$

By Proposition 1.2.9, GCD $\left(\frac{a}{d}, \frac{b}{d}\right) = 1$. Since $\frac{b}{d}$ divides $\frac{a}{d}(x - x_0)$, it follows from Theorem 1.2.8 that $\frac{b}{d}$ divides $x - x_0$. If we put $x - x_0 = n\frac{b}{d}$, where $n \in \mathbb{Z}$, then $anb = bd(y_0 - y)$, and so every solution is of the form

$$x = x_0 + n\frac{b}{d}, \quad \text{and} \quad y = y_0 - n\frac{a}{d}.$$

We now check that this is a solution for every $n \in \mathbb{Z}$. We have

$$\begin{aligned} ax + by &= a\left(x_0 + n\frac{b}{d}\right) + b\left(y_0 - n\frac{a}{d}\right) \\ &= ax_0 + by_0 + n\frac{ab}{d} - n\frac{ab}{d} \\ &= c \end{aligned}$$

since $x = x_0$, $y = y_0$ is a particular solution. Therefore the complete solution is $x = x_0 + n\frac{b}{d}$ and $y = y_0 - n\frac{a}{d}$, where $n \in \mathbb{Z}$. $\qquad\square$

For example, the complete solution to the Diophantine equation

$$481x + 1053y \;=\; 13$$

of Example 1.2.6 is $x = -35 + \frac{1053n}{13}, y = 16 - \frac{481n}{13}$; that is, $x = 81n - 35$, $y = 16 - 37n$ for all $n \in \mathbb{Z}$. Putting $n = -1, 0, 1$ and 2, we see that some particular solutions are

$$(x, y) \;=\; (-116, 53), \; (-35, 16), \; (46, -21) \text{ and } (127, -58).$$

This method of solving an equation, by first finding one particular solution and then finding the complete solution from it, is very common in mathematics. It is used extensively in the solution of differential equations.

Note that the Euclidean Algorithm 1.2.3 and the proof of Theorem 1.2.5 can always be used to find the greatest common divisor, and also one particular solution to the Diophantine equation. However, any method can be used to find the particular solution. It is often quicker to find one solution by inspection, rather than use the Euclidean Algorithm.

1.3.2 Example.   Find, if possible, one solution to each of the following Diophantine equations.

(i) $28x + 35y \;=\; 60$

(ii) $21x + 15y \;=\; 9$

Solution. *(i).*   GCD$(28, 35) = 7$, which does not divide 60. Hence the first equation has no integer solutions.

(ii).   GCD$(21, 15) = 3$, which does divide 9. Hence the second equation does have integer solutions.

We will use the Euclidean Algorithm to find one solution to $21x + 15y = 3$.

$$21 \;=\; 15 + 6$$
$$15 \;=\; 2 \cdot 6 + 3$$

Hence $3 = 15 - 2 \cdot 6 = 15 - 2(21 - 15) = 3 \cdot 15 - 2 \cdot 21$ and $21(-2) + 15(3) = 3$. Multiplying this whole equation by 3 to get 9 on the right side, we obtain

$$21(-6) + 15(9) = 9$$

and we see that $x = -6, y = 9$ is one solution to $21x + 15y = 9$.

Check. $21(-6) + 15(9) = -126 + 135 = 9.$ □

1.3.3 Example. Find the complete solution to the Diophantine equation

$$343x + 259y = 658.$$

Solution. We shall first find the GCD$(343, 259)$ by using the Euclidean Algorithm.

$$\begin{aligned}
343 &= 259 + 84 \\
259 &= 3 \cdot 84 + 7 \\
84 &= 12 \cdot 7 + 0
\end{aligned}$$

Hence GCD$(343, 259) = 7$ and, as $658 = 94 \cdot 7$, the equation does have solutions. Using the above Euclidean Algorithm, we have

$$\begin{aligned}
7 &= 259 - 3 \cdot 84 = 259 - 3(343 - 259) \\
&= 4 \cdot 259 - 3 \cdot 343.
\end{aligned}$$

Multiplying this equality by 94, we have

$$(376)259 - (282)343 = 658.$$

Therefore $x = -282$, $y = 376$ is one solution to the equation. The complete solution is $x = -282 + \frac{259n}{7}, y = 376 - \frac{343n}{7}$; that is,

$$x = 37n - 282, \quad y = 376 - 49n \quad \text{for all } n \in \mathbb{Z}.$$

Check. $343(37n - 282) + 259(376 - 49n) = 12691n - 96726 + 97384 - 12691n = 658.$ □

If GCD$(a, b)|c$, and GCD$(a, b) \neq 1$ it is often easier to divide the whole equation by GCD(a, b), as this reduces the size of the numbers involved. For example, if we divide the equation in the above example by 7, we obtain the equation $49x + 37y = 94$. When this is solved, it will yield exactly the same solutions as those we have already obtained.

The Euclidean Algorithm 1.2.3 can be extended so that at the same time we compute GCD(a, b), we find all the integers x and y such that $ax + by = \text{GCD}(a, b)$. We shall describe this Extended Euclidean Algorithm, give an example to show how it is implemented, and then prove the algorithm

This algorithm can easily be implemented on a programmable calculator or a computer. The program only has to store two consecutive rows in the table.

1.3.4 Extended Euclidean Algorithm.   Let a and b be positive integers.

START: Write down the first two rows in the following table.

1	0	a
0	1	b
s_1	t_1	r_1
s_2	t_2	r_2
$\vdots$	$\vdots$	$\vdots$
s_n	t_n	r_n
s_{n+1}	t_{n+1}	0

FIRST STEP: Divide a by b using the Division Algorithm 1.1.3, so that $a = q_1 b + r_1$, where $0 \leq r_1 < b$. Take the top row and subtract q_1 times the next row from it.

GENERAL STEP: Divide r_{i-2} by r_{i-1} using the Division Algorithm 1.1.3, so that $r_{i-2} = q_i r_{i-1} + r_i$, where $0 \leq r_i < b$. Let row i be the row containing r_i, and let $s_{-1} = 1, t_{-1} = 0, r_{-1} = a, s_0 = 0, t_0 = 1$ and $r_0 = b$. Then row i is obtained from the previous two rows by calculating

$$\text{row } i \;=\; \text{row } (i-2) \;-\; q_i \text{ row } (i-1)$$

with

$$
\begin{aligned}
s_i &= s_{i-2} &-& \quad q_i s_{i-1} \\
t_i &= t_{i-2} &-& \quad q_i t_{i-1} \\
r_i &= r_{i-2} &-& \quad q_i r_{i-1}.
\end{aligned}
$$

STOP: Stop the algorithm when $r_{n+1} = 0$.

CONCLUSION:

(i) $\text{GCD}(a, b) = r_n$.

(ii) Each row (s_i, t_i, r_i) satisfies the equation $as_i + bt_i = r_i$.

(iii) The general integer solution to $ax + by = \text{GCD}(a, b)$ is

$$x = s_n + s_{n+1}m, \quad y = t_n + t_{n+1}m \quad \text{for all } m \in \mathbb{Z}.$$

If a or b is negative, it is easier to solve the equation $|a|x + |b|y = \text{GCD}(a, b)$ and then change the sign of the variables.

1.3.5 Example.   Apply the Extended Euclidean Algorithm to $a = 126$ and $b = 91$ to find all the integer solutions to

$$126x + 91y = \text{GCD}(126, 91).$$

Solution. The Extended Euclidean Algorithm yields the following tables.

s_i	t_i	r_i
1	0	126
0	1	91
1	-1	35
-2	3	21
3	-4	14
-5	7	7
13	-18	0

q_i	Euclidean Algorithm
1	$126 = 1 \cdot 91 + 35$
2	$91 = 2 \cdot 35 + 21$
1	$35 = 1 \cdot 21 + 14$
1	$21 = 1 \cdot 14 + 7$
2	$14 = 2 \cdot 7 + 0$

The next to the last row shows that $\mathrm{GCD}(126, 91) = 7$, and also gives the identity $-5 \cdot 126 + 7 \cdot 91 = 7$. Hence one solution to $126x + 91y = 7$ is $x = -5, y = 7$ and the general solution is

$$x = -5 + 13m, \quad y = 7 - 18m \quad \text{for all } m \in \mathbb{Z}.$$

Check. $126(-5 + 13m) + 91(7 - 18m) = -630 + 1638m + 637 - 1638m = 7.$ $\square$

Proof of the Extended Euclidean Algorithm. The integers $r_1, r_2, \ldots,$ in the third column, are precisely the remainders in the Euclidean Algorithm 1.2.3. Hence they form a strictly decreasing sequence of nonnegative integers and the algorithm must terminate with some $r_{n+1} = 0$. By the proof of the Euclidean Algorithm, the last nonzero remainder r_n will be $\mathrm{GCD}(a, b)$.

We shall now show recursively that each row satisfies the equation $as_i + bt_i = r_i$. Notice that the first two rows satisfy this equation. If the $(i-2)$nd and $(i-1)$st rows satisfy this equation, then

$$s_{i-2}a + t_{i-2}b = r_{i-2}$$
$$s_{i-1}a + t_{i-1}b = r_{i-1}$$

Multiplying the second equation by q_i and subtracting from the first we have

$$(s_{i-2} - q_i s_{i-1})a + (t_{i-2} - q_i t_{i-1})b = r_{i-2} - q_i r_{i-1}$$
$$s_i a + t_i b = r_i.$$

In particular, the nth row satisfies the equation

$$s_n a + t_n b = r_n = \mathrm{GCD}(a, b)$$

and so $x = s_n, y = t_n$ is one solution to $ax + by = \mathrm{GCD}(a, b)$. The $(n+1)$st row satisfies the equation $s_{n+1}a + t_{n+1}b = 0$, so we can add m times this $(n+1)$st row to the nth row to show that $x = s_n + s_{n+1}m, y = t_n + t_{n+1}m$ satisfies $ax + by = \mathrm{GCD}(a, b)$ for all $m \in \mathbb{Z}$.

It is a little more tricky to show that every solution is of this form. Suppose that x and y are integers satisfying $ax + by = \text{GCD}(a, b)$. We know that

$$\begin{array}{ccccc} \text{row } i & = & \text{row } (i-2) & - & q_i \text{ row } (i-1) \\ \text{row } (i-2) & = & \text{row } i & + & q_i \text{ row } (i-1). \end{array}$$

so that

Hence each row is a linear combination of the two rows below it. We can work our way up the rows to show that any row is an integer linear combination of the bottom two rows. Since $(x, y, ax + by)$ is an integer linear combination of the top two rows, it is also an integer linear combination of the bottom two rows. That is

$$(x, y, \text{GCD}(a, b)) \;=\; \ell \text{ row } (n) + m \text{ row } (n+1) \quad \text{for some } \ell, m \in \mathbb{Z}.$$

This implies that

$$\begin{aligned} x &= \ell s_n + m s_{n+1} \\ y &= \ell t_n + m t_{n+1} \\ \text{GCD}(a, b) &= \ell \text{GCD}(a, b) \end{aligned}$$

and so $\ell = 1$ and $x = s_n + s_{n+1}m$, $y = t_n + t_{n+1}m$, for some $m \in \mathbb{Z}$. $\square$

1.3.6 Example.   A customer has a large quantity of dimes and quarters. In how many different ways can the customer pay exactly for an item that is (i) worth \$3.49 or (ii) worth \$2.65?

Solution. (i).   Suppose the customer tenders x dimes and y quarters. To pay for the first item exactly, the customer requires

$$10x + 25y \;=\; 349.$$

But $\text{GCD}(10, 25) = 5$, which does not divide 349 and hence the equation has no solutions. Therefore, as experience would tell us, the customer cannot pay the exact amount without using some cents.

(ii).   For the second item the customer requires

$$10x + 25y \;=\; 265.$$

In this case $\text{GCD}(10, 25) = 5$ which does divide 265. Hence the equation has integral solutions, though not necessarily positive integral solutions. If faced with this problem in a shop, we would not use the Euclidean Algorithm to find a solution, but would obtain one by inspection. For example, $x = 4$, $y = 9$ is one particular solution. The general solution is therefore

$$x \;=\; 4 + 5n, \quad y \;=\; 9 - 2n \quad \text{for } n \in \mathbb{Z}.$$

If we require x and y to be nonnegative, we must have $4 + 5n \geq 0$ and $9 - 2n \geq 0$; that is, $-4/5 \leq n \leq 9/2$. But, as n is integral, $0 \leq n \leq 4$ will yield all the nonnegative solutions, namely

$$(x, y) \ = \ (4, 9), \ (9, 7), \ (14, 5), \ (19, 3) \text{ or } (24, 1).$$

Hence the second item could be paid for in exactly in five different ways, as long as the customer has at least 24 dimes and 9 quarters. $\qquad\square$

What do the negative solutions mean in this case? If we put $n = -1$, we obtain the solution $x = -1, y = 11$. This corresponds to the situation in which the customer offers 11 quarters and receives one dime in change.

1.3.7 Example. A hallway 5 metres long is to be tiled with strips of tile of widths 8 cms and 18 cms. In how many ways can this be done, without cutting some of the tiles to different widths?

Solution. If x strips of tile of width 8 cms and y strips of width 18 cms exactly fill the length of the hallway then

$$8x + 18y \ = \ 500.$$

That is, dividing by the GCD$(8, 18) = 2$,

$$4x + 9y \ = \ 250.$$

By inspection, we see that one solution to the equation $4x + 9y = 1$ is $x = -2, y = 1$. Hence one solution to our desired equation is $x = -500, y = 250$. This is clearly not a feasible solution because it is impossible to have a negative number of tiles. However, this particular solution will allow us to obtain the general integral solution. This is $x = -500 + 9n, y = 250 - 4n$, where $n \in \mathbb{Z}$. The only workable solutions occur when x and y are nonnegative. Hence we need $-500 + 9n \geq 0$ and $250 - 4n \geq 0$; that is

$$\frac{500}{9} \leq n \leq \frac{250}{4} \quad \text{or} \quad 55\tfrac{5}{9} \leq n \leq 62\tfrac{1}{2}.$$

Since n must be integral, it follows that $56 \leq n \leq 62$ and the seven feasible solutions are given in the following table.

n	56	57	58	59	60	61	62
x	4	13	22	31	40	49	58
y	26	22	18	14	10	6	2

For each of these seven ways of choosing the different widths, the tiles, of course, can be permuted amongst themselves when they are laid.

Check. $8 \cdot 58 + 18 \cdot 2 = 464 + 36 = 500$, so $x = 58, y = 2$ is correct. $\qquad\square$

1.3.8 Example. Find all integer solutions to

$$1249x + 379y = 5.$$

Solution. We apply the extended Euclidean algorithm to 1249 and 379.

s_i	t_i	r_i		q_i	Euclidean Algorithm
1	0	1249			
0	1	379			
1	-3	112		3	$1249 = 3 \cdot 379 + 112$
-3	10	43		3	$379 = 3 \cdot 112 + 43$
7	-23	26		2	$112 = 2 \cdot 43 + 26$
-10	33	17		1	$43 = 1 \cdot 26 + 17$
17	-56	9		1	$26 = 1 \cdot 17 + 9$
-27	89	8		1	$17 = 1 \cdot 9 + 8$
44	-145	1		1	$9 = 1 \cdot 8 + 1$
-379	1249	0		8	$8 = 8 \cdot 1 + 0$

From the next to last row we have $44(1249) + (-145)(379) = 1$. Multiplying through by 5 gives us $(220)(1249) + (-725)(379) = 5$, and so a particular solution to the given equation is $x = 220$ and $y = -725$. All the solutions are

$$x = 220 + 379m, \quad y = -725 - 1249m \quad \text{for all } m \in \mathbb{Z}.$$

Check. $1249(220 + 379m) + 379(-725 - 1249m)$
$= 274780 + 473371m - 274775 - 473371m = 5.$ $\square$

1.4 INTEGERS IN DIFFERENT BASES

Another application of the Division Algorithm is in the conversion of a number from base 10 to any other base.

In the standard notation for integers, the symbol 52067 stands for the number

$$5 \cdot 10^4 + 2 \cdot 10^3 + 0 \cdot 10^2 + 6 \cdot 10 + 7.$$

In general, any positive integer can be written as the symbol $r_n r_{n-1} \ldots r_1 r_0$, which stands for

$$r_n 10^n + r_{n-1} 10^{n-1} + \cdots + r_1 10 + r_0$$

where $0 \leq r_i \leq 9$ for $i = 0, 1, 2, \ldots, n$. This system, in which numbers are written in terms of powers of ten, is called the *decimal system* or the *representation of integers in the base ten*.

This system is not the only one that has been used by man. The Babylonians wrote their mathematical and astronomical numbers in the base 60 and the remains of this system can still be seen in our division of the hour and minute into 60 parts. In a more modern context, the internal computations in a digital computer are normally performed in the base 2 and this is called the *binary system*.

For example, the symbol $(1011011)_2$ in the binary system stands for the number

$$
\begin{aligned}
& 1 \cdot 2^6 + 0 \cdot 2^5 + 1 \cdot 2^4 + 1 \cdot 2^3 + 0 \cdot 2^2 + 1 \cdot 2 + 1 \\
= \ & 64 \ + \ 0 \ + \ 16 \ + \ 8 \ + \ 0 \ + \ 2 + 1 \\
= \ & 91 \qquad \text{in the decimal system.}
\end{aligned}
$$

How can a number in the decimal system be converted to another base? Let us look at the digits $r_n \ldots r_2 r_1 r_0$ of a number x in the decimal system. The rightmost digit, r_0, is the remainder when x is divided by 10, so

$$
x \ = \ q_0 10 + r_0.
$$

The next digit, r_1, is the remainder when the quotient, q_0, is divided by 10, so

$$
\begin{aligned}
q_0 & = q_1 10 + r_1 \\
q_1 & = q_2 10 + r_2 \qquad \text{etc.}
\end{aligned}
$$

The digits in the representation of an integer to any other base have similar properties where 10 is replaced by the base in question.

Let us try to convert the decimal 126 to base 4, using this method. Start by dividing 126 by 4 according to the Division Algorithm and then repeatedly divide the quotients by 4.

$$
\begin{aligned}
126 & = \ 31 \cdot 4 \ + \ 2 \\
31 & = \ 7 \cdot 4 \ + \ 3 \\
7 & = \ 1 \cdot 4 \ + \ 3 \\
1 & = \ 0 \cdot 4 \ + \ 1
\end{aligned}
$$

Hence we can write

$$
\begin{aligned}
126 & = \ 31 \cdot 4 + 2 & = \ (7 \cdot 4 + 3) 4 + 2 \\
& = \ 7 \cdot 4^2 + 3 \cdot 4 + 2 & = \ (4 + 3) 4^2 + 3 \cdot 4 + 2 \\
& = \ 1 \cdot 4^3 + 3 \cdot 4^2 + 3 \cdot 4 + 2.
\end{aligned}
$$

Therefore 126 can be written as $(1332)_4$ in the base 4. Notice that these digits are just the remainders in the above equations, starting with the bottom equation.

1.4.1 Theorem.
Let b be a fixed integer greater than 1. Then any positive integer x can be expressed uniquely as $x = r_n b^n + r_{n-1} b^{n-1} + \cdots + r_2 b^2 + r_1 b + r_0$ where $0 \le r_i < b$ for $i = 0, 1, 2, \ldots, n$ and $r_n \neq 0$.

This expression for x is called the *representation of x in base b* and is written as

$$
x = (r_n r_{n-1} \ldots r_2 r_1 r_0)_b.
$$

Proof. Dividing x by b according to the Division Algorithm and repeatedly dividing the quotients by b, we obtain the following list of equations.

$$
\begin{array}{rcll}
x & = & q_0 b + r_0 & \text{where } 0 \leq r_0 < b \\
q_0 & = & q_1 b + r_1 & \text{where } 0 \leq r_1 < b \\
q_1 & = & q_2 b + r_2 & \text{where } 0 \leq r_2 < b \\
& \vdots & & \\
q_{n-2} & = & q_{n-1} b + r_{n-1} & \text{where } 0 \leq r_{n-1} < b \\
q_{n-1} & = & 0 \cdot b + r_n & \text{where } 0 < r_n < b.
\end{array}
$$

Since $b > 1, x > q_0 > q_1 > \ldots$, and the quotients form a strictly decreasing sequence of nonnegative integers, which must eventually reach zero. Using this list of equations we can write

$$
\begin{array}{rcll}
x & = & q_0 b + r_0 & \\
& = & (q_1 b + r_1)b + r_0 & = \quad q_1 b^2 + r_1 b + r_0 \\
& = & (q_2 b + r_2)b^2 + r_1 b + r_0 & = \quad q_2 b^3 + r_2 b^2 + r_1 b + r_0 \\
& \vdots & & \\
x & = & r_n b^n + r_{n-1} b^{n-1} + \cdots + r_2 b^2 + r_1 b + r_0 &
\end{array}
$$

and this is the required expression.

To show that the expression if unique, suppose that

$$
x \quad = \quad r_n b^n + \cdots + r_1 b + r_0 \quad = \quad s_m b^m + \cdots + s_1 b + s_0
$$

where $0 \leq r_i < b, i = 0, 1, \ldots, n$ and $0 \leq s_j < b, j = 0, 1, \ldots, m$. Now

$$
(r_n b^{n-1} + \cdots + r_1)b + r_0 \quad = \quad (s_m b^{m-1} + \cdots + s_1)b + s_0
$$

which are two expressions for x in the form of the Division Algorithm under division by b. Hence, by the uniqueness of the Division Algorithm, the remainders and quotients must be equal. That is $r_0 = s_0$ and

$$
r_n b^{n-1} + \cdots + r_1 \quad = \quad s_m b^{m-1} + \cdots + s_1.
$$

Repeating this procedure we can show that $r_1 = s_1, r_2 = s_2$, etc. Also m must equal n and the expansions for x are identical. $\qquad \square$

We will use the convention that a number without parentheses and a subscript will be in decimal form.

1.4.2 Example.   Express 545 in base 7, and in base 2.

Solution. Repeatedly dividing by 7 we have

$$
\begin{aligned}
545 &= 77 \cdot 7 + 6 \\
77 &= 11 \cdot 7 + 0 \\
11 &= 1 \cdot 7 + 4 \\
1 &= 0 \cdot 7 + 1.
\end{aligned}
$$

Hence $545 = (1406)_7$

Repeatedly dividing by 2 we have

$$
\begin{aligned}
545 &= 272 \cdot 2 + 1 \\
272 &= 136 \cdot 2 + 0 \\
136 &= 68 \cdot 2 + 0 \\
68 &= 34 \cdot 2 + 0 \\
34 &= 17 \cdot 2 + 0 \\
17 &= 8 \cdot 2 + 1 \\
8 &= 4 \cdot 2 + 0 \\
4 &= 2 \cdot 2 + 0 \\
2 &= 1 \cdot 2 + 0 \\
1 &= 0 \cdot 2 + 1.
\end{aligned}
$$

Hence $545 = (1000100001)_2$.

Check. $(1406)_7 = 1 \cdot 7^3 + 4 \cdot 7^2 + 0 \cdot 7 + 6 = 343 + 196 + 6 = 545.$
$(1000100001)_2 = 2^9 + 2^5 + 2^0 = 512 + 32 + 1 = 545.$ ☐

Each digit in a number in the base b can be any one of the symbols $0, 1, \ldots, b - 1$ and therefore numbers in base b require b symbols to represent them. If the base is larger than 10, new symbols are required to represent some of the numbers.

1.4.3 Example. Using the symbols A for ten and B for eleven, express $(1AAB9)_{12}$ in the decimal system, and express 1511 in base 12.

Solution.
$$
\begin{aligned}
(1AAB9)_{12} &= 1(12)^4 + 10(12)^3 + 10(12)^2 + 11 \cdot 12 + 9 \\
&= 20736 + 17280 + 1440 + 132 + 9 \\
&= 39597.
\end{aligned}
$$

To express 1511 in base 12, repeatedly divide by 12 to obtain

$$
\begin{aligned}
1511 &= 125 \cdot 12 + 11 \\
125 &= 10 \cdot 12 + 5 \\
10 &= 0 \cdot 12 + 10.
\end{aligned}
$$

Hence $1511 = (A5B)_{12}$.

Check.
$$
\begin{aligned}
39597 &= 3299 \cdot 12 + 9 \\
3299 &= 274 \cdot 12 + 11 \\
274 &= 22 \cdot 12 + 10 \\
22 &= 1 \cdot 12 + 10 \\
1 &= 0 \cdot 12 + 1.
\end{aligned}
$$
$(A5B)_{12} = 10 \cdot 12^2 + 5 \cdot 12 + 11 = 1440 + 60 + 11 = 1511.$ ☐

Arithmetical calculations can be performed in base b without reference to base 10, if the addition and multiplication tables for base b are known. The tables for base 4 are as follows. Remember that only the digits 0, 1, 2 and 3 are used in base 4 arithmetic.

Base 4 Addition Table

+	$(1)_4$	$(2)_4$	$(3)_4$
$(1)_4$	$(2)_4$	$(3)_4$	$(10)_4$
$(2)_4$	$(3)_4$	$(10)_4$	$(11)_4$
$(3)_4$	$(10)_4$	$(11)_4$	$(12)_4$

Base 4 Multiplication Table

$\cdot$	$(1)_4$	$(2)_4$	$(3)_4$
$(1)_4$	$(1)_4$	$(2)_4$	$(3)_4$
$(2)_4$	$(2)_4$	$(10)_4$	$(12)_4$
$(3)_4$	$(3)_4$	$(12)_4$	$(21)_4$

1.4.4 Example.   Calculate the sum and product of $(2031)_4$ and $(332)_4$ in base 4.

Solution.

$$
\begin{array}{r}
(2031)_4 \\
+ \quad (332)_4 \\
\hline
(3023)_4
\end{array}
\qquad
\begin{array}{r}
(2031)_4 \\
\times \quad (332)_4 \\
\hline
(10122)_4 \\
(122130)_4 \\
(1221300)_4 \\
\hline
(2020212)_4
\end{array}
$$

Check. $(2031)_4 = 2 \cdot 4^3 + 3 \cdot 4 + 1 = 141$ and $(332)_4 = 3 \cdot 4^2 + 3 \cdot 4 + 2 = 62$.
$(3023)_4 = 3 \cdot 4^3 + 2 \cdot 4 + 3 = 203 = 141 + 62.$
$(2020212)_4 = 2 \cdot 4^6 + 2 \cdot 4^4 + 2 \cdot 4^2 + 4 + 2 = 8742 = 141 \cdot 62.$ ☐

1.5   PRIME NUMBERS

One of the most important class of numbers is the class of prime numbers. Most integers can be factored into a product of smaller integers. Numbers which cannot be so factored are called prime numbers. They form the basic building blocks of the number system, because any other integer can be written as a product of primes.

1.5.1 Definition.   An integer $p > 1$ is called a *prime* if its only positive divisors are 1 and p; otherwise it is called *composite*.

The first few primes are 2, 3, 5, 7, 11 while $4 = 2 \cdot 2$, $6 = 2 \cdot 3$, $8 = 2 \cdot 2 \cdot 2$, $9 = 3 \cdot 3$, $10 = 2 \cdot 5$ are composite. The integer 1 is neither prime nor composite; a factor 1 is of no interest in any product.

1.5.2 Proposition. Every integer > 1 can be expressed as a product of primes.

Proof. Suppose that the result is false and let N be the smallest integer, greater than 1, that cannot be written as a product of primes. N cannot be prime itself, so we can write $N = r \cdot s$ where $1 < r \leq s < N$. By our hypothesis, N is the smallest integer that cannot be written as a product of primes; hence r and s can be written as a product of primes. It follows that $N = r \cdot s$ can also be written as a product of primes. This contradiction shows that our hypothesis is false and the theorem must be true. □

It is natural to wonder whether there are only a finite number of primes or whether the set of primes is infinite. This question was answered by Euclid in about 300 B.C., and the following proof is essentially the same as his.

1.5.3 Euclid's Theorem. There are an infinite number of primes.

Proof. Suppose that there are just a finite number of primes, say $p_1, p_2, p_3, \ldots, p_n$. Consider the integer

$$N = p_1 \cdot p_2 \cdot p_3 \cdots p_n + 1$$

This is not a prime because it is larger than all the primes $p_1, p_2, p_3, \ldots, p_n$. On the other hand, N is not divisible by any of the primes p_i, for $1 \leq i \leq n$; if $p_i | N$ then $p_i | (N - p_1 \cdots p_n)$ and so $p_i | 1$, which is impossible. Therefore N cannot be written as a product of primes, contrary to the previous theorem.

Hence our original supposition must be false and the theorem is true. □

There is no known efficient procedure for finding prime numbers. A tedious process known as the *sieve of Eratosthenes* will yield all the primes less than any given number N. It consists of writing down all the numbers from 2 to $N - 1$. Leave 2 alone and cross out every second number (that is, composite numbers that are multiples of 2). The next remaining number, namely 3, will be prime; keep it and cross out every third number starting from 3 (that is, composite multiples of 3). The next remaining number, namely 5, will be prime; keep it and cross out every fifth number after 5. If we proceed in this way we will eventually cross out all the composite numbers and all the primes less than N will remain.

The following important result shows that if a prime divides a product then it must divide one of the factors. This is not true for composite numbers; for example $6 | 15 \cdot 4$ but $6 \nmid 15$ and $6 \nmid 4$.

1.5.4 Theorem. If p is a prime and $p | ab$ then $p | a$ or $p | b$.

Proof. Suppose that the prime p divides ab but does not divide a. Since the only positive divisors of the prime p are 1 and p, the only positive common divisor of p and a is 1; hence $\text{GCD}(a, p) = 1$. It now follows from Theorem 1.2.8 that $p | b$. Therefore either $p | a$ or $p | b$. □

One of the reasons for introducing primes is to enable us to split numbers into factors which are as small as possible. We shall now show that each number can be written as a product of primes in essentially only one way. This may appear obvious; most probably because you have never seen a number being factored into primes in two different ways. (This can be seen by looking at the set of real numbers $S = \{a + b\sqrt{5} \mid a, b \in \mathbb{Z}\}$ instead of the set of integers $\mathbb{Z}$. In S, 4 can be factored as $(\sqrt{5} + 1)(\sqrt{5} - 1)$ as well as $2 \cdot 2$, and the numbers $2, \sqrt{5} + 1$ and $\sqrt{5} - 1$ cannot be further factored, and so are "primes" in the set S.)

As multiplication is commutative, the prime factors in any factorization can be written in different orders; for example, $45 = 3^2 \cdot 5 = 3 \cdot 5 \cdot 3$. However, up to order, the factorization of integers is unique. This Unique Factorization Theorem is so basic it is often referred to as the *Fundamental Theorem of Arithmetic*.

1.5.5 Unique Factorization Theorem.   Every integer, greater than 1, can be expressed as a product of primes and, apart from the order of the factors, this expression is unique.

Proof.   The existence of the factorization was shown in Proposition 1.5.2.

Now suppose that an integer x can be factored into primes in two ways as

$$x = p_1 p_2 \cdots p_n = q_1 q_2 \cdots q_m$$

where all the p's and q's are primes. Since $p_1 | x$, $p_1 | q_1 q_2 \cdots q_m$. By repeated application of Theorem 1.5.4, it follows that p_1 divides at least one of the q's. If necessary, rearrange the q's so that $p_1 | q_1$. Since q_1 is prime and p_1 is a nontrivial factor, it follows that $p_1 = q_1$. Cancelling p_1 and q_1 we have

$$p_2 p_3 \cdots p_n = q_2 q_3 \cdots q_m$$

By continuing in this way, we see that each p must be paired off with one of the q's until there are no factors on either side. Hence $n = m$ and, apart from the order of the factors, the two expressions for x are the same. $\qquad\square$

Note that this theorem does not provide an algorithm for finding the prime factors. The following result shows that we can determine whether an integer x has any factors, other than x or 1, by checking whether it is divisible by all the primes less than or equal to $\sqrt{x}$.

1.5.6 Theorem.   An integer $x > 1$ is either prime or contains a prime factor $\leq \sqrt{x}$.

Proof.   Suppose that p is the smallest prime factor of x. If x is composite, we can write $x = ab$ where a and b are positive integers between 1 and x. Since p is the smallest prime factor, $a \geq p, b \geq p$ and $x = ab \geq p^2$. Hence $p \leq \sqrt{x}$. $\qquad\square$

The above proposition shows that in the sieve of Eratosthenes, we only have to cross out multiples of numbers $\leq \sqrt{N}$ when searching for primes up to N.

The prime factorization of integers can be used to find all the divisors of an integer and the greatest common divisor of two integers.

1.5.7 Proposition. If $a = p_1^{\alpha_1} p_2^{\alpha_2} \cdots p_n^{\alpha_n}$ is the prime factorization of a into powers of distinct primes $p_1, p_2, \ldots, p_n$, then the positive divisors of a are those integers of the form

$$c = p_1^{\gamma_1} p_2^{\gamma_2} \cdots p_n^{\gamma_n} \qquad \text{where} \qquad 0 \leq \gamma_i \leq \alpha_i \text{ for } i = 1, 2, \ldots, n.$$

Proof. If $\gamma_i \leq \alpha_i$ for each i, it is clear that $a = c(p_1^{\alpha_1 - \gamma_1} p_2^{\alpha_2 - \gamma_2} \cdots p_n^{\alpha_n - \gamma_n})$ and so $c|a$.

On the other hand, if c is a divisor of a, let $a = bc$ where

$$b = p_1^{\beta_1} \cdots p_n^{\beta_n} \cdots p_m^{\beta_m} \qquad \text{and} \qquad c = p_1^{\gamma_1} \cdots p_n^{\gamma_n} \cdots p_m^{\gamma_m}$$

and $p_1, \ldots, p_m$ are distinct primes (some of the exponents of the primes may be zero). By applying the Unique Factorization Theorem 1.5.5 to the equation $a = bc$, we see that $\alpha_i = \beta_i + \gamma_i$ for $i = 1, 2, \ldots, n$ and $\beta_i = \gamma_i = 0$ if $i \geq n$. In particular $\gamma_i \leq \alpha_i$ for $i = 1, 2, \ldots, n$. $\square$

1.5.8 Theorem. If $a = p_1^{\alpha_1} \cdots p_n^{\alpha_n}$ and $b = p_1^{\beta_1} \cdots p_n^{\beta_n}$ are prime factorizations of the integers a and b (some of the exponents may be zero), then

$$\text{GCD}(a, b) = p_1^{\delta_1} \cdots p_n^{\delta_n}$$

where $\delta_i = \min(\alpha_i, \beta_i)$ for $i = 1, \ldots, n$.

Proof. Let $d = p_1^{\delta_1} \cdots p_n^{\delta_n}$ where $\delta_i = \min(\alpha_i, \beta_i)$.

Since $\delta_i \leq \alpha_i$ and $\delta_i \leq \beta_i$ for each i, it follows from the previous proposition that $d|a$ and $d|b$. Suppose $c = p_1^{\gamma_1} \cdots p_n^{\gamma_n}$ is another divisor of a and b. Then, by Proposition 1.5.7 again, $\gamma_i \leq \alpha_i$ and $\gamma_i \leq \beta_i$ for each i. Hence $\gamma_i \leq \min(\alpha_i, \beta_i)$ and $c|d$. This proves that $d = \text{GCD}(a, b)$. $\square$

For example,

$$
\begin{aligned}
336 &= 2^4 \cdot 3 \cdot 7 &&= 2^4 \cdot 3^1 \cdot 7^1 \cdot 11^0 \\
2156 &= 2^2 \cdot 7^2 \cdot 11 &&= 2^2 \cdot 3^0 \cdot 7^2 \cdot 11^1 \\
\text{GCD}(336, 2156) &= &&\quad 2^2 \cdot 3^0 \cdot 7^1 \cdot 11^0 = 28.
\end{aligned}
$$

This method does not supersede the Euclidean Algorithm for finding greatest common divisors because it is often too tedious to factor an integer into a product of primes; however this method is useful when the numbers involved are small.

Our investigations into prime numbers and the divisibility properties of integers is the beginning of the branch of mathematics known as Number Theory. Even though the raw material, the set of integers, is apparently elementary, there are many outstanding conjectures about numbers and primes that can be simply stated, but have not yet been solved.

One of these is known as the "Goldbach conjecture". Goldbach, in a letter to Euler in 1742, asked if every even number (greater than 2) can be written as the sum of two primes. It is true in every particular case that has been looked at; for example, $4 = 2 + 2$, $6 = 3 + 3$, $8 = 3 + 5, \ldots, 30 = 23 + 7$, $32 = 29 + 3$. However nobody has proved that it must be true for all even numbers.

Another unsolved problem is that of the number of pairs of primes differing by 2. An examination of a list of prime numbers shows that many primes occur in pairs of the form p and $p + 2$; such pairs are 3 and 5, 11 and 13, 17 and 19, etc. From circumstantial evidence it appears that the number of such prime pairs is infinite, but no proof has been found.

In 1640, Fermat thought that he had discovered a long-sought-for formula that would yield primes for every value of a variable n. He conjectured that

$$F(n) = 2^{2^n} + 1$$

was a prime for all values of n. Now $F(0) = 3$, $F(1) = 5$, $F(2) = 17$, $F(3) = 257$ and $F(4) = 65537$, which are all primes. However, in 1732, Euler discovered that $F(5)$ contains a factor 641 and hence is not prime. In fact, despite extensive computer searches, no more of these "Fermat numbers" were found to be prime. At present, it is unknown whether $F(n)$ is ever prime if $n > 4$.

Exercise Set 1

1 - 8. Find the quotient and remainder when b is divided by a in each of the following cases.

1. $a = 3, b = 13$ **2.** $a = 13, b = 3$

3. $a = 7, b = 7$ **4.** $a = 7, b = 0$

5. $a = 4, b = -12$ **6.** $a = 4, b = -10$

7. $a = 11, b = -246$ **8.** $a = 17, b = -5$

9. If $3p^2 = q^2$ where $p, q \in \mathbb{Z}$, show that 3 is a common divisor of p and q.

10. If $ac|bc$ and $c \neq 0$ prove that $a|b$.

11. Prove that $\text{GCD}(ad, bd) = |d| \cdot \text{GCD}(a, b)$.

12 - 18. *Find the greatest common divisor of each pair of integers.*

12. 5280 and 3600 **13.** 484 and 451
14. 616 and 427 **15.** 1137 and -419
16. 19201 and 3587 **17.** 2^{100} and 100^2
18. 10! and 3^{10}

19 - 26. *In each case write* $\text{GCD}(a, b)$ *in the form* $ax + by$ *where* $x, y \in \mathbb{Z}$.

19. $a = 484, b = 451$ **20.** $a = 5280, b = 3600$
21. $a = 17, b = 15$ **22.** $a = 5, b = 13$
23. $a = 100, b = -35$ **24.** $a = 3953, b = 1829$
25. $a = 51, b = 17$ **26.** $a = 431, b = 0$

27. Prove that $\text{GCD}(a, c) = \text{GCD}(b, c) = 1$ if and only if $\text{GCD}(ab, c) = 1$

28. Prove that any two consecutive integers are coprime.

29. Simplify $\dfrac{95}{646} + \dfrac{40}{391}$.

30. Gear A turns at 1 rev/min and is meshed into gear B. If A has 32 teeth and B has 120 teeth, how often will both gears be simultaneously back in their starting positions?

31 - 36. *Find one integer solution, if possible, to each Diophantine equation.*

31. $21x + 35y = 7$ **32.** $14x + 18y = 5$
33. $x + 14y = 9$ **34.** $11x + 15y = 31$
35. $143x + 253y = 156$ **36.** $91x + 126y = 203$

37 - 42. *Find all the integer solutions to each Diophantine equation.*

37. $7x + 9y = 1$ **38.** $212x + 37y = 1$
39. $15x - 24y = 9$ **40.** $16x + 44y = 20$
41. $243x + 405y = 123$ **42.** $169x - 65y = 91$

43 - 46. *Find all the **nonnegative** integer solutions to each Diophantine equation.*

43. $14x + 9y = 1000$ **44.** $12x + 57y = 423$
45. $38x + 34y = 200$ **46.** $11x - 12y = 13$

47. Can 1000 be expressed as the sum of two positive integers, one of which is divisible by 11 and the other by 17?

48. Can 120 be expressed as the sum of two positive integers, one of which is divisible by 11 and the other by 17?

49. Can 120 be expressed as the sum of two positive integers, one of which is divisible by 14 and the other by 18?

50. Find the smallest positive integer x so that $157x$ leaves remainder 10 when divided by 24.

51. The nickel slot of a pay phone will not accept coins. Can a call costing 95 cents be paid for exactly using only dimes and quarters? If so, in how many ways can it be done?

52 - 54. Convert the following numbers to base 10.

52. $(5613)_7$ **53.** $(100110111)_2$
54. $(9A411)_{12}$ where A is the symbol for ten.

55. How many seconds are there in 4 hours 27 minutes and 13 seconds?

56 - 61. Convert the following numbers to the indicated base.

56. 1157 to base 2   **57.** 241 to base 9
58. 433 to base 5   **59.** 30 to base 3
60. 5766 to base 12, writing A for ten and B for eleven
61. 40239 to base 60

62. Add and multiply $(1011)_2$ and $(110110)_2$ together in base 2.

63. Add and multiply $(3130)_4$ and $(103)_4$ together in base 4.

64. Write out the addition and multiplication tables for base 6 arithmetic and then multiply $(4512)_6$ by $(343)_6$ in base 6.

65. Subtract $(3321)_4$ from $(10020)_4$ in base 4 and check your answer by converting to base 10.

66. If $a = (342)_8$ and $b = (173)_8$, find $a - b$ without converting to base 10. (If you get stuck, listen to the song "The New Math" by Tom Lehrer on the record "That was the year that was".)

67. How many positive divisors does 12 have?

68. How many positive divisors does 6696 have?

69. A nonnegative integer e is called the *least common multiple* of the integers a and b if

    (i) e is a multiple of a and b

    (ii) any multiple of a and b is also a multiple of e.

The least common multiple is denoted by $\mathrm{LCM}(a, b)$. If $a = p_1^{\alpha_1} \cdots p_n^{\alpha_n}$ and $b = p_1^{\beta_1} \cdots p_n^{\beta_n}$, show that $e = p_1^{\varepsilon_1} \cdots p_n^{\varepsilon_n}$ where $\varepsilon_i = \max(\alpha_i, \beta_i)$ for $i = 1, \ldots, n$. Also, show that for any positive integers a and b

$$a \cdot b = \mathrm{LCM}(a, b) \cdot \mathrm{GCD}(a, b).$$

70 - 71. *Factor the following numbers into prime factors and calculate the greatest common divisor and least common multiple of each pair.*

70. 40 and 144   **71.** 5280 and 57800

72. Find $\mathrm{LCM}(12827, 20099)$.

Problem Set 1

73. Prove that $\{ax + by \mid x, y \in \mathbb{Z}\} = \{n \cdot \mathrm{GCD}(a, b) \mid n \in \mathbb{Z}\}$.

74. Show that $\mathrm{GCD}(ab, c) = \mathrm{GCD}(b, c)$ if $\mathrm{GCD}(a, c) = 1$. Is it true in general that

$$\mathrm{GCD}(ab, c) = \mathrm{GCD}(a, c) \cdot \mathrm{GCD}(b, c)\,?$$

75. Show that the Diophantine equation $ax^2 + by^2 = c$ does not have any integer solutions unless $\mathrm{GCD}(a, b) \mid c$. If $\mathrm{GCD}(a, b) \mid c$, does the equation always have an integer solution?

76. For what values of a and b does the Diophantine equation $ax + by = c$ have an infinite number of positive solutions for x and y?

77. For what values of c does $8x + 5y = c$ have exactly one strictly positive solution.

78. An oil company has a contract to deliver 100000 litres of gasoline. Their tankers can carry 2400 litres and they can attach one trailer carrying 2200 litres to each tanker. All the tankers and trailers must be completely full on this contract, otherwise the gas would slosh around too much when going over some rough roads. Find the least number of tankers required to fulfill the contract. Each trailer, if used, must be pulled by a full tanker.

79. A trucking company has to move 844 refrigerators. It has two types of trucks it can use, one carries 28 refrigerators and the other 34 refrigerators. If it only sends out full trucks and all the trucks return empty, list the possible ways of moving all the refrigerators.

80. Show how to measure exactly 2 litres of water from a river using a 27 litre jug and a 16 litre jug. If you could not lift the larger jug when full, but could push it over, could you still measure the 2 litres?

81. Let S be the complete solution set of the Diophantine equation $ax + by = d$. Is

$$cS = \{(cx, cy) \mid (x, y) \in S\}$$

the complete solution set of $ax + by = cd$?

82. Four men and a monkey spend the day gathering coconuts on a tropical island. After they have all gone to sleep at night, one of the men awakens and, not trusting the others, decides to take his share. He divides the coconuts into four equal piles, except for one remaining coconut, which he gives to the monkey. He then hides his share, puts the other piles together and goes back to sleep. Each of the other men awakens during the night and does likewise, and every time there is one coconut left over for the monkey. In the morning all the men awake, divide what's left of the coconuts into four, and again there is one left over that is given to the monkey. Find the minimum number of coconuts that could have been in the original pile.

83. If $a, b, c \in \mathbb{Z}$, the nonnegative integer d is called the *greatest common divisor* of a, b and c, and denoted by $\text{GCD}(a, b, c)$ if

   (i) d divides a, b, and c

   (ii) any divisor of a, b, and c also divides d.

Prove that $\text{GCD}(a, b, c) = \text{GCD}(a, \text{GCD}(b, c))$.

84. Prove that the Diophantine equation $ax + by + cz = e$ has a solution if and only if $\text{GCD}(a, b, c) | e$.

85. If $\text{GCD}(a, b, c) | e$, describe how to find one solution to the Diophantine equation $ax + by + cz = e$.

86. Describe how to find all the solutions to the Diophantine equation

$$ax + by + cz = e.$$

87. Find one integer solution to the Diophantine equation $18x + 14y + 63z = 5$.

88. Find all the ways that $1.67 worth of stamps can be put on a parcel, using 6 cents, 10 cents and 15 cents stamps.

89. Given a balance and weights of 1, 2, 3, 5, and 10 grams, show that any integer gram weight up to 21 grams can be weighed. If the weights were 1, 2, 4, 8 and 16 grams, show that any integer weight up to 31 grams could be weighed.

90. If weights could be put on either side of a balance, show that any integer weight up to 121 grams could be weighed using weights of 1, 3, 9, 27 and 81 grams.

91. If numbers (in their decimal form) are written out in words, such as six hundreds, four tens and three for 643, we require one word for each digit 0, 1, 2, ..., 9, one word for 10, one word for 10^2, etc. We can name all the integers below 1000 with twelve words. What base would use the least number of words to name all the numbers below 1000? What base would use the least number of words to name all the numbers below 10^6?

92. Consider the set of all even integers

$$2\mathbb{Z} = \{2n \mid n \in \mathbb{Z}\}.$$

We can add, subtract and multiply elements of $2\mathbb{Z}$ and the result will always be in $2\mathbb{Z}$, but we cannot always divide. We can define divisibility and factorization in $2\mathbb{Z}$ in a similar way to that in $\mathbb{Z}$. (For example, $2|4$ in $2\mathbb{Z}$, but $2 \nmid 6$ even though $6 = 2 \cdot 3$, because $3 \notin 2\mathbb{Z}$.) A prime in $2\mathbb{Z}$ is a positive even integer that cannot be factored into the product of two even integers.

   (i) Find all the primes in $2\mathbb{Z}$.

   (ii) Can every positive element of $2\mathbb{Z}$ be expressed as a product of these primes?

   (iii) If this factorization into primes can be accomplished, is it unique?

93. Prove that the sum of two consecutive odd primes has at least three prime divisors (not necessarily different).

94. How many zeros are there at the right end of $100! = 100 \cdot 99 \cdot 98 \cdot 97 \cdots 2 \cdot 1$?

95. Show that $1 + \frac{1}{2} + \frac{1}{3} + \cdots + \frac{1}{n}$ can never be an integer if $n > 1$.

96. If $\lfloor x \rfloor$ is the greatest integer less than or equal to x (that is, the integral part of x), then for which values of n does $\lfloor \sqrt{n} \rfloor$ divide n?

97. Let a and b be integers greater than 1, and let $e = \text{LCM}(a, b)$. Prove that

$$0 < \frac{1}{a} + \frac{1}{b} - \frac{1}{e} < 1.$$

98. If a and b are odd positive integers, and the sum of the integers, less than a and greater than b, is 1000, then find a and b.

99 - 102. Either prove each of the following statements about integers, or give a counter example.

99. $a^2 | b^2$ if and only if $a | b$.

100. $\text{GCD}(a, b) = \text{GCD}(a + b, \text{LCM}(a, b))$.

101. $\text{LCM}(\text{GCD}(a, b), \text{GCD}(a, c)) = \text{GCD}(a, \text{LCM}(b, c))$.

102. If $\text{GCD}(a, b) = 1$ and $ax + by = c$ has a positive integer solution then so does $ax + by = d$ when $d > c$.

103. Write a computer program to test whether a given number is prime. Use your program to find the smallest positive integer n for which the number $n^2 - n + 41$ fails to be prime.

104. Using a computer, test whether $F(4) = 2^{2^4} + 1$ and $F(5) = 2^{2^5} + 1$ are prime.

105. If n is a positive integer, denote by $\phi(n)$ the number of positive integers less than or equal to n, which are coprime to n. This is called the *Euler ϕ-function*. For example, $\phi(1) = 1, \phi(2) = 1, \phi(3) = 2$ and $\phi(4) = 2$.

   (i) Find $\phi(7)$, $\phi(12)$, $\phi(16)$, $\phi(25)$ and $\phi(27)$.

   (ii) Show that $\phi(p^r) = p^{r-1}(p - 1)$ for any prime p.

   (iii) If p and q are distinct primes, show that $\phi(pq) = (p - 1)(q - 1)$.

106.   (i) Find two consecutive primes that differ by at least 10.

    (ii) Prove that there are arbitrarily large gaps between two consecutive primes.

107. Let $a < b < c$, where a is a positive integer and b and c are odd primes. Prove that if $a \mid (3b + 2c)$ and $a \mid (2b + 3c)$, then $a = 1$ or 5. Give examples to show that both these values for a are possible.

108. An integer n is *perfect* if the sum of its divisors (including 1 and itself) is $2n$. Show that if $2^p - 1$ is a prime number, then $n = 2^{p-1}(2^p - 1)$ is perfect.

Chapter 2

Congruences

2.1 CONGRUENCE

In 1800, Gauss introduced the notion of congruence, thereby offering a convenient way of dealing with many questions of divisibility.

2.1.1 Definition.   Let m be a fixed positive integer. If $a, b, \in \mathbb{Z}$, we say that "a is *congruent* to b *modulo* m" and write

$$a \equiv b \pmod{m}$$

whenever $m \mid (a - b)$. If $m \nmid (a - b)$, we write $a \not\equiv b \pmod{m}$.

For example, $7 \equiv 3 \pmod 4$, $-6 \equiv 14 \pmod{10}$, $121 \equiv 273 \pmod 2$, but $5 \not\equiv 4 \pmod 3$ and $21 \not\equiv 10 \pmod 2$.

The condition for a to be congruent to b modulo m is equivalent to the condition that

$$a = b + km \qquad \text{for some } k \in \mathbb{Z}.$$

Congruences occur in everyday life. The short hand of a clock indicates the hour modulo 12, while the long hand indicates the minute modulo 60. For example, 20 hours after midnight, the clock indicates 8 o'clock because $20 \equiv 8 \pmod{12}$. In determining which day of the week a particular date falls, we apply congruence modulo 7.

The idea of congruence is not radically different from divisibility, but its usefulness lies in its notation, and the fact that congruence with respect to a fixed modulus has many of the properties of ordinary equality.

49

2.1.2 Proposition.   Let $a, b, c, \in \mathbb{Z}$. Then

(i) $a \equiv a \pmod{m}$

(ii) if $a \equiv b \pmod{m}$ then $b \equiv a \pmod{m}$

(iii) if $a \equiv b \pmod{m}$ and $b \equiv c \pmod{m}$ then $a \equiv c \pmod{m}$.

Proof. (i).   Since $a - a = 0$ and $m|0$ it follows that $a \equiv a \pmod{m}$.

(ii).   If $a \equiv b \pmod{m}$ then $m|(a - b)$ and hence, by Proposition 1.1.2(ii), $m|(-1)(a - b)$; that is, $m|(b - a)$ and $b \equiv a \pmod{m}$.

(iii).   If $a \equiv b$ and $b \equiv c \pmod{m}$ then $m|(a - b)$ and $m|(b - c)$. Hence, by Proposition 1.1.2(ii), $m|(a - b) + (b - c)$; that is, $m|(a - c)$ and $a \equiv c \pmod{m}$. □

2.1.3 Proposition.   If $a \equiv a' \pmod{m}$ and $b \equiv b' \pmod{m}$ then

(i) $a + b \equiv a' + b' \pmod{m}$

(ii) $a - b \equiv a' - b' \pmod{m}$

(iii) $a \cdot b \equiv a' \cdot b' \pmod{m}$.

Proof.   Since $a \equiv a'$ and $b \equiv b' \pmod{m}$ we can write $a = a' + km$ and $b = b' + \ell m$ where $k, \ell \in \mathbb{Z}$. It follows that

$$
\begin{aligned}
a + b &= a' + b' + (k + \ell)m \\
a - b &= a' - b' + (k - \ell)m \\
ab &= a'b' + (kb' + \ell a' + k\ell m)m.
\end{aligned}
$$

The results now follow, since $k + \ell, k - \ell, kb' + \ell a' + k\ell m \in \mathbb{Z}$. □

Although we can add, subtract and multiply congruences with respect to the same modulus, we cannot with impunity divide out an integer from either side of a congruence. For example, $6 \equiv 36 \pmod{10}$ but $1 \not\equiv 6 \pmod{10}$. However the following proposition indicates under what conditions cancellation can occur.

2.1.4 Proposition.   If $ac \equiv bc \pmod{m}$ and $\mathrm{GCD}(c, m) = 1$ then it follows that $a \equiv b \pmod{m}$.

Proof.   If $ac \equiv bc \pmod{m}$ then $m|c(a - b)$. If $\mathrm{GCD}(c, m) = 1$, it follows from Theorem 1.2.8 that $m|(a - b)$ and so $a \equiv b \pmod{m}$. □

For example, $35 \equiv 15 \pmod{4}$ and, since $\mathrm{GCD}(5, 4) = 1$, it follows that $7 \equiv 3 \pmod{4}$.

As would be expected from the fact that $a \equiv b$ (mod m) is equivalent to $a = b + km$, there is a close relationship between congruences modulo m and remainders under division by m.

2.1.5 Proposition. $a \equiv b$ (mod m) if and only if a and b have the same remainders when divided by m.

Proof. Divide a and b by m according to the Division Algorithm to obtain

$$a = km + r \qquad \text{where } 0 \le r < m$$
$$b = \ell m + s \qquad \text{where } 0 \le s < m.$$

Hence $a - b = (k - \ell)m + (r - s)$ where $-m < r - s < m$.

If $a \equiv b$ (mod m) then $m|(a - b)$ and hence $m|(r - s)$. However $-m < r - s < m$ and so $r - s = 0$.

Conversely, if a and b have the same remainders when divided by m then $a - b = (k - \ell)m$ and $a \equiv b$ (mod m). $\qquad \square$

We see from the above proposition, that any integer must be congruent to precisely one of $0, 1, 2, \ldots, m - 1$ modulo m.

2.1.6 Example. What is the remainder when 2^{37} is divided by 7?

Solution. It would be very tedious to calculate 2^{37} and then divide by 7. However we can use the above proposition to find what 2^{37} is congruent to modulo 7.

We know that $2^3 = 8$ and so $2^3 \equiv 1$ (mod 7). By repeated application of Proposition 2.1.3(iii), it follows that $(2^3)^{12} \equiv 1^{12} \equiv 1 \pmod{7}$. Hence

$$2^{37} \equiv 2^{36} \cdot 2 \equiv (2^3)^{12} \cdot 2 \equiv 1 \cdot 2 \equiv 2 \pmod{7}$$

and 2^{37} has remainder 2 when divided by 7. $\qquad \square$

Note that the powers of 2 take on the following forms modulo 7.

$$2 \equiv 2, \quad 2^2 \equiv 4, \quad 2^3 \equiv 1, \quad 2^4 \equiv 2, \quad 2^5 \equiv 4, \quad 2^6 \equiv 1, \text{ etc.} \pmod{7}.$$

2.1.7 Example. What is the remainder when $4^{10} \cdot 7^7$ is divided by 5?

Solution. $4^2 \equiv 16 \equiv 1$ (mod 5) and $7^2 \equiv 49 \equiv -1$ (mod 5). Hence

$$4^{10} \cdot 7^7 \equiv (4^2)^5 \cdot (7^2)^3 \cdot 7 \equiv 1^5 \cdot (-1)^3 \cdot 7 \equiv -7 \equiv 3 \pmod{5}$$

and $4^{10} \cdot 7^7$ has remainder 3 when divided by 5. $\qquad \square$

2.2 ~ TESTS FOR DIVISIBILITY

Congruences can be used to prove some of the familiar tests for divisibility by certain integers. It is well known that any integer is divisible by 2 if and only if its last digit is even. An integer is divisible by 4 if and only if the number determined by its last two digits is divisible by 4.

This test for divisibility by 4 works because $100 \equiv 0 \pmod 4$ and so, for example $56976 \equiv 569 \cdot 100 + 76 \equiv 76 \pmod 4$. Therefore the remainder when 56976 is divided by 4 is the same as that of 76 when divided by 4.

2.2.1 Theorem.   A number is divisible by 9 if and only if the sum of its digits is divisible by 9.

For example, consider the numbers 5895 and 125942. The sums of their digits are $5 + 8 + 9 + 5 = 27$ and $1 + 2 + 5 + 9 + 4 + 2 = 23$ respectively; since 27 is divisible by 9 but 23 is not, it follows that 5895 is divisible by 9 but 125942 is not.

Proof.   Let x be a number with digits $a_r a_{r-1} \ldots a_1 a_0$ so that

$$x = a_r 10^r + a_{r-1} 10^{r-1} + \cdots + a_1 10 + a_0.$$

Now $10 \equiv 1 \pmod 9$ and hence $10^k \equiv 1^k \equiv 1 \pmod 9$ for all $k \geq 0$. Therefore

$$x \equiv a_r + a_{r-1} + \cdots + a_1 + a_0 \pmod 9$$

and $x \equiv 0 \pmod 9$ if and only if the sum of its digits is congruent to zero modulo 9. $\Box$

Note that this not only provides a test for divisibility by 9, it also provides a method for finding the remainder of any number when divided by 9. For example,

$$125942 \equiv 1 + 2 + 5 + 9 + 4 + 2 \equiv 23 \equiv 2 + 3 \equiv 5 \pmod 9$$

and hence 125942 has remainder 5 when divided by 9.

A similar proof also yields the following result for divisibility by 3.

2.2.2 Theorem.   A number is divisible by 3 if and only if the sum of its digits is divisible by 3. $\Box$

The result on the divisibility by 9 provides the basis for an ancient method of checking arithmetical calculations called *casting out nines*. Suppose we wish to check the calculation

$$43296 \times 1742 - 514376 = 74907256.$$

The check proceeds as follows. For each number involved, add the digits together and throw away any multiples of nine. Then perform the original calculation on these remaining numbers. The calculation checks if this new answer agrees with the original answer, after adding digits and casting out any multiples of nine. If the answers do not agree after casting out nines, an error has occurred in the calculation.

In the above example, we add the digits of 43296 to obtain $4 + 3 + 2 + 9 + 6$ and, after casting out nines, we obtain the number 6. If we do this procedure to the other numbers on the left hand side of the equation, our reduced equation becomes

$$6 \times 5 - 8.$$

Perform this simplified calculation to obtain 22 or, after casting out nines again, 4. The sum of the digits of the original answer, after casting out nines, is also 4; hence the calculation checks. This does not guarantee that the calculation is correct; it only provides a partial check.

Let us take another example.

Original calculation : $(442)^3$ $+$ 5176 $=$ 86355064
After casting out nines : 1^3 $+$ 1 $\equiv$ 1 (mod 9)

This reduced congruence is incorrect, so a mistake must have been made in the original calculation.

We see from Theorem 2.2.1 why this method works. The check just performs the original calculation modulo 9. Therefore the method works for any calculation involving addition, subtraction and multiplication. (We can treat exponentiation as repeated multiplication, but we must not reduce the exponent modulo 9.)

2.2.3 Proposition.   A number is divisible by 11 if and only if the alternating sum of its digits is divisible by 11.

Proof.   Let $x = a_r 10^r + a_{r-1} 10^{r-1} + \cdots + a_1 10 + a_0$. Now $10 \equiv -1 \pmod{11}$ so that

$$x \equiv (-1)^r a_r + (-1)^{r-1} a_{r-1} + \cdots - a_3 + a_2 - a_1 + a_0 \pmod{11}.$$

Hence any number is congruent modulo 11 to the alternating sum of its digits and the result follows.   □

For example, 2307151 is divisible by 11 because $2 - 3 + 0 - 7 + 1 - 5 + 1 = -11$, which is divisible by 11.

2.3   EQUIVALENCE RELATIONS

Congruence modulo a fixed integer is an example of an important notion in mathematics, namely the concept of an equivalence relation.

Algebra can be considered as the study of 'operations' and 'relations' in sets. Examples of operations are 'addition', 'subtraction', 'multiplication' and 'exponentiation'; these all combine two elements to form a third. Examples of relations are 'greater than', 'divisible by' and 'equals'; these all compare two elements. Roughly, R is a *relation* on a set S if, for every ordered pair of elements a and b in S, either a is related to b, in which case we write aRb, or a is not related to b and we write $a \not\!R b$. Here are some examples of relations.

1. Let S be the set of real numbers and, for $a, b \in S$, take aRb to mean $a > b$. This the 'greater than' relation.

2. Let $S = \mathbb{Z}$ and take aRb to be $a|b$. This is the divisibility relation.

3. Let S be any set and take aRb to be $a = b$. This is the relation of equality.

4. Let $S = \mathbb{Z}$ and take aRb to be $a \equiv b \pmod{m}$. This is the relation of congruence modulo m.

5. Let S be the set of triangles in the plane and, for two triangles T_1 and T_2, take $T_1 R T_2$ to mean T_1 is congruent to T_2. This is the congruence relation among triangles.

6. Let S be the set of all people in the country and, if a and b are two people, take aRb to mean a is the brother of b.

7. Let S again be the set of all people in the country and take aRb to mean that a has the same surname as b.

8. Let S be the set of all days in a particular year and, for any two days a and b, take aRb to mean that a and b occur on the same day of the week.

2.3.1 Definition.   A relation R on a set S is called an *equivalence relation* if

(i) aRa for all $a \in S$ *(Reflexive Property)*

(ii) if aRb then bRa *(Symmetric Property)*

(iii) if aRb and bRc then aRc.   *(Transitive Property)*

Of the above examples of relations, 3, 4, 5, 7, and 8 are equivalence relations while the others are not. Proposition 2.1.2 shows that congruence modulo m is an equivalence relation.

2.3.2 Definition.   If R is an equivalence relation on a set S and $a \in S$ write

$$[a] = \{x \in S \mid xRa\}.$$

This is called the *equivalence class* of a and consists of all elements in S that are equivalent to a. The element a is called a *representative* of the equivalence class $[a]$.

In the 'equals' relation, the equivalence class of an element consists of a alone. In the relation 'has the same surname', the equivalence class containing John Smith consists of all the people with the surname Smith.

In the equivalence relation of 'congruence modulo m' an equivalence class is called a *congruence class* or sometimes a *residue class*.

In the case of the congruence relation modulo 2

$$
\begin{aligned}
[0] &= \{x \mid x \equiv 0 \pmod 2\} &= \{\ldots, -4, -2, 0, 2, 4, \ldots\} \\
[1] &= \{x \mid x \equiv 1 \pmod 2\} &= \{\ldots, -3, -1, 1, 3, 5, \ldots\} \\
[2] &= \{x \mid x \equiv 2 \pmod 2\} &= \{\ldots, -4, -2, 0, 2, 4, \ldots\} &= [0].
\end{aligned}
$$

In fact, there are only two distinct congruence classes, namely the even integers, and the odd integers. We have $[2r] = [0]$ and $[2r + 1] = [1]$ and any even number is a representative of $[0]$ and any odd number a representative of $[1]$. Furthermore, notice that every integer lies in precisely one congruence class.

2.3.3 Proposition. Let R be an equivalence relation on the set S. If $a, b \in S$, then

(i) $a \in [a]$

(ii) $[a] = [b]$ if and only if aRb

(iii) $[a] \cap [b] = \emptyset$ if and only if $a \not R b$.

Proof. *(i).* The reflexive property states that aRa, for all $a \in S$, so it follows that $a \in [a]$.

(ii). Suppose $[a] = [b]$. Then, by part (i), $a \in [b]$ and aRb. Conversely suppose aRb. Let $x \in [a]$ so that xRa. By the transitive property xRb and hence $x \in [b]$. Therefore $[a] \subseteq [b]$ and, since bRa, it follows similarly that $[b] \subseteq [a]$. Hence $[a] = [b]$.

(iii). Suppose $[a] \cap [b] = \emptyset$. Then $a \notin [b]$ and so $a \not R b$. Conversely suppose $a \not R b$ and let $x \in [a] \cap [b]$. That is, xRa and xRb. By the symmetric and transitive properties, aRx and aRb. This is a contradiction, so x cannot exist and $[a] \cap [b] = \emptyset$. $\qquad\square$

Therefore in any equivalence relation, two equivalence classes are either identical or disjoint, and the set of equivalence classes under an equivalence relation R yields a disjoint decomposition of the set S. A decomposition of a set S into such a disjoint union of subsets is called a *partition* of S.

It follows from Proposition 2.1.5 that the congruence relation modulo m has precisely m distinct congruence classes, namely $[0], [1], [2], \ldots, [m - 2], [m - 1]$, one corresponding to each remainder under division by m.

The partition of the integers into the m congruence classes modulo m can be visualized as follows. Consider the integers evenly spaced on the number line and consider a circle whose circumference has length m. If the number line were to be wrapped around this circle, all the integers in one congruence class would fall on the same part of the circle.

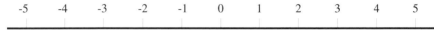

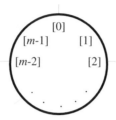

The set of all equivalence classes of a set S under an equivalence relation is called the *quotient set* of S by R and is often denoted S/R. Therefore

$$S/R \;=\; \{[a] \mid a \in S\}.$$

2.4   INTEGERS MODULO m

2.4.1 Definition.   The set of congruence classes of integers under the congruence relation modulo m is called the set of *integers modulo m* and is denoted $\mathbb{Z}_m$.

The set $\mathbb{Z}_m$ is the quotient set of $\mathbb{Z}$ by the congruence relation modulo m and

$$\mathbb{Z}_m \;=\; \{[0], [1], \ldots, [m-1]\}.$$

For example, $\mathbb{Z}_4 = \{[0], [1], [2], [3]\}$ where the four congruence classes are

$$
\begin{aligned}
[0] &= \{\ldots, -8, -4, 0, 4, 8, 12, \ldots\} &= \{4k \mid k \in \mathbb{Z}\} \\
[1] &= \{\ldots, -7, -3, 1, 5, 9, 13, \ldots\} &= \{4k+1 \mid k \in \mathbb{Z}\} \\
[2] &= \{\ldots, -6, -2, 2, 6, 10, 14, \ldots\} &= \{4k+2 \mid k \in \mathbb{Z}\} \\
[3] &= \{\ldots, -5, -1, 3, 7, 11, 15, \ldots\} &= \{4k+3 \mid k \in \mathbb{Z}\}.
\end{aligned}
$$

It will be useful if we were able to perform the operations of addition, subtraction, multiplication and, perhaps, division in $\mathbb{Z}_m$. The obvious way of defining addition and multiplication of two congruence classes modulo m would be as follows.

$$
\begin{aligned}
[a] + [b] &= [a+b] \\
[a] \cdot [b] &= [ab]
\end{aligned}
$$

For example, in $\mathbb{Z}_7$, let $A = [4]$ and $B = [5]$ so that we would have $A + B = [4] + [5] = [4+5] = [9] = [2]$, since $9 \equiv 2 \pmod{7}$ and $A \cdot B = [4] \cdot [5] = [20] = [6]$, since $20 \equiv 6 \pmod 7$. However, these definitions are not as innocuous as they might appear. For example, the congruence class A in $\mathbb{Z}_7$ could equally well be written as [11] and B could be written as [19]. Our definitions would then imply that

$$
\begin{aligned}
A + B &= [11] + [19] &= [30] \\
A \cdot B &= [11] \cdot [19] &= [209].
\end{aligned}
$$

Our definitions would lead to trouble unless $[30] = [9]$ and $[209] = [20]$ in $\mathbb{Z}_7$. In this particular example, it is true that $30 \equiv 9 \pmod 7$ and $209 \equiv 20 \pmod 7$, but how do we know that this will always be the case?

This type of problem arises whenever we define an operation on equivalence classes in terms of representatives. In mathematical language we say that there is the problem of determining whether the operation is *well defined* on equivalence classes.

In the case of $\mathbb{Z}_m$, a congruence class $[a]$ can always be written as $[a']$ if and only if $a' \equiv a \pmod m$. Similarly $[b]$ can be written as $[b']$ if and only if $b' \equiv b \pmod m$. Addition and multiplication in $\mathbb{Z}_m$ will be well defined if $[a + b] = [a' + b']$ and $[ab] = [a'b']$. However Proposition 2.1.3 guarantees that $a + b \equiv a' + b' \pmod m$ and $ab \equiv a'b' \pmod m$ and so the corresponding congruence classes are equal. Hence addition and multiplication are well defined in $\mathbb{Z}_m$.

2.4.2 Example.
Write down the addition and multiplication tables for $\mathbb{Z}_4$ and $\mathbb{Z}_5$.

Solution.

Addition in $\mathbb{Z}_4$

+	[0]	[1]	[2]	[3]
[0]	[0]	[1]	[2]	[3]
[1]	[1]	[2]	[3]	[0]
[2]	[2]	[3]	[0]	[1]
[3]	[3]	[0]	[1]	[2]

Multiplication in $\mathbb{Z}_4$

·	[0]	[1]	[2]	[3]
[0]	[0]	[0]	[0]	[0]
[1]	[0]	[1]	[2]	[3]
[2]	[0]	[2]	[0]	[2]
[3]	[0]	[3]	[2]	[1]

Addition in $\mathbb{Z}_5$

+	[0]	[1]	[2]	[3]	[4]
[0]	[0]	[1]	[2]	[3]	[4]
[1]	[1]	[2]	[3]	[4]	[0]
[2]	[2]	[3]	[4]	[0]	[1]
[3]	[3]	[4]	[0]	[1]	[2]
[4]	[4]	[0]	[1]	[2]	[3]

Multiplication in $\mathbb{Z}_5$

·	[0]	[1]	[2]	[3]	[4]
[0]	[0]	[0]	[0]	[0]	[0]
[1]	[0]	[1]	[2]	[3]	[4]
[2]	[0]	[2]	[4]	[1]	[3]
[3]	[0]	[3]	[1]	[4]	[2]
[4]	[0]	[4]	[3]	[2]	[1]

By looking at the above tables, it is seen that addition of [0] leaves an element unchanged, while multiplication by [0] always gives [0]. This can be proved true for any modulus, because for all $[a] \in \mathbb{Z}_m$

$$
\begin{aligned}
[0] + [a] &= [0 + a] &= [a] \\
[0] \cdot [a] &= [0 \cdot a] &= [0].
\end{aligned}
$$

Hence $[0]$ in $\mathbb{Z}_m$ acts just like the zero element of $\mathbb{Z}$. Furthermore $[1]$ acts like the unit element because

$$[1] \cdot [a] \;=\; [a] \qquad \text{for all } [a] \in \mathbb{Z}_m.$$

If $a \in \mathbb{Z}$, $-a$ is the element of $\mathbb{Z}$ for which $a + (-a) = 0$. In a similar way we can define negatives in $\mathbb{Z}_m$ by $-[a] = [-a]$ because $[a] + [-a] = [a - a] = [0]$. For example, in $\mathbb{Z}_5$, $-[1] = [4]$, $-[2] = [3]$, $-[3] = [2]$, $-[4] = [1]$ and $-[0] = [0]$.

Subtraction can be defined by

$$[a] - [b] \;=\; [a - b]$$

and, by Proposition 2.1.3, this well defined.

If we compare division in $\mathbb{Z}_m$ with division in $\mathbb{Z}$, interesting differences begin to appear. An element a^{-1} is called the *inverse* of an element a if $a \cdot a^{-1} = 1$. The question of division by an element a is equivalent to the existence of its inverse a^{-1}. In $\mathbb{Z}$, the only elements we can always divide by are 1 and -1, as these are the only two elements with inverses.

However,

$$[2] \cdot [3] \;=\; [1] \qquad \text{in } \mathbb{Z}_5$$

so that $[2]$ has an inverse, and $[2]^{-1} = [3]$. Division by $[2]$ in $\mathbb{Z}_5$ is equivalent to multiplication by $[3]$. In fact, in $\mathbb{Z}_5$, every nonzero element has an inverse; $[1]^{-1} = [1]$, $[2]^{-1} = [3]$, $[3]^{-1} = [2]$ and $[4]^{-1} = [4]$. We would never expect zero to have an inverse because zero times anything is always zero.

Looking at the multiplication table of $\mathbb{Z}_4$, we see that $[1]^{-1} = [1]$ and $[3]^{-1} = [3]$ but $[2]$ does not have an inverse. Hence division by $[2]$ is not always possible in $\mathbb{Z}_4$.

We shall show that, if p is prime, every nonzero element of $\mathbb{Z}_p$ has an inverse. A set in which we can perform the operations of addition, subtraction, multiplication, and division by nonzero elements, and in which these operations satisfy certain standard properties, is called a *field*. The set of integers modulo p, $\mathbb{Z}_p$, forms a finite field if and only if p is prime.

We shall now use the concept of congruence to prove the following theorem that was discovered by Fermat in 1640 and can, incidently, be used to show the existence of inverses in $\mathbb{Z}_p$. Fermat could be considered the founder of modern Number Theory. He proved many results in Number Theory, including the one below, but he is perhaps best known for his so-called "Last Theorem". This result was written in the margin of his copy of the work of Diophantus, next to the solution of the Diophantine equation $z^2 + y^2 = z^2$. Fermat claimed that $x^n + y^n = z^n$ has no nonzero integral solutions if $n > 2$. He stated that he had a truly marvelous proof which was too long to write in the margin. Fermat's Last Theorem was finally proved in 1994 by Andrew Wiles, using very advanced mathematics. Most mathematicians are sceptical that Fermat really did have a valid proof.

2.4.3 Fermat's Little Theorem. If p is a prime number that does not divide the integer a, then

$$a^{p-1} \equiv 1 \pmod{p}.$$

Proof. If $p \nmid a$ we shall first show that no two of the numbers $0a, 1a, 2a, \ldots, (p-1)a$ are congruent modulo p. Suppose that

$$ra \equiv sa \pmod{p} \qquad \text{where } 0 \leq s \leq r \leq p - 1.$$

By the definition of congruence, this implies $p|(r - s)a$ and, by Theorem 1.5.4, $p|(r - s)$. Hence $r = s$.

Therefore the congruence classes $[0a], [1a], [2a], \ldots, [(p - 1)a]$ are all distinct. But as $\mathbb{Z}_p$ only contains p congruence classes, it follows that

$$\mathbb{Z}_p = \{[0], [a], [2a], \ldots, [(p - 1)a]\}.$$

Hence the nonzero classes $[a], [2a], \ldots, [(p - 1)a]$ must be a rearrangement of the classes $[1], [2], \ldots, [p - 1]$. In particular,

$$a \cdot 2a \cdot 3a \cdots (p - 1)a \equiv 1 \cdot 2 \cdot 3 \cdots (p - 1) \pmod{p}.$$
$$(p - 1)! a^{p-1} \equiv (p - 1)! \pmod{p}.$$

However $p \nmid (p - 1)!$ because the prime p does not divide any of the factors of $(p - 1)!$ Hence, by Proposition 2.1.4, we can cancel $(p - 1)!$ and obtain

$$a^{p-1} \equiv 1 \pmod{p}. \qquad \square$$

2.4.4 Corollary. For any integer a and prime p

$$a^p \equiv a \pmod{p}.$$

Proof. If $p \nmid a$ this follows from Fermat's Little Theorem. If $p|a$ both sides are congruent to 0 modulo p. $\qquad \square$

2.4.5 Corollary. If $[a]$ is any nonzero element of $\mathbb{Z}_p$, where p is prime, then there exists an element $[b] \in \mathbb{Z}_p$ such that $[a] \cdot [b] = [1]$; that is, every nonzero element of $\mathbb{Z}_p$ has an inverse.

Proof. If $[a] \neq [0]$ in $\mathbb{Z}_p$ then $p \nmid a$ and, by Fermat's Little Theorem,

$$[a][a^{p-2}] = [a^{p-1}] = [1].$$

Hence $[a]^{-1} = [a^{p-2}]$. $\qquad \square$

For example, in $\mathbb{Z}_5$, $[2]^{-1} = [2^3] = [8] = [3]$. If p is large however, Fermat's Theorem gives a rather cumbersome way of finding inverses and it will be easier to find the inverses by inspection, or to use the methods of the next section. In $\mathbb{Z}_{31}$, Fermat's Theorem gives the inverse of $[2]$ as $[2^{29}]$. However, we can see by inspection that

$$[2] \cdot [16] = [32] = [1] \qquad \text{in } \mathbb{Z}_{31}$$

and so $[2]^{-1} = [16]$ and, incidentally, $2^{29} \equiv 16 \pmod{31}$.

2.5 LINEAR CONGRUENCES

A relation of the form

$$ax \equiv c \pmod{m}$$

is called a *linear congruence* in the variable x. A solution to such a congruence is an integer x_0 for which $ax_0 \equiv c \pmod{m}$. Our problem is to determine whether such a linear congruence has a solution and, if so, how to find all the solutions.

We first notice that if x_0 is any solution and $x_1 \equiv x_0 \pmod{m}$, then x_1 is also a solution; this follows immediately from Proposition 2.1.3 because $ax_1 \equiv ax_0 \equiv c \pmod{m}$. Therefore, if x_0 is a solution, so is every element of the congruence class x_0 modulo m. Since there are only m distinct congruence classes, the problem reduces to the finite one of determining which of these congruence classes are solutions.

Any linear congruence $ax \equiv c \pmod{m}$ can be viewed as an equation

$$[a][x] = [c] \quad \text{in } \mathbb{Z}_m$$

and the problem of finding an integer x that satisfies the congruence is equivalent to the problem of finding an equivalence class $[x] \in \mathbb{Z}_m$ that satisfies the equation.

One crude method of solving any congruence modulo m (whether linear or not) is to take one element from each congruence class, say $0, 1, 2, \ldots, m - 1$, and test whether they satisfy the congruence. This method is very effective if m is small, but soon becomes tedious for large m.

2.5.1 Example.   Solve the congruence

$$4x \equiv 2 \pmod{6}.$$

Solution.   We check whether the congruence is satisfied if $x \equiv 0$, 1, 2 , 3, 4 or 5 (mod 6).

Modulo 6						
$x \equiv$	0	1	2	3	4	5
$4x \equiv$	0	4	2	0	4	2

Therefore $4x \equiv 2$ (mod 6) if $x \equiv 2$ or 5 (mod 6). An equivalent way of writing this solution is

$$x = 6k + 2 \quad \text{or} \quad 6k + 5 \quad \text{where } k \in \mathbb{Z}. \qquad \square$$

2.5.2 Example. Solve the equation

$$[2][x] = [1] \quad \text{in } \mathbb{Z}_4$$

Solution. This equation is equivalent to the congruence $2x \equiv 1 \pmod 4$.

Modulo 4				
$x \equiv$	0	1	2	3
$2x \equiv$	0	2	0	2

We see that $2x$ is never congruent to 1 modulo 4 and hence the equation has no solution in $\mathbb{Z}_4$.

The nonexistence of a solution to $[2][x] = [1]$ in $\mathbb{Z}_4$ expresses the fact that [2] has no inverse in $\mathbb{Z}_4$. $\qquad \square$

How do we solve a linear congruence if the modulus is large? The following results show that a one variable linear congruence is equivalent to a Diophantine equation in two variables.

2.5.3 Proposition. The linear congruence $ax \equiv c$ (mod m) has a solution $x = x_0$, if and only if the linear Diophantine equation $ax + my = c$ has a solution $x = x_0, y = y_0$ for some integer y_0.

Proof. By the definition of congruence, the relation $ax \equiv c$ (mod m) holds if and only if $m|(c - ax)$ or, equivalently, if and only if $my = c - ax$ for some $y \in \mathbb{Z}$. Hence $ax_0 \equiv c$ (mod m) if and only if there exists $y_0 \in \mathbb{Z}$ such that $ax_0 + my_0 = c$. $\qquad \square$

2.5.4 Linear Congruence Theorem. The one variable linear congruence

$$ax \equiv c \pmod m$$

has a solution if and only if $\text{GCD}(a, m)|c$.

If $x_0 \in \mathbb{Z}$ is one solution, then the complete solution is

$$x \equiv x_0 \quad \left(\text{mod } \frac{m}{d} \right) \quad \text{where } d = \text{GCD}(a, m)$$

or equivalently

$$x \equiv x_0, \ x_0 + \tfrac{m}{d}, \ x_0 + 2\tfrac{m}{d}, \ \ldots, \ x_0 + (d-1)\tfrac{m}{d} \pmod m;$$

that is, there are $d = \text{GCD}(a, m)$ non-congruent solutions modulo m.

Proof. By Proposition 2.5.3 the congruence is equivalent to $ax + my = c$ and, by Theorem 1.3.1, this has a solution if and only if $\mathrm{GCD}(a, m) | c$.

If x_0 is one particular integer solution then there exists an integer y_0 such that $ax_0 + my_0 = c$ and, by Theorem 1.3.1, the complete solution to $ax + my = c$ is

$$x = x_0 + k\frac{m}{d}, \qquad y = y_0 - k\frac{a}{d} \qquad \text{for all } k \in \mathbb{Z}, \quad \text{where } d = \mathrm{GCD}(a, m).$$

Therefore the complete solution to $ax \equiv c \pmod{m}$ is $x = x_0 + k\frac{m}{d}$ for every integer k. This is equivalent to $x \equiv x_0 \left(\bmod \frac{m}{d}\right)$.

We shall now show that the solution set

$$S = \left\{ x \in \mathbb{Z} \;\middle|\; x \equiv x_0 \left(\bmod \frac{m}{d}\right) \right\}$$

to this congruence is the same as the set

$$T = \left\{ x \in \mathbb{Z} \;\middle|\; x \equiv x_0 + k\frac{m}{d} \pmod{m} \quad \text{for } k \in \mathbb{Z} \right\}.$$

If $x \in S$ then there exists an integer k with $x = x_0 + k\frac{m}{d}$; hence $x \in T$. If $x \in T$ then there exist integers k and ℓ with $x = x_0 + k\frac{m}{d} + \ell m = x_0 + (k + \ell d)\frac{m}{d}$; hence $x \in S$. Therefore we have $S = T$.

We now show that the numbers $x_0 + \frac{m}{d}, x_0 + 2\frac{m}{d}, \ldots, x_0 + (d - 1)\frac{m}{d}$ are in distinct congruence classes modulo m. We have $x_0 + k_1 \frac{m}{d} \equiv x_0 + k_2 \frac{m}{d} \pmod{m}$ if and only if $m \mid (k_1 - k_2)\frac{m}{d}$, which happens if and only if $d \mid k_1 - k_2$, or equivalently $k_1 \equiv k_2 \pmod{d}$. Hence the solution set consists precisely of the d congruence classes modulo m containing $x_0 + k\frac{m}{d}$, for $k = 0, 1, 2, \ldots, d - 1$. $\qquad\square$

If we cannot find one particular solution to $ax \equiv c \pmod{m}$ by any other means, we can always use the Euclidean Algorithm to solve $ax + my = c$.

Note that if $\mathrm{GCD}(a, m) = 1$ then the congruence $ax \equiv c \pmod{m}$ always has a solution, whatever the value of c. Furthermore there is exactly one solution modulo m.

In particular, if the modulus is a prime p then $\mathrm{GCD}(a, p) = 1$ whenever $p \nmid a$. Hence, if p is prime, all congruences of the form $ax \equiv c \pmod{p}$ have solutions, as long as $a \not\equiv 0 \pmod{p}$. Multiplying each side of the congruence by a^{p-2} and applying Fermat's Theorem 2.4.3, we obtain the solution

$$x \equiv a^{p-2}c \pmod{p}.$$

2.5.5 Example.   Solve the congruence

$$63x \equiv 20 \pmod{7}.$$

Solution. $\mathrm{GCD}(63, 7) = 7$ which does not divide 20. Therefore the congruence has no solutions. $\qquad\square$

2.5.6 Example. Find the inverse of [18] in $\mathbb{Z}_{31}$ and write it in the form $[r]$, where $0 \le r < 31$.

Solution. We have to find the equivalence class $[x]$ for which $[18][x] = [1]$ in $\mathbb{Z}_{31}$ or equivalently solve the congruence

$$18x \equiv 1 \pmod{31}.$$

Since $\text{GCD}(18, 31) = 1$, this congruence does have a solution and there is only one congruence class of solutions modulo 31.

The congruence is equivalent to the Diophantine equation

$$18x + 31y = 1.$$

Apply the Euclidean Algorithm to 18 and 31.

$$
\begin{aligned}
31 &= 18 + 13 \\
18 &= 13 + 5 \\
13 &= 2 \cdot 5 + 3 \\
5 &= 3 + 2 \\
3 &= 2 + 1
\end{aligned}
$$

Hence

$$
\begin{aligned}
1 &= 3 - 2 = 3 - (5 - 3) & &= 2 \cdot 3 - 5 \\
&= 2(13 - 2 \cdot 5) - 5 & &= 2 \cdot 13 - 5 \cdot 5 \\
&= 2 \cdot 13 - 5(18 - 13) & &= 7 \cdot 13 - 5 \cdot 18 \\
&= 7(31 - 18) - 5 \cdot 18 & &= 7 \cdot 31 - 12 \cdot 18
\end{aligned}
$$

Therefore $(-12) \cdot 18 \equiv 1 \pmod{31}$ and $x \equiv -12 \equiv 19 \pmod{31}$ is a solution to $18x \equiv 1 \pmod{31}$.

The inverse of [18] in $\mathbb{Z}_{31}$ is therefore [19].

Check. $18 \cdot 19 = 342 = 11 \cdot 31 + 1$ so $18 \cdot 19 \equiv 1 \pmod{31}$. $\qquad \square$

2.5.7 Example. Solve $20x \equiv 8 \pmod{44}$.

Solution. $\text{GCD}(20, 44) = 4$ which does divide 8. Therefore there are exactly 4 noncongruent classes of solutions modulo 44. The congruence is equivalent to the Diophantine equation $20x + 44y = 8$ or $5x + 11y = 2$.

Now $11 = 2 \cdot 5 + 1$, so $11 - 2 \cdot 5 = 1$ and $2 \cdot 11 - 4 \cdot 5 = 2$. Hence we see by inspection that $x = -4$, $y = 2$ is one solution to the Diophantine equation. By Theorem 2.5.4, the complete solution to the congruence can either be written as

$$x \equiv -4 \pmod{\tfrac{44}{4}}$$

that is

$$x \equiv 7 \pmod{11}$$

or as

$$x \equiv 40,\ 40 + 11,\ 40 + 22,\ 40 + 33 \pmod{44}$$

that is

$$x \equiv 40,\ 7,\ 18,\ 29 \pmod{44}.$$

Check. $20 \cdot 7 = 140 = 3 \cdot 44 + 8$ so $20 \cdot 7 \equiv 8 \pmod{44}$.   □

Although we have a method for completely solving a *linear* congruence, there is no effective method for solving any *polynomial* congruence such as

$$a_n x^n + a_{n-1} x^{n-1} + \cdots + a_1 x + a_0 \equiv 0 \pmod{m}.$$

However, as with linear congruences, if x_0 is one solution so is any integer congruent to x_0 modulo m. This follows from Proposition 2.1.3, because if $x_0 \equiv x_1$ $\pmod{m}$ then $x_0^2 \equiv x_1^2$, $x_0^3 \equiv x_1^3$ and in general $x_0^r \equiv x_1^r \pmod{m}$; hence

$$a_n x_0^n + a_{n-1} x_0^{n-1} + \cdots + a_1 x_0 + a_0 \equiv a_n x_1^n + a_{n-1} x_1^{n-a} + \cdots + a_1 x_1 + a_0 \pmod{m}.$$

Therefore the solutions to any polynomial congruence occur in congruence classes and, if the modulus is small, we can solve the congruent by exhaustively trying each congruence class.

2.5.8 Example.   Solve $x^2 \equiv 1 \pmod 8$.

Solution.

Modulo 8								
$x \equiv$	0	1	2	3	4	5	6	7
$x^2 \equiv$	0	1	4	1	0	1	4	1

Hence the solution is $x \equiv 1, 3, 5$ or $7 \pmod 8$.   □

2.5.9 Example.   For which integer x is $x^7 + x^3 + 2x^2 + 4$ divisible by 7?

Solution.   We have to solve the congruence

$$x^7 + x^3 + 2x^2 + 4 \equiv 0 \pmod{7}.$$

Since the modulus is prime, it follows from Corollary 2.4.4 to Fermat's Theorem that $x^7 \equiv x \pmod 7$ for all $x \in \mathbb{Z}$. Therefore the congruence is equivalent to

$$x^3 + 2x^2 + x + 4 \equiv 0 \pmod{7}.$$

Modulo 7							
$x \equiv$	0	1	2	3	4	5	6
$x^2 \equiv$	0	1	4	2	2	4	1
$x^3 \equiv$	0	1	1	6	1	6	6
$x^3 + 2x^2 + x + 4 \equiv$	4	1	1	3	6	2	4

We see from the above table that the congruence has no solution and therefore the original integer polynomial is never divisible by 7.   □

2.6 THE CHINESE REMAINDER THEOREM

The Chinese astronomer and mathematician Sun-Tsu, in the first century A.D., posed the problem of finding the two smallest positive integers which have remainders 2,3 and 2 when divided by 3, 5 and 7 respectively. This is a problem involving three simultaneous congruences. Such questions often arose in ancient calendars that depended on astronomical cycles of different lengths. The solutions to such problems are still useful in the computer age for solving complicated Diophantine equations.

We shall first show how to solve two simultaneous congruences whose moduli are coprime and then show how this solution can be extended to any number of simultaneous congruences with coprime moduli.

2.6.1 Chinese Remainder Theorem. If $\mathrm{GCD}(m_1, m_2) = 1$ then, for any choice of the integers a_1 and a_2, the simultaneous congruences

$$x \equiv a_1 \pmod{m_1}$$
$$x \equiv a_2 \pmod{m_2}$$

have a solution. Moreover, if $x = x_0$ is one integer solution, then the complete solution is

$$x \equiv x_0 \pmod{m_1 m_2}.$$

Proof. We prove this result here in general, though the idea of the proof may be seen more easily by looking at a numerical example, say Example 2.6.2.

The integer x satisfies the first congruence if and only if

$$x = a_1 + m_1 y \qquad \text{for some } y \in \mathbb{Z}.$$

This number x also satisfies the second congruence if and only if

that is, if and only if
$$a_1 + m_1 y \equiv a_2 \pmod{m_2}$$
$$m_1 y \equiv a_2 - a_1 \pmod{m_2}.$$

Since $\mathrm{GCD}(m_1, m_2) = 1$, it follows from Theorem 2.5.4 that this congruence always has a solution, say $y = b$, and the complete solution for y will then be

$$y = b + m_2 z \qquad \text{for } z \in \mathbb{Z}.$$

Therefore $x = a_1 + m_1 b$ is one solution to the simultaneous congruences, and any integer x satisfies the simultaneous congruences if and only if

$$x = a_1 + m_1(b + m_2 z)$$
$$= (a_1 + m_1 b) + m_1 m_2 z \qquad \text{for } z \in \mathbb{Z}.$$

This is exactly one congrunce class modulo $m_1 m_2$. Hence, if $x = x_0$ is one solution, then $x \equiv x_0 \pmod{m_1 m_2}$ is the complete solution. $\qquad\square$

We can follow the method of the above proof to solve particular examples.

2.6.2 Example. Solve the simultaneous congruences

$$x \equiv 2 \pmod 9$$
$$x \equiv 3 \pmod 7$$

Solution. The first congruence is equivalent to $x = 2 + 9y$ where $y \in \mathbb{Z}$. Substituting this into the second congruence we have

$$2 + 9y \equiv 3 \pmod 7 \quad \text{or} \quad 2y \equiv 1 \pmod 7.$$

By inspection, we see that this has solution $y \equiv 4 \pmod 7$ or $y = 4 + 7z$ for all $z \in \mathbb{Z}$. The solution to both congruences is therefore

$$x = 2 + 9(4 + 7z) = 38 + 63z \qquad \text{for all } z \in \mathbb{Z}$$

or equivalently

$$x \equiv 38 \pmod{63}.$$

Check.   If $x = 38 + 63z$ then $x \equiv 2 \pmod 9$ and $x \equiv 3 \pmod 7$.   □

2.6.3 Example.

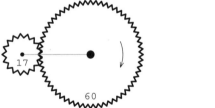 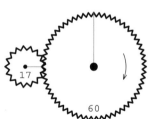

A small gear with 17 teeth is meshed into a large gear with 60 teeth. The large gear starts rotating at one revolution per minute. How long will it be before the small gear is back to its original position and the large gear is one quarter of a revolution past its initial position?

Solution. The gears are moving at the rate of one tooth per second. After x seconds the smaller gear will be back to its initial position if $x \equiv 0 \pmod{17}$ and the larger gear will be one quarter of a revolution past its initial position if $x \equiv 15 \pmod{60}$.

We can solve these two simultaneous congruences. The second congruence implies that $x = 15 + 60y$ where $y \in \mathbb{Z}$. Substituting this value of x into the first congruence, we have

$$15 + 60y \equiv 0 \pmod{17}.$$

That is, $9y \equiv 2$ (mod 17) or $18y \equiv y \equiv 4$ (mod 17). Therefore

$$y = 4 + 17z \quad \text{for } z \in \mathbb{Z}$$

and

$$x = 15 + 60(4 + 17z) = 15 + 60 \cdot 4 + 60 \cdot 17z.$$

The first positive solution occurs when $z = 0$ and the elapsed time is 4 minutes and 15 seconds. $\quad\square$

2.6.4 Proposition. If $\text{GCD}(m_1, m_2) = 1$ then

$$x \equiv a \pmod{m_1 m_2} \quad \Longleftrightarrow \quad \begin{cases} x \equiv a \pmod{m_1} \\ x \equiv a \pmod{m_2}. \end{cases}$$

Proof. First, suppose that $x \equiv a$ (mod $m_1 m_2$). This is equivalent to $m_1 m_2 | (x - a)$. Hence $m_1 | (x - a)$ and $m_2 | (x - a)$, which is equivalent to the two simultaneous congruences $x \equiv a$ (mod m_1) and $x \equiv a$ (mod m_2).

Conversely, given the two simultaneous congruences, it is clear that $x = a$ is one integer solution. If follows from the Chinese Remainder Theorem 2.6.1 that $x \equiv a$ (mod $m_1 m_2$). $\quad\square$

The above result is not true if $\text{GCD}(m_1, m_2) \neq 1$; for example, if $x \equiv 0$ (mod 4) and $x \equiv 0$ (mod 6), what is x congruent to modulo 24?

2.6.5 Example. Find the two smallest positive integers which have remainders 1, 2 and 6 when divided by 3, 5 and 7 respectively.

Solution. The integers must satisfy the following three congruences.

$$x \equiv 1 \pmod{3}$$
$$x \equiv 2 \pmod{5}$$
$$x \equiv 6 \pmod{7}$$

Let us solve the first two of these congruences. The first implies that $x = 1 + 3y$ where $y \in \mathbb{Z}$ and, substituting this in the second, we have $1 + 3y \equiv 2$ (mod 5). Hence $3y \equiv 1$ (mod 5), which has solution $y \equiv 2$ (mod 5) or $y = 2 + 5z$ for $z \in \mathbb{Z}$. Therefore the solution to the first two congruences is

$$x = 1 + 3(2 + 5z) = 7 + 15z \quad \text{for } z \in \mathbb{Z}$$

or equivalently

$$x \equiv 7 \pmod{15}$$

and we have reduce the three simultaneous congruences to two simultaneous congruences. We can now solve these two as before.

We have $x = 7 + 15z$ where $z \in \mathbb{Z}$ and when this is substituted into the congruence $x \equiv 6 \pmod 7$ we have
$$7 + 15z \equiv 6 \pmod 7.$$
This has solution $z \equiv 6 \pmod 7$ or $z = 6 + 7t$ where $t \in \mathbb{Z}$.

The solution to the original three congruences is therefore
$$x = 7 + 15(6 + 7t) = 97 + 105t \qquad \text{for } t \in \mathbb{Z}$$
or equivalently
$$x \equiv 97 \pmod{105}.$$
The two smallest positive integers satisfying the congruences are 97 and 202.

Check. $97 \equiv 1 \pmod 3$, $97 \equiv 2 \pmod 5$ and $97 \equiv 6 \pmod 7$.   □

We can extend the method of the previous example to solve n simultaneous congruences by repeatedly reducing two congruences modulo m_i and m_j to one modulo $m_i m_j$. We state the result without further proof.

2.6.6 Chinese Remainder Theorem.   Let $m_1, m_2, \ldots, m_n$ be positive integers such that $\mathrm{GCD}(m_i, m_j) = 1$ if $i \neq j$. Then for any integers $a_1, a_2, \ldots, a_n$ the simultaneous congruences

$$
\begin{aligned}
x &\equiv a_1 &&\pmod{m_1} \\
x &\equiv a_2 &&\pmod{m_2} \\
&\ \vdots \\
x &\equiv a_n &&\pmod{m_n}
\end{aligned}
$$

always have a solution. Moreover, if $x = x_0$ is one solution, then the complete solution is $x \equiv x_0 \pmod{m_1 m_2 \ldots m_n}$.   □

2.6.7 Example.   Solve the congruence $x^3 \equiv 53 \pmod{120}$.

Solution.   Instead of solving this by trying all 120 congruence classes in turn, we can split the congruence up into congruences with coprime moduli. After solving the individual congruences we can fit them together again using the Chinese Remainder Theorem.

The number 120 factors into primes as $2^3 \cdot 3 \cdot 5$ and hence can be written as the product of the numbers 3, 5 and 8, which are coprime in pairs. If $x^3 \equiv 53 \pmod{120}$ then $x^3 = 53 + 120k$, for some integer k. Therefore

$$
\begin{aligned}
x^3 &\equiv 53 \equiv 2 &&\pmod 3 \\
x^3 &\equiv 53 \equiv 3 &&\pmod 5 \\
x^3 &\equiv 53 \equiv 5 &&\pmod 8.
\end{aligned}
$$

We first solve these three individual congruences. By Fermat's Theorem 2.4.3, $x^3 \equiv x \pmod 3$, so $x \equiv 2 \pmod 3$ is the solution to the first one.

Modulo 5				
$x \equiv$	0	1	2	3	4
$x^3 \equiv$	0	1	3	2	4

Modulo 8							
$x \equiv$	0	1	2	3	4	5	6	7
$x^3 \equiv$	0	1	0	3	0	5	0	7

From these tables we see that the solutions to the second and third congruences are $x \equiv 2$ (mod 5) and $x \equiv 5$ (mod 8).

Use the Chinese Remainder Theorem to solve the simultaneous congruences

$$x \equiv 2 \pmod{3}, \quad x \equiv 2 \pmod{5}, \quad x \equiv 5 \pmod{8}.$$

By Proposition 2.6.4 the solution to the first two is $x \equiv 2$ (mod 15), or $x = 2 + 15y$ where $y \in \mathbb{Z}$. Substituting this into the third congruence we have

$$
\begin{aligned}
2 + 15y &\equiv 5 \pmod{8} \\
-y &\equiv 3 \pmod{8}.
\end{aligned}
$$

Hence $y \equiv 5$ (mod 8) or $y = 5 + 8z$ for $z \in \mathbb{Z}$.

The solution to the three simultaneous congruences, and hence to the original problem, is

$$x = 2 + 15(5 + 8z) = 77 + 120z \qquad \text{for } z \in \mathbb{Z}$$

or equivalently $x \equiv 77$ (mod 120).

Check. $77^2 \equiv 5929 \equiv 49$ (mod 120) and $77^3 \equiv 77 \cdot 49 \equiv 3773 \equiv 53$ (mod 120). $\square$

The Chinese Remainder Theorem can be used to speed up the solution to a complicated system of Diophantine equations on a computer. The first task is to obtain an estimate of the size of the integer solution required. This allows the moduli that will be used to be chosen judiciously. The system of equations are then solved as congruences with the chosen moduli, and the answer obtained from the Chinese Remainder Theorem.

For example, if a system of Diophantine equations was known to have positive solutions less than 2000, the system could first be solved modulo 11, then solved modulo 13 and finally modulo 17. By using the Chinese Remainder Theorem the answer can be found modulo $11 \cdot 13 \cdot 17$, that is, modulo 2431. Since the required solution lay between 0 and 2000, it is known exactly. Such a method will often save valuable computing time, especially if the moduli chosen are prime.

Exercise Set 2

1. Which of the following integers are congruent modulo 4?

$$-12, \ -11, \ -9, \ -6, \ -4, \ -1, \ 0, \ 1, \ 2, \ 3, \ 5, \ 7, \ 10$$

2. Which of the following integers are congruent modulo 6?

$$-147, \ -91, \ -22, \ -14, \ -2, \ 2, \ 4, \ 5, \ 21, \ 185$$

3. What is the remainder when 8^{24} is divided by 3?

4. Let $N = 3^{729}$. What is the last digit in the decimal representation of N? What are the last digits in the base 9 and base 8 representations of N?

5. What is the remainder when 10^{45} is divided by 7?

6. Is $6^{17} + 17^6$ divisible by 3 or 7?

7. Show that an integer of the form $5n + 3$, where $n \in \mathbb{P}$, can never be a perfect square.

8 - 11. For each of the following congruences, determine whether there exists a positive integer k so that the congruence is satisfied. If so, find the smallest such k.

8. $2^k \equiv 1 \pmod{11}$ 9. $3^k \equiv 1 \pmod{17}$

10. $2^k \equiv 1 \pmod{14}$ 11. $2^k \equiv 1 \pmod{29}$

12 - 16. Find tests for determining whether an integer given in the stated base is divisible by the following numbers.

12. Dividing by 8 in base 10   13. Dividing by 12 in base 10

14. Dividing by 7 in base 10   15. Dividing by 7 in base 8

16. Dividing by 13 in base 12

17 - 20. Determine whether the following numbers are divisible by 2, 3, 4, 5, 6, 8, 9, 10 or 11.

17. 514000   18. 111111

19. 179652   20. 7654321

21. Check the following calculation by casting out nines.

$$12453 \times 7057 - 84014651 = 3869170$$

22 - 26. *Determine whether the following relations on $\mathbb{Z}$ are reflexive, symmetric or transitive. If any are equivalence relations, determine their quotient set.*

   22. aRb if and only if $a - b \neq 1$.
   23. aRb if and only if $a \leq b$.
   24. aRb if and only if $a - b$ is a multiple of 3.
   25. aRb if and only if $|a - b| < 3$.
   26. aRb if and only if $a|b$.

27 - 30. *Construct addition and multiplication tables for each of the following sets of integers modulo m and find, if possible, multiplicative inverses of each of the elements in the set.*

   27. $\mathbb{Z}_2$ **28.** $\mathbb{Z}_3$
   29. $\mathbb{Z}_7$ **30.** $\mathbb{Z}_8$

31. If $d = \text{GCD}(a, m)$ and $d|c$ show that the congruence $ax \equiv c \pmod{m}$ is equivalent to

$$\frac{a}{d}x \equiv \frac{c}{d} \left(\text{mod } \frac{m}{d}\right).$$

32 - 41. *Solve each of the following congruences.*

   32. $3x \equiv 5 \pmod{13}$ **33.** $4x \equiv 6 \pmod{14}$
   34. $5x \equiv 7 \pmod{15}$ **35.** $29x \equiv 43 \pmod{128}$
   36. $1713x \equiv 871 \pmod{2000}$ **37.** $1426x \equiv 597 \pmod{2000}$
   38. $x^2 \equiv 6x \pmod{8}$ **39.** $x^2 + 2x \equiv 3 \pmod{8}$
   40. $4x^3 + 2x + 1 \equiv 0 \pmod{5}$ **41.** $x^9 + x^7 + x^6 + 1 \equiv 0 \pmod{2}$

   42. Find the inverse of $[4]$ in $\mathbb{Z}_{11}$.

   43. Find the inverse of $[2]$ in $\mathbb{Z}_{41}$.

   44. Find the inverse of $[23]$ in $\mathbb{Z}_{41}$.

45 - 47. *Solve the following equations in the given set of integers modulo m.*

   45. $[4][x] + [8] = [1]$ in $\mathbb{Z}_9$.
   46. $[3][x] = [18]$ in $\mathbb{Z}_{19}$.
   47. $([x] - [2])([x] - [3]) = [0]$ in $\mathbb{Z}_6$.

   48. For what values of a does $x^2 \equiv a \pmod{7}$ have a solution?

49 - 54. Solve the following simultaneous congruences.

49. $x \equiv 4 \pmod 5$
$\quad\ \ x \equiv 3 \pmod 4$

51. $x \equiv 1 \pmod 2$
$\quad\ \ x \equiv 2 \pmod 3$
$\quad\ \ x \equiv 3 \pmod 7$

53. $2x \equiv 4 \pmod 7$
$\quad\ 18x \equiv 43 \pmod{23}$

50. $x \equiv 46 \pmod{51}$
$\quad\ \ x \equiv 27 \pmod{52}$

52. $2x \equiv 11 \pmod{13}$
$\quad\ 3x \equiv 7 \pmod 9$
$\quad\ 7x \equiv 5 \pmod 8$

54. $161x \equiv 49 \pmod{200}$
$\quad\ \ 74x \equiv 1 \pmod{53}$

55. Find the two smallest positive integral solutions of $x \equiv 5 \pmod 7$ and $x \equiv 24 \pmod{25}$.

Problem Set 2

56. If p is a prime, prove that $x^2 \equiv y^2 \pmod p$ if and only if $x \equiv \pm y \pmod p$.

57. If p is an odd prime, show that $x^2 \equiv a \pmod p$ has a solution for exactly half the values of a between 1 and $p - 1$ inclusive. Furthermore, if $1 \le a \le p - 1$ and $x^2 \equiv a \pmod p$ has a solution, show that it has exactly two congruence classes of solutions modulo p.

58. Does $x^3 \equiv a \pmod p$ always have a solution for every value of a, whenever p is prime?

59. Choose any integer larger than 10, subtract the sum of its digits from it, cross out any one nonzero digit from the result and let the sum of the remaining digits be s. From a knowledge of s alone, is it possible to find the digit that was crossed out?

60. Prove that $21 | (3n^7 + 7n^3 + 11n)$ for all integers n.

61. Prove that $n^{91} \equiv n^7 \pmod{91}$ for all integers n. Is $n^{91} \equiv n \pmod{91}$ for all integers n?

62. For which positive values of k is $n^k \equiv n \pmod 6$ for all integers n?

63. For which positive values of k is $n^k \equiv n \pmod 4$ for all integers n?

64. For which positive values of k is $n^k \equiv n \pmod 7$ for all integers n?

65. Prove, without using a calculator or computer, that 641 divides the Fermat number $F(5) = 2^{2^5} + 1$.

66. Show that the product of two numbers of the form $4n + 1$ is still of that form. Hence show that there are infinitely many primes of the form $4n + 3$.

67. Define a relation on the set of real numbers by

$$aRb \text{ if and only if } a - b = 2k\pi \text{ for some } k \in \mathbb{Z}.$$

(a) Prove that this is an equivalence relation.

(b) Which of the following are related?

$$5\pi \text{ and } -10\pi, \ -\pi \text{ and } \pi, 3 \text{ and } 9, \ \tfrac{2}{3}\pi \text{ and } -\tfrac{1}{3}\pi, \ \tfrac{11}{6}\pi \text{ and } \tfrac{23}{6}\pi?$$

(c) Two real numbers are equivalent if and only if they represent the same angle in radians. The equivalence classes therefore consist of the different angles. Denote the equivalence class containing a by $[a]$.

Show that addition of angles is well defined by

$$[a] + [b] = [a + b].$$

(d) Show, by a counterexample, that multiplication of angles if *not* well defined by

$$[a] \cdot [b] = [ab].$$

68. (a) Find a relation R, on a set S, that is symmetric and transitive, but not reflexive.

(b) If there is an example to part (a), the following "proof", that every symmetric and transitive relation is reflexive, must be fallacious. Find the error. "Let R be a symmetric and transitive relation on the set S. For any $a, b \in S$, aRb implies that bRa, because R is symmetric. But aRb and bRa imply that aRa, because R is transitive. Since aRa, R must also be reflexive."

69. If $m = pq$ is a composite number, where $1 < p \le q < m$, show that $\mathbb{Z}_m$ is not a field by showing that division by nonzero elements is not always possible in $\mathbb{Z}_m$.

70. Solve the following system of simultaneous equations in $\mathbb{Z}_{12}$.

$$
\begin{aligned}
[8][x] &+ [3][y] = [9] \\
[6][x] &+ [5][y] = [2]
\end{aligned}
$$

71. Solve the following system of simultaneous equations in $\mathbb{Z}_{11}$.

$$
\begin{aligned}
[3][x] &+ [4][y] = [5] \\
[7][x] &+ [5][y] = [4]
\end{aligned}
$$

72. One common error in copying numbers is the transposition of adjacent digits. For example, 9578 might be copied as 9758. Will the method of casting out nines discover such an error? Discuss other methods of checking for errors.

73 - 76. *Each new book published is given an* **International Standard Book Number** (ISBN) *which consists of 10 digits arranged in four groups, such as* 0-123-45678-9. *The first group of digits is a code for the language of the book; 0 stands for English, 2 for French, etc. The second group is a code for the publisher and the third group is the publisher's number for the book. The final digit is a* **check digit**. *This digit provides a check on the other digits to ensure that they are copied correctly. This check digit is chosen so that for any* ISBN $a_1 a_2 a_3 \ldots a_9 a_{10}$

$$1a_1 + 2a_2 + 3a_3 + \cdots + 9a_9 + 10a_{10} \equiv 0 \pmod{11}$$

or equivalently

$$a_1 + 2a_2 + 3a_3 + \cdots + 9a_9 \equiv a_{10} \pmod{11}.$$

The check digit can be any one of the digits 0, 1, 2, ..., 9 *or* X, *where* X *stands for the number* 10.

73. Is 0-467-51402-X a valid ISBN?

74. Is 1-56-004151-5 a valid ISBN?

75. What is the check digit for 14-200-0076-?

76. What is the check digit for 0-4101-1286-?

77. *(Euler-Fermat Theorem)* If $\text{GCD}(a, n) = 1$, prove that

$$a^{\phi(n)} \equiv 1 \pmod{n}$$

where $\phi(n)$ is the Euler ϕ-function defined in Problem 105 of Chapter 1.

78. If $\text{GCD}(m, n) = 1$, prove that $\phi(mn) = \phi(m)\phi(n)$.

Using Problem 105 of Chapter 1, deduce that if N has the prime decomposition

$$N = p_1^{\alpha_1} \cdots p_r^{\alpha_r}$$

then $\phi(N) = p_1^{\alpha_1 - 1} \cdots p_r^{\alpha_r - 1}(p_1 - 1) \cdots (p_r - 1)$.

79. *(Wilson's Theorem)* If p is prime, prove that

$$(p - 1)! \equiv -1 \pmod{p}.$$

80. If p and q are integers, not divisible by 3 or 5, prove that $p^4 \equiv q^4 \pmod{15}$.

81. Solve the simultaneous congruences

$$\begin{aligned} 9x &\equiv 21 &\pmod{6} \\ 4x &\equiv 9 &\pmod{13}. \end{aligned}$$

82. Solve the simultaneous congruences

$$
\begin{aligned}
3x &\equiv 7 \quad &(\text{mod } 11) \\
8x &\equiv 3 \quad &(\text{mod } 9).
\end{aligned}
$$

83. Two watches, one of which gains 2 minutes per day and the other which loses 3 minutes per day, read the correct time. When will both watches next give the same time? When will they next both give the correct time?

84. Solve $x^3 \equiv 17 \pmod{99}$.

85. Solve $x^2 \equiv 7 \pmod{99}$.

86. If $\text{GCD}(m, n) = d$, when do the simultaneous congruences

$$
\begin{aligned}
x &\equiv a \quad &(\text{mod } m) \\
x &\equiv b \quad &(\text{mod } n)
\end{aligned}
$$

have a solution?

87. Let $M = m_1 m_2 \ldots m_n$, where $\text{GCD}(m_i, m_j) = 1$ whenever $i \neq j$, and let $M_i = M/m_i$. Let $y \equiv b_i \pmod{m_i}$ be a solution to $M_i y \equiv 1 \pmod{m_i}$. Prove that the simultaneous congruences

$$
\begin{aligned}
x &\equiv a_1 \quad &(\text{mod } m_1) \\
x &\equiv a_2 \quad &(\text{mod } m_2) \\
&\ \ \vdots \\
x &\equiv a_n \quad &(\text{mod } m_n)
\end{aligned}
$$

have the solution

$$
x \equiv a_1 b_1 M_1 + a_2 b_2 M_2 + a_3 b_3 M_3 + \cdots + a_n b_n M_n \pmod{M}.
$$

88. Solve the simultaneous equations

$$
\begin{aligned}
100x &- 9y &= 4264 \\
11x &+ 109y &= 909
\end{aligned}
$$

  (i) modulo 9
  (ii) modulo 11
  (iii) in integers, using (i) and (ii), given the fact that x and y have unique solutions and both are positive integers less than 100.

89. A basket contains a number of eggs and, when the eggs are removed 2, 3, 4, 5 and 6 at a time, there are 1, 2, 3, 4 and 5 respectively, left over. When the eggs are removed 7 at a time there are none left over. Assuming none of the eggs broke during the preceding operations, determine how many eggs there were in the basket.

90. Use Problem 87 to solve each of these three simultaneous congruences.

(a) $x \equiv 2 \pmod{7}$, $x \equiv 5 \pmod{11}$, $x \equiv 11 \pmod{17}$

(b) $x \equiv 0 \pmod{7}$, $x \equiv 8 \pmod{11}$, $x \equiv 10 \pmod{17}$

(c) $x \equiv 5 \pmod{7}$, $x \equiv 6 \pmod{11}$, $x \equiv 14 \pmod{17}$

91 - 92. Use Problem 87 to find the solution to these simultaneous congruences.

91. $x \equiv a_1 \pmod{9}$, $x \equiv a_2 \pmod{11}$.

92. $x \equiv a_1 \pmod{3}$, $x \equiv a_2 \pmod{8}$, $x \equiv a_3 \pmod{25}$.

93. Find positive integers a, b, m_1, m_2 such that

$$
\begin{aligned}
a &\equiv b \pmod{m_1} \\
a &\equiv b \pmod{m_2} \\
a &\not\equiv b \pmod{m_1 m_2}.
\end{aligned}
$$

94. Find all the integral solutions to the Diophantine equation $5x^2 + x + 6 = 7y$.

95.   (a) Prove that if p and q are coprime, and x is an integer such that

$$
\begin{aligned}
x &\equiv p \pmod{q} \\
x &\equiv q \pmod{p}
\end{aligned}
$$

then $x \equiv p + q \pmod{pq}$.

(b) Show by means of a counterexample that the condition that p and q are coprime is necessary.

96. Solve the congruence

$$x^3 - 29x^2 + 35x + 38 \equiv 0 \pmod{195}.$$

97. If p is prime and k is the smallest positive integer such that $a^k \equiv 1 \pmod{p}$ then prove that k divides $p - 1$.

98. Find the remainder when $2^{2^{405}}$ is divided by 23.

Chapter 3

Induction and the Binomial Theorem

3.1 MATHEMATICAL INDUCTION

In this book we are assuming that the reader knows the properties of the positive integers. However, we will study explicitly the property known as the Principle of Mathematical Induction, as this has several important consequences.

In everyday parlance, "induction" means the inference of a general law from particular cases. "Empirical induction" is commonly used in the sciences to formulate a general theory. For example, tables for the times and heights of future high tides, at particular points on the coast, are constructed from many previous observations.

In quite a different way, "Mathematical Induction" allows us to *prove* a statement true for all positive integers. This depends on the following property of the positive integers $\mathbb{P}$. You should convince yourself that it is a plausible property.

3.1.1 Inductive Property of the Positive Integers.   Let S be a subset of the positive integers $\mathbb{P}$.

If   (i) $1 \in S$
and   (ii) $k + 1 \in S$ whenever $k \in S$

then S is the entire set $\mathbb{P}$.

We do not prove this, but take it as one of the defining properties of $\mathbb{P}$.

As an example, we now show how this can be used to prove that the sum of the first n positive integers is $n(n + 1)/2$.

3.1.2 Example.   Prove that $1 + 2 + \cdots + n \;=\; \dfrac{n(n + 1)}{2}$ for all $n \in \mathbb{P}$.

Solution.   Let $P(n)$ be the statement "$1 + 2 + \cdots + n = \frac{n(n+1)}{2}$".

We would like to prove that the statement $P(n)$ is true for all $n \in \mathbb{P}$. Let S be the set of positive integers for which $P(n)$ is true; that is

$$S \;=\; \{n \in \mathbb{P} \mid P(n) \text{ is true}\}.$$

(i). $1 \in S$ because $P(1)$ is "$1 = \frac{1 \cdot 2}{2}$" which is true.

(ii).   Now suppose that $k \in S$, so that $P(k)$ is true and $1 + 2 + \cdots + k = \frac{k(k+1)}{2}$. We have

$$1 + 2 + \cdots + k + (k+1) \;=\; \frac{k(k+1)}{2} + (k+1) \;=\; \frac{(k+1)(k+2)}{2}$$

which shows that $P(k+1)$ is true, and so $k + 1 \in S$.

It now follows from the Inductive Property of $\mathbb{P}$ that $S = \mathbb{P}$ and so $P(n)$ is true for all $n \in \mathbb{P}$. $\qquad\qquad\qquad\qquad\qquad\qquad\qquad\qquad\qquad\qquad\qquad\qquad$ $\square$

We can formulate the above process into the following principle.

3.1.3 Principle of Mathematical Induction.   Let $P(n)$ be a statement that depends on the integer n.

If   (i) $P(1)$ is true

and   (ii) $P(k+1)$ is true whenever $P(k)$ is true

then $P(n)$ is true for all $n \in \mathbb{P}$.

Proof.   We shall show that this principle follows from the Inductive Property of $\mathbb{P}$. If $S = \{n \in \mathbb{P} \mid P(n) \text{ is true}\}$ then

           (i) $1 \in S$

and   (ii) $k + 1 \in S$ whenever $k \in S$.

Hence, by 3.1.1, $S = \mathbb{P}$ and $P(n)$ is true for all $n \in \mathbb{P}$. $\qquad\qquad\qquad\qquad$ $\square$

This principle of induction has already been implicitly used in the Euclidean Algorithm 1.2.3, Theorem 1.2.5, the Extended Euclidean Algorithm 1.3.4, Theorem 1.4.1, twice in Theorem 1.5.5, and in the Chinese Remainder Theorem 2.6.1.

Besides being useful in *proving* results, induction can be used in making *definitions*. For example, for each positive integer n, "n factorial" is defined to be the product of the first n positive integers. It is written as $n!$ so that

$$n! \;=\; 1 \cdot 2 \cdot 3 \cdot 4 \cdots (n-1) \cdot n.$$

Alternatively, n factorial can be defined inductively by

           (i) $1! = 1$

and   (ii) $(k+1)! = (k!)(k+1)$ for all $k \in \mathbb{P}$.

3.1.4 Example. Prove that $n! \geq 2^{n-1}$ for all $n \in \mathbb{P}$.

Solution. (i). When $n = 1, 1! = 1$ and $2^{1-1} = 1$. Hence the statement $n! \geq 2^{n-1}$ is true when $n = 1$.

(ii). Suppose that $k! \geq 2^{k-1}$. Then

$$(k + 1)! = (k + 1)(k!) \geq (k + 1)2^{k-1}.$$

But $k + 1 \geq 2$ whenever $k \in \mathbb{P}$ so

$$(k + 1)! \geq 2 \cdot 2^{k-1} = 2^k.$$

That is, the statement $n! \geq 2^{n-1}$ is true for $n = k + 1$ whenever it is true for $n = k$.

Therefore, by the Principle of Mathematical Induction, the result if true for all $n \in \mathbb{P}$. □

The Principle of Mathematical Induction can be visualized by means of the following "Domino Principle". Suppose a line of dominoes, numbered by the positive integers, are standing on end on a table.

If (i) the first domino is pushed over
and (ii) the dominoes are close enough that whenever the kth domino falls
it knocks over the $(k + 1)$st domino
then all the dominoes will fall down.

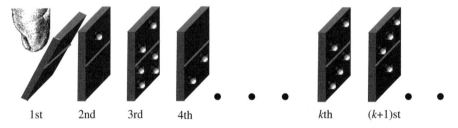

| 1st | 2nd | 3rd | 4th | kth | $(k+1)$st |

The Domino Principle

3.1.5 Example. Find the sum of the odd positive integers from 1 to $2n - 1$.

Solution. Since n can be any positive integer, there are an infinite number of sums that we have to calculate. Let us look at the first few to see if there is any pattern to the sums.

$$\begin{aligned}
1 &= 1 &= 1^2 \\
1 + 3 &= 4 &= 2^2 \\
1 + 3 + 5 &= 9 &= 3^2 \\
1 + 3 + 5 + 7 &= 16 &= 4^2 \\
1 + 3 + 5 + 7 + 9 &= 25 &= 5^2
\end{aligned}$$

By observing the above pattern, we can formulate a general result. The above five cases suggest that

$$1 + 3 + 5 + \cdots + (2n - 1) \;=\; n^2.$$

However we have not yet proved that this formula is true for all n; we have only verified it in five cases. We must apply some general argument, such as Mathematical Induction, to verify that the formula always holds.

(i).   We have seen that the formula holds if $n = 1$.

(ii).   Suppose that the formula holds when $n = k$; that is suppose

$$1 + 3 + 5 + \cdots + (2k - 1) \;=\; k^2.$$

Then

$$
\begin{aligned}
1 + 3 + 5 + \cdots + (2k - 1) + (2k + 1) &= k^2 + (2k + 1) \\
&= (k + 1)^2.
\end{aligned}
$$

Therefore the formula also holds for $n = k + 1$.

Hence, by Mathematical Induction,

$$1 + 3 + 5 + \cdots + (2n - 1) \;=\; n^2 \quad \text{for all } n \in \mathbb{P}. \qquad \square$$

Mathematicians have a notation that often simplifies the writing of the sum of a long series of terms. It is called the *sigma notation* or *summation notation* as it employs the capital Greek letter sigma, $\sum$.

The sum

$$1 + 3 + 5 + \cdots + (2n - 1)$$

whose rth term if $(2r - 1)$ is written as

$$\sum_{r=1}^{n} (2r - 1)$$

and is read as "the sum, from $r = 1$ to $r = n$, of $(2r - 1)$".

In general, if $f(r)$ is an expression involving the integer r then

$$\sum_{r=k}^{\ell} f(r) = f(k) + f(k + 1) + \cdots + f(\ell - 1) + f(\ell)$$

that is, the sum of all the terms obtained by substituting the integers from k to ℓ for r in the expression $f(r)$.

For example,

$$\sum_{i=5}^{8}(2^i + 3) \;=\; 35 + 67 + 131 + 259.$$

The result proved in Example 3.1.2 can be written as

$$\sum_{r=1}^{n} r \;=\; \frac{n(n+1)}{2}.$$

3.1.6 Example.   If x and y are integers, prove that $x^{2n-1} + y^{2n-1}$ is divisible by $x + y$ for all $n \in \mathbb{P}$.

Solution.   We shall prove this result by induction on n.

(i).   When $n = 1$ the result is true, because $(x + y)|(x + y)$.

(ii).   Suppose that $(x + y)|(x^{2k-1} + y^{2k-1})$. Then

$$\begin{aligned}
x^{2k+1} + y^{2k+1} &= x^2(x^{2k-1} + y^{2k-1}) - x^2 y^{2k-1} + y^{2k+1} \\
&= x^2(x^{2k-1} + y^{2k-1}) - y^{2k-1}(x^2 - y^2).
\end{aligned}$$

Since $(x + y)|(x^{2k-1} + y^{2k-1})$ by the induction hypothesis, and $(x + y)|(x^2 - y^2)$, it follows that $(x + y)|(x^{2k+1} + y^{2k+1})$. Therefore, by the Principle of Mathematical Induction, $(x + y)|(x^{2n-1} + y^{2n-1})$ for all $n \in \mathbb{P}$. $\square$

3.1.7 Example.   An ancient puzzle called the *Tower of Hanoi* consists of three pegs on a stand and n punctured discs of different sizes that are placed in decreasing order on one of the pegs. The object of the puzzle is to transfer the pile of discs to another peg, by moving one disc at a time, and without placing any disc on top of a smaller disc. Show that it is possible to solve this puzzle in $2^n - 1$ moves.

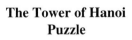

The Tower of Hanoi Puzzle

Proof.   We shall prove this by induction on the number of discs.

(i).   If $n = 1$ then one disc can be transferred to another peg in $2^1 - 1 = 1$ move.

(ii).   Suppose that it is possible to transfer k discs to another peg in $2^k - 1$ moves.

Now suppose that there are $k + 1$ discs on one peg. Leave the largest disc alone and transfer the k other discs to another peg. Since any of the discs can be placed on the largest one, the large disc does not affect the problem and the transfer of the k smaller discs can be accomplished in $2^k - 1$ moves. Now move the largest disc to the vacant peg and finally move the k smaller discs back onto the largest disc in $2^k - 1$ more moves.

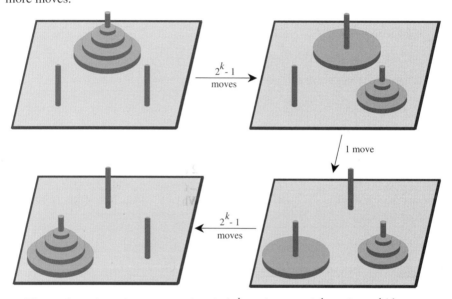

The total number of moves required is $(2^k - 1) + 1 + (2^k - 1) = 2^{k+1} - 1$.

It therefore follows from Mathematical Induction that the problem can always be solved in $2^n - 1$ moves. $\qquad\qquad\qquad\qquad\qquad\qquad\qquad\qquad\qquad\qquad\qquad\qquad$ $\square$

Slight variations of the Principle of Mathematical Induction given in 3.1.3 are sometimes useful. For example, if $P(n)$ is a statement depending on the integer n and

      (i) $P(t)$ is true for some fixed integer t (positive, negative or zero)

and   (ii) $P(k + 1)$ is true whenever $P(k)$ is true, for $k \geq t$

then it follows that $P(n)$ is true for all integers $n \geq t$.

Sometimes it is not possible to prove the statement $P(k + 1)$ from the statement $P(k)$, although $P(k + 1)$ could be proved from some or all of the statements $P(k), P(k - 1), \ldots, P(2), P(1)$. In this case the following variation of the induction principle is useful.

3.1.8 Second Principle of Mathematical Induction. Let $P(n)$ be a
statement that depends on the positive integer n.

If   (i) $P(1)$ is true
and   (ii) $P(k+1)$ is true whenever $P(r)$ is true, for all $1 \leq r \leq k$

then $P(n)$ is true for all $n \in \mathbb{P}$.

Proof. Let $Q(n)$ be a statement "$P(r)$ is true for $1 \leq r \leq n$." Then the hypotheses on $P(n)$ imply that

     (i) $Q(1)$ is true
and   (ii) $Q(k+1)$ is true whenever $Q(k)$ is true

Hence, by the Principle of Mathematical Induction 3.1.3, $Q(n)$ is true for all $n \in \mathbb{P}$ and, in particular, $P(n)$ is true for all $n \in \mathbb{P}$. $\qquad\square$

3.1.9 Example. A sequence of integers $x_1, x_2, x_3, x_4 \ldots$ is defined by $x_1 = 2$, $x_2 = 5$, and $x_k = x_{k-1} + 2x_{k-2}$ for all $k \geq 3$. Prove that

$$x_n = \frac{7 \cdot 2^{n-1} + (-1)^n}{3} \qquad \text{for all } n \in \mathbb{P}.$$

Proof. (i). When $n = 1$, $x_1 = (7 \cdot 2^0 - 1)/3 = 2$ and the result is true.
     We cannot use the inductive formula $x_k = x_{k-1} + 2x_{k-2}$ until we reach x_3. We shall therefore have to verify the result for $n = 2$. When $n = 2$, $x_2 = (7 \cdot 2 + 1)/3 = 5$ and the result is true.

(ii). We can calculate the terms in the sequence after x_2 if we know the preceding *two* terms. We shall therefore apply the Second Principle of Mathematical Induction to prove the result in general whenever $n \geq 3$.
     Suppose that $x_r = (7 \cdot 2^{r-1} + (-1)^r)/3$, whenever $1 \leq r \leq k$. Then, if $k \geq 2$,

$$\begin{aligned}
x_{k+1} &= x_k + 2x_{k-1} \\
&= \frac{7 \cdot 2^{k-1} + (-1)^k}{3} + \frac{2[7 \cdot 2^{k-2} + (-1)^{k-1}]}{3} \\
&= \frac{7 \cdot 2^{k-1} + (-1)^k + 7 \cdot 2^{k-1} - 2(-1)^k}{3} \\
&= \frac{7 \cdot 2^k - (-1)^k}{3} = \frac{7 \cdot 2^k + (-1)^{k+1}}{3}.
\end{aligned}$$

Therefore the result is true for $n = k + 1$.
     By the Second Principle of Mathematical Induction 3.1.8, it follows that

$$x_n = \frac{7 \cdot 2^{n-1} + (-1)^n}{3} \qquad \text{for all } n \in \mathbb{P}. \qquad\square$$

3.2 RECURSION

One example of mathematical induction that is frequently used in computer science is recursion. Most programming languages allow the use of recursive functions or procedures.

A *recursive routine* is one that calls itself. It obviously must call itself with different arguments, otherwise it would enter an infinite loop. The routine evaluates itself with the new, usually smaller arguments, which would then call itself with different arguments again. This recursion continues until the routine reaches some *base* or *stopping case*. There may be one or more of these stopping cases.

For example, consider the function $f(n)$ that is the sum of the first n integers. This can be defined in several different ways.

Iteration:	$f(n)$ =	$1 + 2 + 3 + \cdots + n$
Recursion:	$f(n)$ =	$f(n-1) + n$ if $n > 1$; and $f(1) = 1$
Closed form:	$f(n)$ =	$n(n+1)/2$

In this case, the recursive definition of the function $f(n)$ calls the same function, but with its argument reduced by one. There is one stopping case, namely $f(1)$.

In a similar way the *factorial function* can be defined in two ways.

Iteration:	$n!$ =	$1 \cdot 2 \cdot 3 \cdots n$
Recursion:	$n!$ =	$n(n-1)!$ if $n > 1$; and $0! = 1$

The *greatest common divisor* of n integers can be defined recursively for $n > 2$ by

$$\mathrm{GCD}(x_1, x_2, \ldots, x_n) \quad = \quad \mathrm{GCD}(\mathrm{GCD}(x_1, x_2, \ldots, x_{n-1}), x_n).$$

In this case the number of arguments change. The stopping case occurs when $n = 2$; we already know the definition of $\mathrm{GCD}(x_1, x_2)$.

To prove that a recursive function produces the correct value, we usually have to use induction. We have to

(i) check the *base* or *stopping cases*; that is, show that the function is correct when there are no recursive calls;

(ii) check the *recursive steps*, assuming inductively that the function gives the correct values for the smaller arguments.

3.2.1 Example.   Prove that the recursive function $f(n)$ defined by

$$f(n) \quad = \quad f(n-1) + n \quad \text{if } n > 1; \quad \text{and } f(1) = 1$$

is equal to $\frac{n(n+1)}{2}$ for all $n \geq 1$.

Solution. (i).   When $n = 1$, $f(1) = 1$ and also $\frac{n(n+1)}{2} = 1$. Hence the result is true when $n = 1$.

(ii). Assume, as induction hypothesis, that $f(k) = \frac{k(k+1)}{2}$, for some $k > 0$. Then

$$
\begin{aligned}
f(k+1) &= f(k+1) + k + 1 \\
&= \frac{k(k+1)}{2} + k + 1 \\
&= \frac{(k+1)(k+2)}{2}
\end{aligned}
$$

Hence the result is true for $n = k + 1$. Therefore, by the Principle of Mathematical Induction, $f(n) = \frac{n(n+1)}{2}$ for all $n \geq 1$. $\qquad\square$

In computer science, the integer function MOD denotes the remainder when one integer is divided by another using the Division Algorithm 1.1.3. If a is a positive integer and b a nonnegative integer then b MOD $a = r$, where $b = qa + r$, with $0 \leq r < a$. Proposition 1.2.2 yields the following recursive algorithm for computing the greatest common divisor. Since b MOD a is always smaller than a, the algorithm will terminate, as the first variable always decreases.

3.2.2 Recursive Euclidean Algorithm. If a and b are nonnegative integers, their greatest common divisor can be calculated recursively using

$$
\text{GCD}(a, b) = \begin{cases} b & \text{if } a = 0 \\ \text{GCD}(b \text{ MOD } a, a) & \text{if } a \neq 0 \end{cases}
$$

The pseudo-code for the recursive GCD function is as follows.

Function GCD (a, b)

if $a = 0$
    then return b
else return GCD $(b$ MOD $a, a)$

For example,

$$
\begin{aligned}
\text{GCD}(66, 39) &= \text{GCD}(39, 66) &= \text{GCD}(27, 39) &= \text{GCD}(12, 27) \\
&= \text{GCD}(3, 12) &= \text{GCD}(0, 3) &= 3.
\end{aligned}
$$

In the above examples, the recursive function calls *one* copy of itself; this is called *one-way recursion*. It is also possible for the function to call multiple copies of itself. In *two-way recursion* the function calls two copies of itself. One example of this is the *Quicksort Algorithm* that is used to sort large lists, say to alphabetize a long list of words. This algorithm splits the list into two parts, and then applies the Quicksort Algorithm to both halves separately. These separately sorted halves then have to be merged together.

3.3   THE BINOMIAL THEOREM

A binomial is a sum of two quantities, such as $a+b$. The square and cube of a binomial have the following familiar expansions.

$$
\begin{aligned}
(a + b)^2 &= a^2 + 2ab + b^2 \\
(a + b)^3 &= a^3 + 3a^2b + 3ab^2 + b^3
\end{aligned}
$$

The Binomial Theorem yields the expansion of $(a + b)^n$ for each positive integral exponent. The coefficients that occur in the binomial expansions are called binomial coefficients and can be conveniently written in terms of factorials.

3.3.1 Definition.   If $0 \leq r \leq n$ then the *binomial coefficient* $\binom{n}{r}$ is defined by

$$
\binom{n}{r} = \frac{n!}{r!(n - r)!}
$$

where $0!$ is defined to be 1.

The binomial coefficient $\binom{n}{r}$ is pronounced "n choose r" because it is also the number of *combinations of n things chosen r at a time*; that is $\binom{n}{r}$ is the number of different r element subsets in a set containing n elements. Other common notations for $\binom{n}{r}$ are $_nC_r$ and $C(n,r)$.

3.3.2 Proposition.   The following properties of the binomial coefficients follow directly from the definition, when $0 \leq r \leq n$.

(i) $\displaystyle \binom{n}{r} = \frac{n(n - 1)(n - 2) \cdots (n - r + 2)(n - r + 1)}{1 \cdot 2 \cdot 3 \cdots (r - 1) \cdot r}.$

(ii) $\displaystyle \binom{n}{0} = \binom{n}{n} = 1.$

(iii) $\displaystyle \binom{n}{n - r} = \binom{n}{r}.$ $\square$

We need the following important identity between the binomial coefficients in order to use induction to prove the Binomial Theorem.

3.3.3 Proposition.   If $1 \leq r \leq n$ then

$$
\binom{n}{r - 1} + \binom{n}{r} = \binom{n + 1}{r}.
$$

Proof. The proof is by straightforward calculation.

$$
\begin{aligned}
\binom{n}{r-1} + \binom{n}{r} &= \frac{n!}{(r-1)!(n-r+1)!} + \frac{n!}{r!(n-r)!} \\
&= \frac{r(n!) + (n-r+1)(n!)}{r!(n-r+1)!} \\
&= \frac{(n+1)(n!)}{r!(n-r+1)!} = \frac{(n+1)!}{r!(n+1-r)!} \\
&= \binom{n+1}{r}.
\end{aligned}
$$
□

This identity has a nice combinatorial interpretation. The number $\binom{n+1}{r}$ is the number of different r element subsets that can be chosen from an $n+1$ element set. Label the elements of the set as $L_1, L_2, \ldots, L_n, L_{n+1}$. If L_{n+1} is in the chosen subset, then there are $\binom{n}{r-1}$ ways of chosing the remaining $r-1$ elements from $L_1, L_2, \ldots, L_n$. If L_{n+1} is not in the chosen subset, then there are $\binom{n}{r}$ ways of chosing an r element subset from $L_1, L_2, \ldots, L_n$. Hence the total number of r element subsets in an $n+1$ element set is $\binom{n}{r-1} + \binom{n}{r}$.

It is not clear from our definition that the binomial coefficients are always integers.

3.3.4 Proposition. $\binom{n}{r}$ is an integer for $0 \le r \le n$.

Proof. We shall prove this by induction on n.

(i). If $n = 1$, then $\binom{1}{0} = 1$ and $\binom{1}{1} = 1$ which are both integers.

(ii). Suppose that $\binom{k}{r}$ is an integer if $0 \le r \le k$. Then, it follows from Proposition 3.3.3, that if $1 \le r \le k$,

$$
\binom{k+1}{r} = \binom{k}{r-1} + \binom{k}{r}
$$

which is the sum of two integers and so is also an integer. Finally $\binom{k+1}{0} = \binom{k+1}{k+1} = 1$ are integers.

Therefore, by Mathematical Induction, $\binom{n}{r}$ is an integer for all $n \in \mathbb{P}$ and $0 \le r \le n$. □

3.3.5 Binomial Theorem. If a and b are any numbers and $n \in \mathbb{P}$ then

$$
(a+b)^n = \binom{n}{0}a^n + \binom{n}{1}a^{n-1}b + \cdots + \binom{n}{r}a^{n-r}b^r + \cdots + \binom{n}{n-1}ab^{n-1} + \binom{n}{n}b^n.
$$

Proof. We shall prove it by induction on n.

(i). If $n = 1$ then

$$\tbinom{1}{0}a + \tbinom{1}{1}b \;=\; a + b \;=\; (a+b)^1$$

and the theorem holds.

(ii). Suppose the theorem is true for $n = k$; that is

$$(a+b)^k \;=\; \binom{k}{0}a^k + \binom{k}{1}a^{k-1}b + \cdots + \binom{k}{r}a^{k-r}b^r + \cdots + \binom{k}{k}b^k.$$

Now

$$(a+b)^{k+1} \;=\; (a+b)(a+b)^k \;=\; a(a+b)^k + b(a+b)^k$$

$$
\begin{aligned}
=\;\; & \tbinom{k}{0}a^{k+1} + \tbinom{k}{1}a^k b + \cdots + \tbinom{k}{r}a^{k-r+1}b^r + \cdots + \tbinom{k}{k}ab^k \\
& + \tbinom{k}{0}a^k b + \cdots + \tbinom{k}{r-1}a^{k-r+1}b^r + \cdots + \tbinom{k}{k-1}ab^k + \tbinom{k}{k}b^{k+1} \\
=\;\; & a^{k+1} + \tbinom{k+1}{1}a^k b + \cdots + \tbinom{k+1}{r}a^{k-r+1}b^r + \cdots + \tbinom{k+1}{k}ab^k + \quad b^{k+1}
\end{aligned}
$$

using Proposition 3.3.3. Hence the theorem is true for $n = k + 1$.

By the Principle of Mathematical Induction the theorem is true for all $n \in \mathbb{P}$. $\quad\square$

Using the sigma notation, the Binomial Theorem can be written as

$$(a+b)^n \;=\; \sum_{r=0}^{n} \binom{n}{r} a^{n-r} b^r.$$

Writing down the first few cases of the theorem, and adding $(a + b)^0$ we obtain the following.

$$
\begin{aligned}
(a+b)^0 &= 1 \\
(a+b)^1 &= a + b \\
(a+b)^2 &= a^2 + 2ab + b^2 \\
(a+b)^3 &= a^3 + 3a^2b + 3ab^2 + b^3 \\
(a+b)^4 &= a^4 + 4a^3b + 6a^2b^2 + 4ab^3 + b^4 \\
(a+b)^5 &= a^5 + 5a^4b + 10a^3b^2 + 10a^2b^3 + 5ab^4 + b^5
\end{aligned}
$$

If the binomial coefficients alone are written out, as above, we obtain what is known as *Pascal's Triangle*.

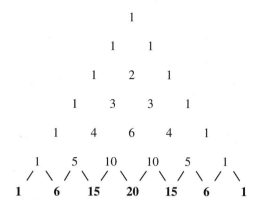

It follows from Proposition 3.3.3 that each row can be obtained from the previous row; each element is the sum of the two elements to its immediate left and right in the preceding row.

3.3.6 Example.   Expand $(3x - 2y)^4$.

Solution.   By the Binomial Theorem

$$
\begin{aligned}
(3x - 2y)^4 &= (3x)^4 + 4(3x)^3(-2y) + 6(3x)^2(-2y)^2 + 4(3x)(-2y)^3 + (-2y)^4 \\
&= 81x^4 - 216x^3y + 216x^2y^2 - 96xy^3 + 16y^4.
\end{aligned}
$$
$\square$

3.3.7 Example.   Calculate $(2.01)^5$ to 3 decimal places.

Solution.   By the Binomial Theorem,

$$
\begin{aligned}
(2.01)^5 &= (2 + .01)^5 \\
&= 2^5 + 5 \cdot 2^4(.01) + 10 \cdot 2^3(.01)^2 + 10 \cdot 2^2(.01)^3 + 5 \cdot 2(.01)^4 + (.01)^5 \\
&= 32 + .8 + .008 + .00004 + .0000001 + .0000000001 \\
&= 32.808 \qquad \text{to 3 decimal places.}
\end{aligned}
$$
$\square$

3.3.8 Example.   If k is an integer and kx^3y^4 is a term in the expansion of $(2x + 5y^2)^n$, then find the values of n and k.

Solution.   The rth term in the expansion of $(2x + 5y^2)^n$ is

$$
\binom{n}{r}(2x)^{n-r}(5y^2)^r = \binom{n}{r}2^{n-r} \cdot 5^r x^{n-r}y^{2r}.
$$

If this equals kx^3y^4 then we must have $n - r = 3$ and $2r = 4$; that is $r = 2$ and $n = 5$. Hence

$$k = \binom{n}{r}2^{n-r}5^r = \binom{5}{2}2^3 \cdot 5^2 = \frac{5 \cdot 4}{1 \cdot 2} \cdot 2^3 \cdot 5^2 = 2^4 \cdot 5^3$$
$$= 2000. \qquad \Box$$

The reason why the binomial coefficient $\binom{n}{r}$ is equal to the number of combinations of n objects taken r at a time, can be seen by writing out $(a + b)^n$ as

$$(a + b)^n = (a + b)(a + b)(a + b) \cdots (a + b)$$

where there are n factors. When the factors on the right hand side are multiplied out, the term $a^{n-r}b^r$ will occur whenever we choose an "a" from $n - r$ factors and a "b" from the remaining r factors. Hence the number of times $a^{n-r}b^r$ will occur is equal to the number of ways of choosing r b's from the n factors.

We have proved the Binomial Theorem for positive integral values of the exponent. It is possible to expand a binomial to a negative integer power or, in fact, any real power. In these cases we cannot obtain an expansion involving only a finite number of terms, but instead we obtain an infinite series. For example, if n is a real number then

$$(1 + x)^n = 1 + nx + \frac{n(n - 1)}{2!}x^2 + \frac{n(n - 1)(n - 2)}{3!}x^3 + \cdots .$$

If n is a positive integer, this series terminates and we obtain the terms given in the Binomial Theorem. If n is not a positive integer, the coefficient of x^r is $\frac{n(n-1)(n-2)\cdots(n-r+1)}{r!}$ and this never vanishes; hence we obtain an infinite series. It can be shown that the sum of the series on the right hand side approaches the value $(1 + x)^n$ *provided that* $-1 < x < 1$. If n lies outside this range, then the binomial expansion is meaningless.

Consider

$$\frac{1}{(1 + x)^2} = (1 + x)^{-2} = 1 - 2x + \frac{(-2)(-3)}{2!}x^2 + \frac{(-2)(-3)(-4)}{3!}x^3 + \cdots$$
$$= 1 - 2x + 3x^2 - 4x^3 + \cdots .$$

This expansion is valid if $-1 < x < 1$. However, if we put $x = -2$ in the above expression, the right hand side becomes

$$1 + 4 + 12 + 32 + \cdots$$

which certainly does not approach $\frac{1}{(1-2)^2} = 1$.

Exercise Set 3

1 - 3. *Calculate the following.*

1. $\dbinom{5}{3}$

2. $\dbinom{10}{6}$

3. $\dfrac{8!}{(4!)^2}$

4. $100! - 99!$

5. Show that $\dfrac{1}{n}\dbinom{n}{r} = \dfrac{1}{r}\dbinom{n-1}{r-1}$.

6. Show that $\dbinom{n}{r}\dbinom{r}{s} = \dbinom{n}{s}\dbinom{n-s}{r-s}$.

7. Find n if $\dbinom{n+2}{n} = 36$.

8 - 10. *Write the following in sigma notation.*

8. $\dfrac{1}{2} + \dfrac{3}{4} + \dfrac{5}{6} + \cdots + \dfrac{99}{100}$.

9. $8 + 15 + 24 + 35 + \cdots + (n^2 - 1)$.

10. $a^k + a^{2k} + a^{4k} + a^{8k} + a^{16k} + \cdots + a^{256k}$.

11 - 19. *Prove, by induction, the following results for all $n \in \mathbb{P}$.*

11. $1^2 + 2^2 + 3^2 + \cdots + n^2 = \dfrac{n(n+1)(2n+1)}{6}$

12. $1^3 + 2^3 + 3^3 + \cdots + n^3 = \left[\dfrac{n(n+1)}{2}\right]^2$

13. $1^4 + 2^4 + 3^4 + \cdots + n^4 = \dfrac{n(n+1)(6n^3 + 9n^2 + n - 1)}{30}$

14. $1^2 + 3^2 + 5^2 + \cdots + (2n-1)^2 = \dfrac{n(2n-1)(2n+1)}{3}$

15. $1 \cdot 2 + 2 \cdot 3 + 3 \cdot 4 + \cdots + n(n+1) = \dfrac{n(n+1)(n+2)}{3}$

16. $\dfrac{1}{2} + \dfrac{2}{2^2} + \dfrac{3}{2^3} + \cdots + \dfrac{n}{2^n} = 2 - \left(\dfrac{n+2}{2^n}\right)$

17. $\sum_{r=1}^{n} r(r!) = (n+1)! - 1$

18. $6 | (2n^3 + 3n^2 + n)$

19. A set with n elements contains 2^n subsets (including the set itself and $\emptyset$).

20 - 23. *Are the following true for all positive integral values of n? If so, prove the result; if not, give a counterexample.*

20. $n! \geq 2n$ **21.** $3|(2^{2n} - 1)$

22. $7|(5^n + n + 1)$ **23.** $(a + b)|(a^{2n} - b^{2n})$

24. Prove that the sum of the first n terms of the *arithmetic progression*

$$a + (a + d) + (a + 2d) + \cdots + [a + (n - 1)d]$$

is $\frac{n}{2}[2a + (n - 1)d]$; that is, $\frac{n}{2}$ times the sum of the first and last terms.

25. Prove that the sum of the first n terms of the *geometric progression*

$$a + aq + aq^2 + \cdots + aq^{n-1}$$

is $\dfrac{a(1 - q^n)}{1 - q}$, when $q \neq 1$.

26. *(Fermat's Little Theorem)* If p is a prime, use induction on n and the Binomial Theorem to prove that $n^p \equiv n \pmod{p}$ for all $n \in \mathbb{P}$.

27. Use induction to prove that $a^m \cdot a^n = a^{m+n}$ for all $n \in \mathbb{P}$.

28. A sequence of integers $x_1, x_2, x_3, \ldots$ is defined by $x_1 = 3$, $x_2 = 7$ and

$$x_k = 5x_{k-1} - 6x_{k-2} \quad \text{for } k \geq 3.$$

Prove that $x_n = 2^n + 3^{n-1}$ for all $n \in \mathbb{P}$.

29. If n points lie in a plane and no three are collinear, prove that there are $\frac{1}{2}n(n-1)$ lines joining these points.

30. Find an expression for

$$1 - 3 + 5 - 7 + 9 - 11 + \cdots + (-1)^{n-1}(2n - 1)$$

and prove that it is correct.

31. The notation $\prod_{r=1}^{n} a_r$ stands for the *product* of all the terms obtained by substituting the integers from 1 to n for r in the expression a_r. That is,

$$\prod_{r=1}^{n} a_r = a_1 \cdot a_2 \cdot a_3 \cdots a_n.$$

Prove that $\displaystyle\prod_{r=1}^{n} (1 + x^{2^r}) = \dfrac{1 - x^{2^{r+1}}}{1 - x^2}$, if $x^2 \neq 1$.

32. Find an expression for $\displaystyle\prod_{r=2}^{n} \left(1 - \dfrac{1}{r^2}\right)$ and prove that your expression is correct.

33. *(Peano Axioms)* In 1889 the Italian Mathematician Guiseppe Peano developed the properties of the integers from five axioms. He started with the undefined concepts of "set", "positive integer", "belongs to" and "successor". The integer that immediately follows the integer n is called the successor of n and is denoted by $n^\dagger$. His axiom system is based on the fact that every positive integer has a successor and furthermore, every positive integer can be obtained by starting with 1 and taking the successor enough times. The five axioms of the set $\mathbb{P}$ are as follows.

Axiom 1. $1 \in \mathbb{P}$.

Axiom 2. For each $n \in \mathbb{P}$ there exists an integer $n^\dagger \in \mathbb{P}$ called the *successor* of n.

Axiom 3. There is no $n \in \mathbb{P}$ such that $n^\dagger = 1$.

Axiom 4. If $m, n \in \mathbb{P}$ and $m^\dagger = n^\dagger$ then $m = n$.

Axiom 5. *(Mathematical Induction)* If S is any subset of $\mathbb{P}$ and

(i) $1 \in S$

(ii) $k^\dagger \in S$ whenever $k \in \mathbb{S}$

then $S = \mathbb{P}$.

All the properties of $\mathbb{P}$ can be obtained from these axioms. Addition in $\mathbb{P}$ is defined by

$$n + 1 = n^\dagger \quad \text{for every } n \in \mathbb{P}$$

and $n + m^\dagger = (n + m)^\dagger$ whenever $n + m$ is defined. For example, $1 + 1 = 1^\dagger$ and this would be denoted by 2. Then $2 + 1 = 2^\dagger$ which would be denoted by 3, etc.

Using the axioms, prove that

(a) $m + n \in \mathbb{P}$ for all $m, n \in \mathbb{P}$.

(b) $n + 1 = 1 + n$ for all $n \in \mathbb{P}$.

(c) $m + n = n + m$ for all $n, m \in \mathbb{P}$.

(d) $m + (n + p) = (m + n) + p$ for all $n, m, p \in \mathbb{P}$.

(e) Define multiplication in $\mathbb{P}$ and then prove that

$$(m + n) \cdot p = m \cdot p + n \cdot p \quad \text{for all } m, n, p \in \mathbb{P}.$$

34 - 38. *Expand the following by the Binomial Theorem.*

34. $(2a + b)^6$

35. $(a - 1)^5$

36. $\left(x + \dfrac{1}{x} \right)^8$

37. $(4x^2 - 3y^3)^4$

38. $(a + b + c)^3$

39. Calculate $(2.99)^4$ to 3 decimal places.

40. Calculate $(1.02)^{10}$ to 3 decimal places.

41. Find the fifth term in the expansion of $\left(2x^6 - \dfrac{5}{x^5} \right)^{11}$.

42. Find the term containing x^5 in the expansion of $\left(x^2 + \dfrac{3}{x} \right)^6$.

43. If p is a prime, prove that

$$(a + b)^p \equiv a^p + b^p \pmod{p} \quad \text{for all } a, b \in \mathbb{Z}.$$

44. A man earns a starting salary of \$10,000 a year and receives an annual wage increase of 10%. Find his salary, to the nearest dollar, after 10 years.

45. Prove that

$$\binom{n}{0} + \binom{n}{1} + \binom{n}{2} + \cdots + \binom{n}{n} = 2^n$$

and that

$$\binom{n}{0} - \binom{n}{1} + \binom{n}{2} - \cdots + (-1)^n \binom{n}{n} = 0.$$

Problem Set 3

46. Prove that $\displaystyle\sum_{r=1}^{n} rx^r = \dfrac{x - (n + 1)x^{n+1} + nx^{n+2}}{(1 - x)^2}$ for all $n \in \mathbb{P}$, where x is a number different from 1.

47. Prove that $\sqrt[n]{2} \leq 1 + \dfrac{1}{n}$ for all $n \in \mathbb{P}$.

48. Find an expression for $1^2 - 3^2 + 5^2 - 7^2 + \cdots + (-1)^{n-1}(2n - 1)^2$ and prove that your expression is correct.

49. Prove that a convex n-gon contains $\frac{1}{2}n(n - 3)$ diagonals. (A convex n-gon is a polygon with n sides such that all the line segments, joining two nonadjacent vertices, lie inside the polygon.)

50. Generalize the following sequence of identities and prove your generalization.

$$1 = 1, \quad 3 + 5 = 8, \quad 7 + 9 + 11 = 27, \quad 13 + 15 + 17 + 19 = 64$$

51. Prove that the product of r consecutive integers is divisible by $r!$.

52. Find an expression for

$$\sum_{i=1}^{n} i(i + 1)(i + 2) \cdots (i + r - 1)$$

and prove by induction that your expression is correct.

53. If $x \equiv 1 \pmod 2$, prove that $x^{2^n} \equiv 1 \pmod{2^{n+2}}$ for all $n \in \mathbb{P}$.

54. Is $2^n - 1$ the minimum number of moves required to solve the Tower of Hanoi puzzle in Example 3.1.7? Give reasons for your answer.

55. If the three pegs in the Tower of Hanoi puzzle are labelled A, B and C and n discs are initially on peg A, then what is the first move in order to transfer the discs to peg B in $2^n - 1$ moves?

56. *(Pigeonhole Principle)* Prove the following statement by induction on n. "If $n + 1$ objects are placed in n boxes (or pigeonholes) then one box must contain at least two objects."

57. *(Leibniz Rule)* If you have some knowledge of the calculus, prove by induction, that

$$D^n(f \cdot g) = \sum_{r=0}^{n} \binom{n}{r} D^{n-r} f \cdot D^r g$$

where Df is the derivative of the function f. Assume that all the necessary derivatives exist.

58. Use integrals to show that

$$\frac{n}{(n + 1)(2n + 1)} < \sum_{r=n+1}^{2n} \frac{1}{r^2} < \frac{1}{2n}.$$

Estimate the value of $\sum_{r=1}^{3n} \frac{1}{r^2}$, stating how accurate your estimate is.

59 - 67. *The Fibonacci sequence is the sequence of integers $f_1, f_2, f_3, \ldots$ defined by $f_1 = 1$, $f_2 = 1$, and $f_n = f_{n-1} + f_{n-2}$, for $n \geq 3$.*

59. Find the first 15 numbers in the Fibonacci Sequence.

60. Prove that $\text{GCD}(f_n, f_{n+1}) = 1$ for all $n \in \mathbb{P}$.

61. Look at the Euclidean Algorithm applied to f_{14} and f_{15}. What do you notice about the sequence of remainders?

62. Prove that $f_{n+1} < \left(\dfrac{7}{4}\right)^n$ for all $n \in \mathbb{P}$.

63. If $\alpha = \dfrac{1 + \sqrt{5}}{2}$ and $\beta = \dfrac{1 - \sqrt{5}}{2}$, prove that $f_n = \dfrac{\alpha^n - \beta^n}{\sqrt{5}}$ for all $n \in \mathbb{P}$.

64. If $\alpha = \dfrac{1 + \sqrt{5}}{2}$, prove that $f_n = \left\lfloor \dfrac{\alpha^n}{\sqrt{5}} \right\rfloor$ for all $n \in \mathbb{P}$, where $\lfloor x \rfloor$ is the greatest integer less than or equal to x. Compute f_{28}, f_{29}, and f_{30}, and verify that $f_{30} = f_{28} + f_{29}$.

65. Prove that $\sum_{r=1}^{n} f_r^2 = f_n f_{n+1}$ for all $n \in \mathbb{P}$.

66. Prove that $\sum_{r=1}^{n} f_{2r-1} = f_{2n}$ for all $n \in \mathbb{P}$.

67. Prove that $f_{n+5} \equiv 3f_n \pmod{5}$ for all $n \in \mathbb{P}$.

68. The downtown portion of a city consists of a rectangular area m blocks long and n blocks wide. If all the streets in each direction are through streets, find the number of different shortest routes from one corner of the downtown area to the opposite corner.

69. One evening, the village squire called together all the men of the village and told them that adultery had been committed in the village. Furthermore he decreed that whenever a husband found that he had been cuckolded, he was to ceremonially plunge his wife into the village pond, in the ducking stool, at noon the following day.

All the men in the village were married and well versed in logic and mathematics, including induction. As is well known in small communities, when a wife indulges in adultery, all save her husband, know about it.

At the first midday after the meeting, no wife was ducked and, indeed, except for much thought, nothing happened till just before noon on the 40th day. Then every husband was seen dragging his wife to the ducking stool.

How many men lived in the village?

70. *(Trinomial Theorem)* Prove that

$$(a+b+c)^n = \sum_{p+q+r=n} \frac{n!}{p!q!r!} a^p b^q c^r$$

for all $n \in \mathbb{P}$, where the sum is taken over all nonnegative values of p, q and r for which $p + q + r = n$.

71. What is the maximum number of regions that a plane can be divided into by n straight lines?

72. What is the maximum number of regions that three dimensional space can be divided into by n planes?

(See the video by G. Polya entitled "Let us teach guessing".)

73. Prove that if $a_1, a_2, \ldots, a_n$ are real numbers such that $0 \le a_i \le 1$ for $1 \le i \le n$, then

$$(1-a_1)(1-a_2)\cdots(1-a_n) \ge 1 - (a_1 + a_2 + \cdots + a_n).$$

74. A sequence $x_1, x_2, x_3, \ldots$ of real numbers is defined by $x_1 = 1$ and

$$x_{n+1} = \frac{n}{n+1}x_n + 1, \quad \text{if } n \ge 1.$$

Prove that $x_n = \dfrac{n+1}{2}$ for all positive integers n.

75. A sequence $y_1, y_2, y_3, \ldots$ of integers is defined by $y_1 = 4$, and $y_{n+1} = y_n^2 - 2$, if $n \ge 1$. Prove that

$$y_n = (2+\sqrt{3})^{2^{n-1}} + (2-\sqrt{3})^{2^{n-1}}$$

for all positive integers n.

76. Prove that

$$\left(1 - \frac{1}{4}\right)\left(1 - \frac{1}{9}\right)\left(1 - \frac{1}{16}\right)\cdots\left(1 - \frac{1}{n^2}\right) = \frac{n+1}{2n}$$

for all integers $n \ge 2$.

77. Show that

$$1 + \frac{1}{2^2} + \frac{1}{3^2} + \cdots + \frac{1}{n^2} \le 2 - \frac{1}{n}$$

for all integers $n \ge 1$.

78 - 82.   Find the value of each recursive mystery function myst $(x_1, x_2, \ldots, x_n)$ *on any n-tuple* $(x_1, x_2, \ldots, x_n)$ *and prove that your value is correct.*

78. myst $(x_1, x_2, \ldots, x_n)$ $= \begin{cases} x_1 & \text{if } n = 1 \\ x_n - \text{myst}(x_1, x_2, \ldots, x_{n-1}) & \text{if } n > 1 \end{cases}$

79. myst $(x_1, x_2, \ldots, x_n)$ $= \begin{cases} x_1 & \text{if } n = 1 \\ x_n \, \text{myst}(x_1, x_2, \ldots, x_{n-1}) & \text{if } n > 1 \end{cases}$

80. myst $(x_1, x_2, \ldots, x_n)$ $= \begin{cases} x_1 & \text{if } n = 1 \\ x_n & \text{if } x_n > \text{myst}(x_1, x_2, \ldots, x_{n-1}) \\ \text{myst}(x_1, x_2, \ldots, x_{n-1}) & \text{otherwise} \end{cases}$

81. myst $(x_1, x_2, \ldots, x_n)$ $= \begin{cases} x_1 & \text{if } n = 1 \\ x_1 - 2\,\text{myst}(x_2, x_3, \ldots, x_n) & \text{if } n > 1 \end{cases}$

82. myst $(x_1, x_2, \ldots, x_n)$ $= \begin{cases} x_1 & \text{if } n = 1 \\ \text{myst}(x_1, x_2, \ldots, x_{n-1}) \\ \quad + \text{myst}(x_2, x_3, \ldots, x_n) & \text{if } n > 1 \end{cases}$

83. Find a recursive definition for the function

$$e(n) = 1 + \frac{1}{1!} + \frac{1}{2!} + \cdots + \frac{1}{n!}$$

that gives an approximation to e, the base of natural logarithms.

84. Discuss the following recursive definition of the GCD for $a \geq 0$ and $b \geq 0$. Is it correct? Is it efficient?

$$\text{GCD}(a, b) = \begin{cases} b & \text{if } a = 0 \\ \text{GCD}(b, a) & \text{if } b < a \\ \text{GCD}(b - a, a) & \text{if } b \geq a > 0 \end{cases}$$

Chapter 4

Rational and Real Numbers

4.1 RATIONAL NUMBERS

In the previous chapters, we have been concerned with the properties of the integers. Whole numbers are excellent for counting, but they are not sufficient for measuring quantities such as length or weight. We need to be able to divide such quantities into any number of equal parts. Therefore we extend our number system to include fractions of the form a/b, where a and b are whole numbers. The fraction a/b represents the number a divided into b equal parts. The integer a is called the *numerator* and the integer b is called the *denominator* of the fraction.

Mathematically, this is equivalent to saying that the integers $\mathbb{Z}$ are inadequate because equations of the form $bx = a$ cannot always be solved in $\mathbb{Z}$. The fraction or rational number a/b that we introduce is a solution to this equation $bx = a$.

As is well known, fractions can be added, subtracted and multiplied by the following rules.

$$\frac{a}{b} + \frac{c}{d} = \frac{ad + bc}{bd}$$

$$\frac{a}{b} - \frac{c}{d} = \frac{ad - bc}{bd}$$

$$\frac{a}{b} \cdot \frac{c}{d} = \frac{ac}{bd}$$

Furthermore any fraction can be divided by a nonzero fraction by the rule

$$\frac{a}{b} \div \frac{c}{d} = \frac{ad}{bc}.$$

One snag is that fractions, such as 1/2 and 2/4, look different but are both solutions to the same equation $2x = 1$. We should like them both to represent the same number.

This suggests that the correct mathematical description of a fraction or rational number should be as an equivalence class. These equivalence classes should be such that a/b and c/d are the same whenever $ad = bc$.

4.1.1 Definition.   Define the equivalence relation, $\sim$, on the set $\mathbb{Z} \times (\mathbb{Z} - \{0\}) = \{(a, b) \mid a, b \in \mathbb{Z}, b \neq 0\}$ by $(a, b) \sim (c, d)$ if and only if $ad = bc$.

The equivalence classes are called *rational numbers* and the equivalence class containing (a, b) is denoted by $\frac{a}{b}$ or a/b. The set of all rational numbers is denoted by $\mathbb{Q}$, so that

$$\mathbb{Q} \ = \ \left\{ \frac{a}{b} \ \middle| \ a, b \in \mathbb{Z}, b \neq 0 \right\}.$$

The reader should check that the relation $\sim$ on $\mathbb{Z} \times (\mathbb{Z} - \{0\})$ is indeed an equivalence relation, so that this is a valid definition.

Since the operations of addition, subtraction, multiplication and division are all defined in terms of representatives of equivalence classes, we have to check that these operations are all well defined. We have to show that if we take two different forms for the same rational number then the result of performing the operations on these is the same. For example, using the definition of addition

$$\begin{array}{rcccc}
\frac{1}{2} + \frac{1}{2} & = & \frac{2+2}{2\cdot 2} & = & \frac{4}{4} \\[2mm]
\frac{2}{4} + \frac{-3}{-6} & = & \frac{2(-6)+4(-3)}{4(-6)} & = & \frac{-24}{-24}.
\end{array}$$

In general, we can check that if $a_1/b_1 = a_2/b_2$ and $c_1/d_1 = c_2/d_2$ then

$$\frac{a_1}{b_1} + \frac{c_1}{d_1} \ = \ \frac{a_2}{b_2} + \frac{c_2}{d_2}$$

and obtain similar results for the other operations.

When rational numbers of the form $n/1$ are added, subtracted and multiplied, we see that the result is also a number with denominator 1;

$$\frac{n}{1} + \frac{m}{1} = \frac{n+m}{1}, \qquad \frac{n}{1} - \frac{m}{1} = \frac{n-m}{1}, \qquad \frac{n}{1} \cdot \frac{m}{1} = \frac{nm}{1}.$$

We can identify the integer n with the rational number $n/1$, and, because of the above results, the operations of addition, subtraction and multiplication of integers can be performed either on the integers themselves or on the corresponding rational numbers with denominator 1. Therefore the set $\mathbb{Z}$ can be considered as a subset of $\mathbb{Q}$, or $\mathbb{Q}$ can be thought of as an extension of $\mathbb{Z}$.

The zero rational number is $0/1$ or, equivalently, $0/b$ for any $b \neq 0$. The unit is the number $1/1$ or, equivalently, a/a for any $a \neq 0$. Addition, subtraction and multiplication of rational numbers have the usual arithmetic properties, and division by nonzero rationals is always possible, so the set of rational numbers, $\mathbb{Q}$, forms a field.

The rational numbers were constructed so that linear equations of the form $bx = a$ could be solved where $a, b \in \mathbb{Z}, b \neq 0$. However they do more, because any linear equation with *rational* coefficients,

$$\frac{b}{d}x = \frac{a}{c} \quad \text{where } \frac{a}{c}, \frac{b}{d} \in \mathbb{Q}, b \neq 0$$

has a rational solution $x = ad/bc$.

4.1.2 Proposition.   Any nonzero rational number r can be expressed in a unique way as a fraction $r = a/b$ with $b > 0$ and $\text{GCD}(a, b) = 1$.

In this case, we say that the fraction has been reduced to its *lowest terms*.

Proof.   By the definition of rational numbers, r can be written in the form p/q where p and q are nonzero integers. Furthermore we can assume $q > 0$ for otherwise we could replace p/q by $(-p)/(-q)$.

Let $d = \text{GCD}(p, q)$ and $p = ad, q = bd$ where $a, b \in \mathbb{Z}$ and $b > 0$. Then

$$r = \frac{p}{q} = \frac{ad}{bd} = \frac{a}{b}.$$

This is the required form for r because $\text{GCD}(a, b) = \text{GCD}\left(\frac{p}{d}, \frac{q}{d}\right) = 1$, by Proposition 1.2.9.

To show that this form is unique, suppose that

$$r = \frac{a_1}{b_2} = \frac{a_2}{b_2} \quad \text{where } a_1, a_2, b_1, b_2 \in \mathbb{Z}, b_1, b_2 > 0.$$

and $\text{GCD}(a_1, b_1) = \text{GCD}(a_2, b_2) = 1$. Then $a_1 b_2 = a_2 b_1$ and it follows from Theorem 1.2.8 that $b_1 | b_2$ and $b_2 | b_1$. Hence, by Proposition 1.1.2 (ii), $b_1 = b_2$ and so also $a_1 = a_2$. $\qquad \square$

4.2   REAL NUMBERS

We can give a geometrical picture of the rational numbers as points on a "number line" as follows. Mark off two points on a straight line and label the left hand point 0 and the right hand point 1. We shall take the distance between these two points as the unit length. The positive integer n is represented by the point that is n units to the right of 0 and the negative integer $-n$ as the point that is n units to the left of 0. The rational number a/b, where $a, b \in \mathbb{Z}$ and $b > 0$, is represented by the point that is one bth part of the distance from 0 to the integer point a.

Any interval of the line, however small, contains rational points. We can find such a point by choosing n large enough so that the interval form 0 to $1/n$ is smaller than the interval in question. Then, at least one rational point of the form m/n, with $m \in \mathbb{Z}$, must lie in the interval. We express this fact by saying that the rational numbers are dense in the line.

In fact, every interval contains an infinite number of rational points. For example the interval between $\frac{88}{100}$ and $\frac{89}{100}$ contains the points $\frac{881}{1000}, \frac{882}{1000}, \ldots, \frac{889}{1000}$, and $\frac{8801}{10000}$, $\frac{8802}{10000}, \ldots$ etc.

The surprising fact is that there are points on the line that do not correspond to any rational number. One such point corresponds to the distance of the hypotenuse of a right angled triangle whose other two sides both have unit length.

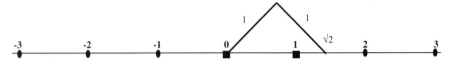

If x is this length, it follows from Pythagoras' Theorem that $x^2 = 1^2 + 1^2 = 2$. We shall now show that this equation has no rational solution.

4.2.1 Theorem.   There is no $x \in \mathbb{Q}$ such that $x^2 = 2$.

Proof.   Suppose that there is a rational number x such that $x^2 = 2$. By Proposition 4.1.2, write x in its lowest terms as a/b where $\text{GCD}(a, b) = 1$.

Now $\left(\frac{a}{b}\right)^2 = 2$ so that $a^2 = 2b^2$. Therefore $2|a^2$ and, since 2 is prime, $2|a$. Put $a = 2c$ so that $4c^2 = 2b^2$ and $2c^2 = b^2$. It now follows that $2|b$ and so $\text{GCD}(a, b)$ contains a factor 2.

This contradicts the hypotheses on a and b and so it follows that there is no rational number x such that $x^2 = 2$.   □

We can express this result by saying that $\sqrt{2}$ is not a rational number. It is now clear that the rational numbers are not sufficient for many purposes, and we must extend our number system to include all the points on the number line.

The system of numbers that correspond to all the points of the number line is called the set of *real numbers* and denoted by $\mathbb{R}$. This will include the set of rational numbers $\mathbb{Q}$ as a proper subset.

Those real numbers that are not rational numbers are called *irrational numbers.* We have shown that $\sqrt{2}$ is irrational. It is possible, but more difficult, to show that π is an irrational number.

The construction of the system of real numbers, $\mathbb{R}$, in which we can perform the operations of addition, subtraction, multiplication and division, is beyond the scope of this book. Instead, we shall assume that the real numbers are known, just as we assumed that the integers were known.

Since $\sqrt{2}$ cannot be written in the form a/b for $a, b \in \mathbb{Z}$, it follows that $m\sqrt{2}/n$ is not rational for all nonzero integers m and n. Therefore, by choosing n large enough, we can show that any interval contains irrational numbers of the form $m\sqrt{2}/n$. In fact, every interval contains infinitely many rational numbers and infinitely many irrational numbers, and the rational and irrational numbers are both dense on the number line.

4.3 RATIONAL EXPONENTS

One of the properties of the real numbers is the fact that every positive real number has a unique positive nth root, for each positive integer n.

4.3.1 Definition. If $n \in \mathbb{P}$ and $a \geq 0$, then $x = \sqrt[n]{a}$ denotes the unique positive nth root of a; that is, x is the positive solution to the equation

$$x^n = a.$$

If $n = 2$, we usually denote $\sqrt[2]{a}$ just by $\sqrt{a}$.

For example, $\sqrt{9} = +3$, $\sqrt[3]{125} = +5$ and $\sqrt[4]{16} = +2$. Note that the square of -3 is also equal to 9 and the fourth power of -2 is equal to 16; however, by definition, $\sqrt{9}$ and $\sqrt[4]{16}$ refer to only the positive roots.

If n is odd and $a > 0$, there is only one real nth root of a and this is positive. If n is odd and $a < 0$ we can define $\sqrt[n]{a}$ to be the unique real number whose nth power is a. For example, $\sqrt[3]{-125} = -5$.

It is often useful to express the root of a number by means of exponents. If n is a positive integer and $a \in \mathbb{R}$, then we write a^n to stand for $a \cdot a \cdots a$ (n factors) and a^{-n} to stand for $1/a^n$. We also define a^0 to be 1 for all nonzero a. If $a, b \in \mathbb{R}$ and $m, n \in \mathbb{Z}$ then the exponents satisfy the following properties.

$$a^m \cdot a^n = a^{m+n}$$
$$(a^m)^n = a^{mn}$$
$$(ab)^m = a^m b^m$$

These properties can be proved by induction for positive m and n, and then proved for negative m and n.

Since $(\sqrt[n]{a})^n = a$ it is natural to define $a^{1/n}$ to be $\sqrt[n]{a}$ so that the second exponential law above would still hold.

4.3.2 Definition. If $a \geq 0$ and $m, n \in \mathbb{Z}, n > 0$ define

$$a^{m/n} = (\sqrt[n]{a})^m$$

For example, $27^{2/3} = (\sqrt[3]{27})^2 = 3^2 = 9$ and $4^{3/4} = (\sqrt[4]{4})^3 = (\sqrt{2})^3 = 2\sqrt{2}$.

Since a rational number is an equivalence class, we have to check that the definition of a^r for rational r does not depend on how we write r. For example, we would want $27^{2/3}$ to equal $27^{6/9}$.

4.3.3 Lemma. $a^{m/n} = \sqrt[n]{a^m}$.

Proof. Let $x = a^{m/n}$ so that

$$x^n = ((\sqrt[n]{a})^m)^n = (\sqrt[n]{a})^{mn} = ((\sqrt[n]{a})^n)^m = a^m.$$

Since a^m has only one positive nth root $x = \sqrt[n]{a^m}$. □

4.3.4 Proposition.   If $m/n = r/s$ and $a \geq 0$ then

$$a^{m/n} = a^{r/s}.$$

Proof. Let $x = a^{m/n}$ so that, by Lemma 4.3.3, $x^n = a^m$. Now $x^{ns} = a^{ms} = a^{nr}$ and $(x^s)^n = (a^r)^n$. Since a positive number has only one positive nth root, $x^s = a^r$. Therefore $x = \sqrt[s]{a^r}$ and, by Lemma 4.3.3, $x = a^{r/s}$. □

With the above definition of rational exponents, it can be shown that three exponential laws

$$\begin{aligned}
a^r \cdot a^s &= a^{r+s} \\
(a^r)^s &= a^{rs} \\
(ab)^r &= a^r b^r
\end{aligned}$$

still hold when $a, b \in \mathbb{R}$ and $r, s \in \mathbb{Q}$.

4.3.5 Example.   Simplify $125^{-\frac{2}{3}} + 8^{\frac{7}{6}}$.

Solution.

$$\begin{aligned}
125^{-\frac{2}{3}} + 8^{\frac{7}{6}} &= (5^3)^{-\frac{2}{3}} + (2^3)^{\frac{7}{6}} = 5^{-2} + 2^{\frac{7}{2}} \\
&= \frac{1}{5^2} + 2^3 \cdot 2^{\frac{1}{2}} = \frac{1}{25} + 8\sqrt{2}.
\end{aligned}$$

□

4.3.6 Example.   Expand $(x^{\frac{1}{3}} + \sqrt{2}y^{\frac{1}{6}})^3$.

Solution.   By the Binomial Theorem

$$\begin{aligned}
(x^{\frac{1}{3}} + \sqrt{2}y^{\frac{1}{6}})^3 &= (x^{\frac{1}{3}})^3 + 3(x^{\frac{1}{3}})^2(\sqrt{2}y^{\frac{1}{6}}) + 3(x^{\frac{1}{3}})(\sqrt{2}y^{\frac{1}{6}})^2 + (\sqrt{2}y^{\frac{1}{6}})^3 \\
&= x + 3\sqrt{2}x^{\frac{2}{3}}y^{\frac{1}{6}} + 6x^{\frac{1}{3}}y^{\frac{1}{3}} + 2\sqrt{2}y^{\frac{1}{2}}.
\end{aligned}$$

□

4.3.7 Example.   Simplify $\dfrac{2\sqrt{7} - \sqrt{5}}{\sqrt{7} + \sqrt{5}}$.

Solution. Any expression with a denominator of the form $(\sqrt{a} + \sqrt{b})$ can be simplified by a process called 'rationalizing the denominator'. Since

$$(\sqrt{a} + \sqrt{b})(\sqrt{a} - \sqrt{b}) \;=\; (\sqrt{a})^2 - (\sqrt{b})^2 \;=\; a - b$$

we can multiply numerator and denominator by $(\sqrt{a} - \sqrt{b})$ to eliminate the square roots in the denominator.

Hence

$$\frac{2\sqrt{7} - \sqrt{5}}{\sqrt{7} + \sqrt{5}} \;=\; \frac{(2\sqrt{7} - \sqrt{5})(\sqrt{7} - \sqrt{5})}{(\sqrt{7} + \sqrt{5})(\sqrt{7} - \sqrt{5})} \;=\; \frac{14 - 3\sqrt{35} + 5}{7 - 5} \;=\; \frac{19 - 3\sqrt{35}}{2}. \qquad \square$$

4.4 DECIMAL EXPANSIONS

Positive integers are written in base 10 using powers of 10; in a similar way, we can write certain rational numbers as decimals using positive and negative powers of 10. For example, the decimal **3905.6402** represents the number

$$\mathbf{3} \times 10^3 + \mathbf{9} \times 10^2 + \mathbf{0} \times 10^1 + \mathbf{5} \times 10^0 + \mathbf{6} \times 10^{-1} + \mathbf{4} \times 10^{-2} + \mathbf{0} \times 10^{-3} + \mathbf{2} \times 10^{-4}.$$

All such finite decimal expansions represent rational numbers whose denominator can be written as some power of 10. For example,

$$2.52 \;=\; 2 + 5 \times 10^{-1} + 2 \times 10^{-2} \;=\; 2 + \frac{5}{10} + \frac{2}{100} \;=\; \frac{252}{100} \;=\; \frac{63}{25}$$

and $3905.6402 = 39056402/10^4$. Therefore we would only expect to be able to represent in this way, fractions which, when written in their lowest terms, have denominators which divide some power of 10.

However we can still use the idea of decimals to represent all real numbers; but we now have to allow infinite decimal expansions, whose successive finite terms provide better and better approximations to the real number.

Suppose that we wish to find the decimal expansion of a positive real number α lying between 0 and 1.

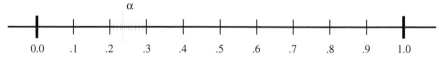

First subdivide the unit interval into 10 equal parts. The number will lie in one of these intervals. Say α lies in the third interval so that

$$.2 \le \alpha \le .3.$$

Subdivide this third interval into 10 equal parts, each of length 10^2. Suppose α lies in the fourth such interval so that

$$.23 \leq \alpha \leq .24.$$

Proceeding in this way, we obtain an infinite sequence of digits $a_1, a_2, a_3, \ldots$ such that, for each n,

$$.a_1 a_2 a_3 \ldots a_{n-1} a_n \leq \alpha \leq .a_1 a_2 a_3 \ldots a_{n-1} \tilde{a}_n \quad \text{where} \quad \tilde{a}_n = a_n + 1.$$

4.4.1 Definition.   The expression $b.a_1 a_2 \ldots$, where each a_i is a digit from 0 to 9, is called the *decimal expansion* of the real number α if

$$b.a_1 a_2 \ldots a_n \leq \alpha \leq (b.a_1 a_2 \ldots a_n) + 10^{-n} \quad \text{for all } n \in \mathbb{P}.$$

Decimal expansions of negative numbers can be obtained by placing a minus sign before the expansion.

For example, the decimal expansion of $\sqrt{2}$ begins $1.4142\ldots$ because

$$(1.4142)^2 = 1.99996164 < 2 < 2.00024449 = (1.4143)^2$$

and so

$$1.4142 < \sqrt{2} < 1.4143.$$

A decimal $b.a_1 a_2 \ldots$ is called *terminating* if there exists an integer n such that $a_i = 0$ for all $i \geq n$. A decimal is called *recurrent* or *periodic* if there exist positive integers p and n such that $a_{i+p} = a_i$ for all $i \geq n$. Note that a terminating decimal is also a periodic decimal.

Certain numbers have two different decimal expansions. For example, $.25000\ldots$ and $.24999\ldots$ are both decimal expansions of 1/4. From our discussion on approximating a real number by a decimal, we see that, when we subdivide an interval into 10 subintervals, it may happen that our real number lies in two subintervals. In that case, there is a choice for the decimal expansion. For example, when the interval from .2 to .3 is subdivided into 10 equal parts we see that the number 1/4 lies in the fifth *and* sixth subdivision; hence the first two places of the expansion of 1/4 are .24 *or* .25.

It is well known that we can find a decimal expansion of a rational number by a process of long division. For example 1/11 has the decimal expansion $0.090909\ldots$ which we shall write as $0.\dot{0}\dot{9}$ where the dots over a string of digits indicate that these digits are to be repeated indefinitely. We also have

$$
\begin{aligned}
1/3 &= 0.333\ldots &= 0.\dot{3} \\
1/7 &= 0.1428571428571\ldots &= 0.\dot{1}4285\dot{7} \\
1/8 &= 0.125000\ldots &= 0.125 \\
32/15 &= 2.1333\ldots &= 2.1\dot{3}
\end{aligned}
$$

We shall show that a rational number always has a periodic (or terminating) decimal expansion. The converse is also true; a periodic expansion always represents a rational number. We can find the rational number by the methods used in the following examples.

4.4.2 Example.   Find the rational number with the decimal expansion $0.\dot{1}\dot{7}$.

Solution.   Let $x = 0.\dot{1}\dot{7}$. This has period of length 2, so multiply it by 10^2 to obtain $100x = 17.\dot{1}\dot{7}$. Therefore

$$
\begin{aligned}
100x - x &= 17.\dot{1}\dot{7} - 0.\dot{1}\dot{7} \\
99x &= 17 \\
x &= \frac{17}{99}.
\end{aligned}
$$

Check.   If we divide 17 by 99, using long division, we see that $17/99 = 0.\dot{1}\dot{7}$. $\square$

4.4.3 Example.   Find the rational number whose decimal expansion is $1.1\dot{2}1\dot{6}$.

Solution.   Let $x = 1.1\dot{2}1\dot{6}$ so that $1000x = 1121.6\dot{2}1\dot{6}$. Therefore

$$
\begin{aligned}
1000x - x &= 1121.6\dot{2}1\dot{6} - 1.1\dot{2}1\dot{6} = 1120.5 \\
999x &= \frac{2241}{2} \\
x &= \frac{2241}{2 \cdot 999} = \frac{249}{2 \cdot 111} = \frac{83}{2 \cdot 37} = \frac{83}{74}.
\end{aligned}
$$

Check.   Dividing 83 by 74 we obtain the expansion $1.1\dot{2}1\dot{6}$. $\square$

4.4.4 Theorem.   A real number is rational if and only if its decimal expansion is periodic (or terminating). Hence a real number is irrational if and only if it has a nonperiodic infinite decimal expansion.

Proof.   Let us look at the process of long division to find the decimal expansion of the rational number m/n, where $m, n \in \mathbb{P}$.

We first divide m by n and obtain a remainder r_0. We then divide $10r_0$ by n to obtain a remainder r_1 and continue in the following manner.

$$
\begin{aligned}
m &= bn + r_0 \quad \text{where} \quad 0 \leq r_0 < n \\
10r_0 &= a_1 n + r_1 \quad \text{where} \quad 0 \leq r_1 < n \\
10r_1 &= a_2 n + r_2 \quad \text{where} \quad 0 \leq r_2 < n \\
&\vdots \\
10r_{i-1} &= a_i n + r_i \quad \text{where} \quad 0 \leq r_i < n \\
&\vdots
\end{aligned}
$$

The decimal expansion of m/n is $b.a_1a_2\ldots\ldots$ First notice that $0 \le a_i < 10$ for all $i \in \mathbb{P}$. This follows because $0 \le r_{i-1} < n$ and so $0 \le 10r_{i-1} < 10n$. Now we have

$$
\begin{aligned}
\frac{m}{n} &= b + \frac{r_0}{n} \\
&= b + \frac{a_1}{10} + \frac{r_1}{10n} \\
&= b + \frac{a_1}{10} + \frac{a_2}{10^2} + \frac{r_2}{10^2 n}
\end{aligned}
$$

and, by induction, we can show that

$$
\frac{m}{n} = b + \frac{a_1}{10} + \frac{a_2}{10^2} + \cdots + \frac{a_i}{10^i} + \frac{r_i}{10^i n}
$$

for all $i \in \mathbb{P}$. Since $0 \le r_i < n$, it follows that m/n lies between $b.a_1a_2\ldots a_i$ and $(b.a_1a_2\ldots a_i) + 10^{-i}$.

Each remainder, r_i, must be one of the n integers $0, 1, 2, \ldots, n-1$ and therefore, after at most n steps, one of the remainders must equal an earlier remainder; say $r_{j+p} = r_j$. Thereafter, the computations just repeat themselves and $a_{i+p} = a_i$ for all $i \ge j$. This shows that the decimal expansion of any rational number is periodic.

Conversely, suppose that we have a periodic decimal expansion $x = b.a_1a_2\ldots$ where $a_{i+p} = a_i$ for all $i \ge j$. Then $(10^p - 1)x$ will be a terminating decimal represented by some rational number $k/10^\ell$. Therefore x will be represented by the rational number $k/10^\ell(10^p - 1)$. $\qquad\square$

4.4.5 Example.   Illustrate the above theorem by finding the decimal expansion of 83/74.

Solution.   Write out the division of 83 by 74 as in the above theorem.

$83 = 1\cdot74 + \textbf{\textit{9}}$

$90 = 1\cdot74 + \textbf{\textit{16}}$

$160 = 2\cdot74 + \textbf{\textit{12}}$

$120 = 1\cdot74 + \textbf{\textit{46}}$

$460 = 6\cdot74 + \textbf{\textit{16}}$

$160 = 2\cdot74 + \textbf{\textit{12}}$

repeating remainders

```
            1.1216216...
    74 / 83.0000000
         74
         9 0
         7 4
         1 60
         1 48
          120
           74
          460
          444
          160
          148
          120
```

The decimal expansion of 83/74 is therefore $1.1\overset{\cdot}{2}1\overset{\cdot}{6}$.

Check. This agrees with Example 4.4.3. $\square$

For those readers familiar with infinite series, the decimal expansion $b.a_1 a_2 \ldots$ can be interpreted as the infinite series

$$b + \frac{a_1}{10} + \frac{a_2}{10^2} + \cdots + \frac{a_r}{10^r} + \cdots.$$

This series always converges if $0 \leq a_r \leq 9$. (Why?)

For example, $0.\dot{3}$ is the infinite geometric series

$$\frac{3}{10} + \frac{3}{10^2} + \frac{3}{10^3} + \cdots = \frac{3}{10} \left(1 + \frac{1}{10} + \frac{1}{10^2} + \cdots \right)$$

whose sum is $\frac{3}{10}(\frac{1}{1-\frac{1}{10}}) = \frac{3}{10} \cdot \frac{10}{9} = \frac{1}{3}$.

In fact, all infinite periodic decimals can be written as an infinite geometric series, after a certain point.

Exercise Set 4

1. Verify that the relation $\sim$ on $\mathbb{Z} \times (\mathbb{Z} - \{0\})$, defined by $(a, b) \sim (c, d)$ if and only if $ad = bc$, is indeed an equivalence relation.

2. Verify that addition, subtraction, multiplication and division are all well defined in $\mathbb{Q}$. For example, for addition, it has to be verified that if $(a_1, b_1) \sim (a_2, b_2)$ and $(c_1, d_1) \sim (c_2, d_2)$ then $(a_1 d_1 + b_1 c_1, b_1 d_1) \sim (a_2 d_2 + b_2 c_2, b_2 d_2)$.

3. Prove that $\sqrt{3}$ is irrational.

4. Prove that $\sqrt[3]{4}$ is irrational.

5. Prove that $\sqrt{6}$ is irrational.

6. Is $\sqrt{2} + \sqrt{3}$ rational or irrational? Give reasons.

7. If a is rational and b is irrational, prove that $a + b$ is irrational.

8. If a is rational and b is irrational, prove that ab is irrational, except for one case. What is the exceptional case?

9. Define a relation $\perp$ on the real numbers $\mathbb{R}$ by $a \perp b$ if and only if $a - b \in \mathbb{Q}$. Prove that this is an equivalence relation. Which of the following are related?

(a) 3 and $4/5$

(b) $1 + \sqrt{5}$ and $1 - \sqrt{5}$

(c) $\sqrt{2}$ and $\sqrt{2} + 1$

(d) $\sqrt{2}$ and $\sqrt{3}$

(e) $\dfrac{1}{\sqrt{2}}$ and $\dfrac{\sqrt{2} - 1}{2}$

10. If a is a positive rational number, let $\tilde{a} = \frac{2+a}{1+a}$. Prove that $\tilde{a}^2$ is closer to 2 then a^2 is. By starting with $a = 1$, use this to find a sequence of rational numbers approximating $\sqrt{2}$.

11. The amount of light that enters a camera is determined by the f-number of the aperture. An aperture of $f/8$ means that the effective diameter of the lens is 1/8 of its focal length. The exposure time increases with the square of the f-number. If the largest aperture of a camera is $f/2$ and the smallest $f/16$, find the intermediate f-numbers that are needed so that, when the aperture is reduced one stop, the exposure time is doubled.

12. The international paper size A0 has an area of 1 square metre and is such that when cut in two, the ratio of the long side to the short side remains unchanged. What is the ratio of the long side to the short side, and what is the size of the A0 paper (to the nearest mm.). The standard A4 size typing paper is obtained by cutting A0 into half 4 times. What are its dimensions?

13 - 19. Simplify the following.

13. $\sqrt{2^8}$

14. $(49)^{1/4}$

15. $\left(\dfrac{1}{81}\right)^{-3/4}$

16. $\dfrac{7^{-2/5} \cdot 7^{1/2}}{7^{1/12}}$

17. $\dfrac{2\sqrt{3} + 3\sqrt{2}}{\sqrt{3} + \sqrt{2}}$

18. $\dfrac{\sqrt{5}}{3 - \sqrt{5}}$

19. $\sqrt{\sqrt{2}} \cdot \sqrt{8\sqrt{2}}$

20. Rationalize the denominator of $\dfrac{1}{\sqrt{2} + \sqrt{3} + \sqrt{5}}$.

21 - 22. Simplify the following, assuming $a > 0$.

21. $a^{5/4}(3a^2 - a^{1/4})$

22. $(a^{2/3} + a^{1/2})^3$

23 - 26. *Express the following rational numbers as periodic (or terminating) decimals. Which of these numbers have two different decimal expansions?*

23. $1/12$ **24.** $3/16$
25. $7/40$ **26.** $5/19$

27 - 32. *Express the following decimals as rational numbers in their lowest terms.*

27. 2.105 **28.** $0.\dot{4}\dot{2}$
29. $0.4\dot{2}$ **30.** $0.\dot{7}69\dot{2}3\dot{0}$
31. $0.13\dot{1}6\dot{2}$ **32.** $1.50\dot{5}\dot{1}$

Problem Set 4

33. We have shown how to construct the rational numbers from the integers by means of an equivalence relation on $\mathbb{Z} \times (\mathbb{Z} - \{0\})$. Show how the integers could be constructed from the positive integers $\mathbb{P}$ by means of an equivalence relation on $\mathbb{P} \times \mathbb{P}$.

34. Could we have introduced positive rational numbers by means of an equivalence relation on $\mathbb{P} \times \mathbb{P}$, before introducing negative numbers?

35.   (a) Find irrational numbers a and b with $a + b$ rational.
          (b) Find irrational numbers a and b with ab rational.
          (c) Are there any irrational numbers a and b with a^b rational?

36. Let $a, b, c, d \in \mathbb{Q}$ where $\sqrt{b}$ and $\sqrt{d}$ exist and are irrational. If $a + \sqrt{b} = c + \sqrt{d}$, prove that $a = c$ and $b = d$.

37.   (a) If $m, n \in \mathbb{Z}$ and $\mathrm{GCD}(m, n) = 1$, prove that $\mathrm{GCD}(m^2, n^2) = 1$.
          (b) If $r \in \mathbb{Q}$ and $r^2 \in \mathbb{Z}$, prove that $r \in \mathbb{Z}$.
          (c) Prove that $\sqrt{p}$ is irrational whenever p is prime.

38. Resolve the following contradiction.

$$-1 \; = \; \sqrt[3]{-1} \; = \; (-1)^{1/3} = (-1)^{2/6} \; = \; \sqrt[6]{(-1)^2} \; = \; \sqrt[6]{1} \; = \; 1$$

39. Rationalize the denominator of $\dfrac{\sqrt[3]{12} + 1}{\sqrt[3]{3} - \sqrt[3]{2}}$.

40. When does a/b have a terminating decimal expansion?

41. (a) Use Fermat's Theorem to show that, for every prime p other than 2 or 5, there is some positive integer r for which $p|(10^r - 1)$.

    (b) Is it true that, for all integers n, other than multiples of 2 and 5, there is some positive integer r for which $n|(10^r - 1)$?

    (c) What is the relationship between these questions and decimal expansions?

42. Let $\mathrm{GCD}(10, n) = 1$ and let r be the least positive integer such that $10^r \equiv 1 \pmod{n}$.

    (a) Prove that $1/n$ has a recurring decimal expansion with period r.

    (b) If n is prime, prove that $r|(n - 1)$.

    (c) Find the periods of 1/13, 1/17, 2/31 and 1/47.

43. Find a method for converting a rational number m/n into an expansion in base 6. Use your method to expand 1/4 in base 6.

44. Find the expansions of 1/7 in (a) base 10, (b) base 9, (c) base 8 and (d) base 7.

45. Convert $(.125)_6$ from base 6 to a decimal in base 10.

46. Calculate π in base 2 correct to 6 binary places, after the point.

47. Convert the decimal .15 to base 3.

48. Calculate the first 5 places of the decimal number 0.241 in base 8. Will the expansion terminate, repeat indefinitely or be non-periodic?

49. Convert $(2.4\dot{6}\dot{7})_8$ from base 8 to a rational number in base 10.

50. Convert $(.11\dot{0}1\dot{0})_2$ from base 2 to a rational number in base 10.

51. Let $x_1 = \sqrt{44}$ and $x_{n+1} = \sqrt{3x_n + 1}$, for $n \geq 1$. Prove that x_n is irrational for every $n \geq 1$.

52. Find three positive fractions with denominators 5, 7, and 9, whose sum is $491/315$.

Chapter 5

Functions and Bijections

5.1 FUNCTIONS

One of the basic notions of modern mathematics is that of a function. To a mathematician in 1800, a function referred to an algebraic or trigonometrical formula involving one or more variables. Numbers could be substituted for each of the variables and the resulting numerical value of the function could be calculated from the given formula. Although such functions are still very important today, it became necessary to broaden the scope of a function to include relationships that could not be expressed by a simple formula, and to allow variables that were not necessarily numbers.

5.1.1 Definition. Let X and Y be sets. A *function*, f, from X to Y is denoted by $f : X \to Y$ and consists of a rule that assigns to each element $x \in X$, a unique element $f(x) \in Y$.

The set X is called the *domain* of f, while the set Y is called the *codomain* of f. If we write $y = f(x)$, then the element $y \in Y$ is called the *value* of the function f at the point x.

Whenever a specific element is assigned to the variable x, the corresponding value of y is determined by the function; hence x is sometimes called the *independent variable* and y is called the *dependent variable*.

For example, if f is the function from the real numbers, $\mathbb{R}$, to the real numbers in which f assigns to each real number its cube, we would say that $f : \mathbb{R} \to \mathbb{R}$ was defined by $f(x) = x^3$. The value of f at 3 would be 27, while the value of f at $-\sqrt{2}$ would be $-2\sqrt{2}$.

It often happens that the set of values of a function is not the whole codomain, but a proper subset of it. The set of values of a function $f : X \to Y$ is called the *image* of f and is denoted by $f(X)$. It is a subset of the codomain Y and

$$f(X) = \{f(x) \mid x \in X\} \subseteq Y.$$

(The term 'range' is also used to mean the image. However, since many authors refer to the codomain as the range, we shall avoid its use.)

A telephone directory assigns to each name a telephone number and, assuming that no person has two telephone numbers, it can be considered a function whose domain is the set of subscribers, and whose codomain is the set of possible telephone numbers. The image consists of those telephone numbers in actual use.

Let X be the set of all human beings who have ever lived. If x is any person, let $m(x)$ be the mother of x. Then $m : X \to X$ is a function because, assuming that applied genetics has not advanced too far, each person has a unique mother. The image of this function, $m(X)$, consists of the set of all mothers.

Notice however, that the rule $c(x) =$ 'child of x' would *not* define a function from X to X, for two reasons. Some parents have many children, while some people have no children. Therefore, for child-free people, c is not defined, while c does not assign a unique element to parents who have more than one child.

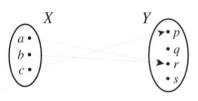

If $X = \{a, b, c\}$ and $Y = \{p, q, r, s\}$, then this diagram defines a function

$$f : X \longrightarrow Y.$$

Here $f(a) = r$, $f(b) = r$ and $f(c) = p$. The codomain is $Y = \{p, q, r, s\}$ but the image is $f(X) = \{p, r\}$.

A table of squares and cubes of integers from 1 to 100 defines a function f whose domain is the set of $\{1, 2, \ldots, 100\}$ and whose codomain is $\mathbb{P} \times \mathbb{P}$. The value of the function at the integer n is the pair of positive integers (n^2, n^3). For example, $f(1) = (1, 1)$, $f(2) = (4, 8)$, $f(3) = (9, 27)$, etc.

Elementary calculus usually deals with functions whose domains and codomains are subsets of the real numbers. Such functions are called 'real valued functions of a real variable'. However, in calculus, it it customary not to refer explicitly to the domain or codomain of such functions. The domain of such a function is usually taken to be the largest subset of $\mathbb{R}$ for which the given formula makes sense (that is, gives a real value). For example, if

$$f(x) \;=\; \frac{\sqrt{x - 2}}{x - 4}$$

then the domain of f cannot be the whole of $\mathbb{R}$, because $\sqrt{x - 2}$ is not real if $x < 2$, and $f(x)$ is not defined when $x = 4$. We would take the domain of f to be $X = \{x \in \mathbb{R} \mid x \geq 2, x \neq 4\}$, which is the union of the two intervals $\{x \mid 2 \leq x < 4\}$ and $\{x \mid x > 4\}$. The codomain of a real valued function of a real variable is not very crucial (unless one is dealing with the inverse of the function) and it can usually be taken to be the whole real line $\mathbb{R}$.

5.1.2 Definition.   Two functions f and g are said to be *equal* if they have the same domains, the same codomains and, for every element x in the domain, $f(x) = g(x)$.

For example, $f : \mathbb{R} \to \mathbb{R}$ defined by $f(x) = x^2$ and $g : \mathbb{Z} \to \mathbb{Z}$ defined by $g(x) = x^2$ are not considered equal functions, even though they have the same formula.

However the functions $f : \mathbb{P} \to \mathbb{P}$, defined by $f(n) = \mathrm{LCM}(2, n)$, and $g : \mathbb{P} \to \mathbb{P}$, defined by $g(n) = (3 - (-1)^n)n/2$, are equal functions because they have the same domains and codomains and $f(n) = g(n)$ for all $n \in \mathbb{P}$.

There are several synonyms for the word 'function', the commonest being *mapping*, *transformation* and *correspondence*.

5.2 THE GRAPH OF A FUNCTION

The reader will undoubtedly have drawn the graph of a real valued function such as $f : \mathbb{R} \to \mathbb{R}$ where $f(x) = x^2$. This is constructed by plotting the points (x, y) in the plane $\mathbb{R} \times \mathbb{R}$ where $y = f(x) = x^2$. We can, in a similar way, define the graph of a general function. However, we will not always be able to represent such a graph on a two dimensional piece of paper.

5.2.1 Definition. The *graph* of the function $f : X \to Y$ is the subset of the Cartesian product $X \times Y$ consisting of pairs $(x, f(x))$, for all $x \in X$. That is, the graph of f is the set $\{(x, f(x)) \in X \times Y \mid x \in X\}$.

Whenever f is a real valued function of a real variable, then X and Y are subsets of $\mathbb{R}$, and the above definition of the graph of f agrees with the usual notion of the graph as a subset of the plane $\mathbb{R} \times \mathbb{R}$.

For example, if $f : X \to \mathbb{R}$ is the function defined by

$$f(x) = \sqrt{x + 4}$$

where $X = \{x \in \mathbb{R} \mid x \geq -4\}$, then the graph of f is the subset of $X \times \mathbb{R}$ consisting of

$$\{(x, \sqrt{x + 4}) \mid x \geq -4\}.$$

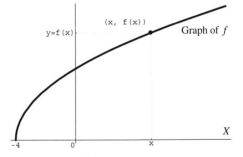

It is customary for the horizontal axis in a graph to represent the domain, and the vertical axis to represent the codomain. A point y, in the codomain, lies in the image of the function if the horizontal line through y intersects the graph. The image is therefore the projection of the graph on the vertical axis.

In the case of the above function $f : X \to \mathbb{R}$ where $f(x) = \sqrt{x + 4}$, the projection of the graph onto the vertical axis is the set of nonnegative real numbers; that is, $f(X) = \{y \in \mathbb{R} \mid y \geq 0\}$.

The illustration below is the graph of the function $f : \mathbb{R} \to \mathbb{R}$ defined by

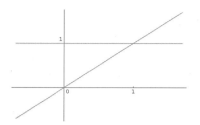

$$f(x) = \begin{cases} 1 \text{ if } x \text{ is rational} \\ x \text{ if } x \text{ is irrational.} \end{cases}$$

The image of f consists of the irrational numbers together with the point 1.

5.2.2 Example.   Illustrate the graph of the function $f : \mathbb{Z}_4 \to \mathbb{Z}_4$, defined by $f([x]) = [x^2]$, and find the image of f.

Solution.   There are only 4 points in the domain and codomain and $f([0]) = [0]$, $f([1]) = [1]$, $f([2]) = [0]$ and $f([3]) = [1]$.

The graph of f is a four element subset of the sixteen element set $\mathbb{Z}_4 \times \mathbb{Z}_4$. We can represent $\mathbb{Z}_4 \times \mathbb{Z}_4$ by the 4×4 array as shown. The graph of f consists of the solid dots.

The image of f is the set $\{[0], [1]\}$.

```
[3] | o   o   o   o
[2] | o   o   o   o
[1] | o   •   o   •
[0] | •   o   •   o
    |_____
     [0] [1] [2] [3]
```

5.2.3 Example.   Sketch the graph of the *absolute value function* from $\mathbb{R}$ to $\mathbb{R}$ whose value at x is denoted by $|x|$ where

$$|x| = \begin{cases} x \text{ if } x \geq 0 \\ -x \text{ if } x < 0. \end{cases}$$

Solution.

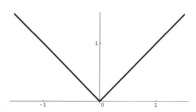

The graph of a function contains all the information about the function. In fact, the concept of a function may be defined by means of its graph. The following is an alternative to Definition 5.1.1, and it is more precise in the sense that it avoids the use of the undefined terms 'rule' and 'assigns.' However it is not usually as conceptually useful as the former definition.

5.2.4 Definition.   A *function f* with domain X and codomain Y is a subset of $X \times Y$ in which each element of X occurs precisely once as the first element of an ordered pair in f.

Hence, using this definition, we can write

$$f = \{(x, f(x)) \in X \times Y \mid x \in X\}$$

though we shall usually still refer to this subset as the graph of f.

For example, the function $f : \mathbb{Z}_4 \to \mathbb{Z}_4$, in Example 5.2.2, can be written as

$$f = \{([0], [0]), ([1], [1]), ([2], [0]), ([3], [1])\}.$$

It is fairly easy to recognize which subsets of $X \times Y$ do define the graph of some function; each vertical line through a point of the domain must meet the graph precisely once. If there is a vertical line through a point of the domain which does not intercept the subset or intercepts the subset in more than one point, then the subset cannot be a graph.

The figures below illustrate some graphs of functions from X to Y.

SUBSETS THAT ARE GRAPHS

The figures below illustrate subsets of $X \times Y$ that are not the graph of any function from X to Y.

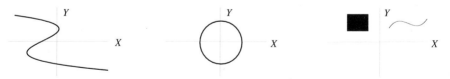

SUBSETS THAT ARE NOT GRAPHS

We now have various ways in which to describe a function. For example, the function $f : \mathbb{R} \to \mathbb{R}$ defined by $f(x) = x^3$ could also be written as

- $f : \mathbb{R} \longrightarrow \mathbb{R}$ with $y = x^3$

- $f : \mathbb{R} \longrightarrow \mathbb{R}$ with $x \mapsto x^3$

- $f = \{(x, x^3) \mid x \in \mathbb{R}\} \subset \mathbb{R} \times \mathbb{R}$

- $f = \{(x, y) \mid y = x^3,\ x \in \mathbb{R}\} \subset \mathbb{R} \times \mathbb{R}.$

5.3 COMPOSITION OF FUNCTIONS

If $f : X \to Y$ and $g : Y \to Z$ are two functions such that the codomain of f is equal to the domain of g, then we can form a new function

$$g \circ f : X \longrightarrow Z$$

called the *composite* of f and g, which is defined by

$$(g \circ f)(x) \;=\; g(f(x)).$$

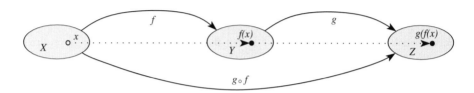

Observe the order of the composite $g \circ f$; the function f is applied first and then g is applied to the result. It may seem rather odd for the composite to be written in this order, but it appears more natural when one looks at the definition $(g \circ f)(x) = g(f(x))$.

Two functions cannot always be composed; this can only happen in the special case in which the codomain of the first is equal to the domain of the second. Even if $g \circ f$ is defined, where $f : X \to Y$ and $g : Y \to Z$, then the composite in the reverse order, $f \circ g$, will not be defined unless $X = Z$.

5.3.1 Example.   Let $f : \mathbb{R}_{\geq 0} \to \mathbb{R}$ be defined by $f(x) = \sqrt{x}$, where the domain, $\mathbb{R}_{\geq 0}$, is the set of nonnegative real numbers. Let $g : \mathbb{R} \to \mathbb{R}$ be defined by $g(x) = 3x - 1$. Determine whether the composites $g \circ f$ or $f \circ g$ are defined. If so, find their values.

Solution.   The codomain of f is equal to $\mathbb{R}$, the domain of g; hence

$$g \circ f : \mathbb{R}_{\geq 0} \longrightarrow \mathbb{R}$$

is defined and $(g \circ f)(x) = g(f(x)) = g(\sqrt{x}) = 3\sqrt{x} - 1$. However the codomain of g is not equal to the domain of f, so $f \circ g$ is not defined.   □

5.3.2 Example.   Let $f : \mathbb{R} \to \mathbb{R}$ and $g : \mathbb{R} \to \mathbb{R}$ be functions defined by $f(x) = x^2$ and $g(x) = 4x - 5$. Are $g \circ f$ and $f \circ g$ defined? If so, find their values.

Solution.   Since the codomain of f and the domain of g are both equal to $\mathbb{R}$, and the codomain of g and the domain of f are also equal to $\mathbb{R}$, both composites are defined and are functions from $\mathbb{R}$ to $\mathbb{R}$. Now

$$(g \circ f)(x) \;=\; g(f(x)) \;=\; g(x^2) \;=\; 4x^2 - 5$$

while

$$(f \circ g)(x) \;=\; f(g(x)) \;=\; f(4x - 5) \;=\; (4x - 5)^2 \;=\; 16x^2 - 40x + 25. \quad \square$$

Note that, even if $g \circ f$ and $f \circ g$ are defined, they do not, in general, define equal functions. Thus the operation of composition is *not commutative*. However, whenever the composition of three functions is defined, the composition is *associative*.

5.3.3 Theorem.   Let $f : X \to Y$, $g : Y \to Z$ and $h : Z \to T$ be three functions. Then

$$h \circ (g \circ f) \;=\; (h \circ g) \circ f : X \longrightarrow T.$$

In other words, the placing of the brackets is unimportant.

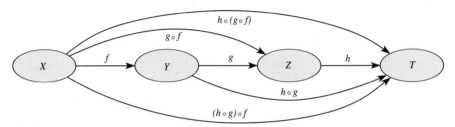

Proof.   Notice that the functions $g \circ f$, $h \circ (g \circ f)$, $h \circ g$, and $(h \circ g) \circ f$ are all defined and that $h \circ (g \circ f)$ and $(h \circ g) \circ f$ have the same domain and codomain.

Now, if $x \in X$,

$$[h \circ (g \circ f)](x) \;=\; h(g \circ f(x)) \;=\; h(g(f(x)))$$
$$[(h \circ g) \circ f](x) \;=\; (h \circ g)(f(x)) \;=\; h(g(f(x))).$$

Hence, by Definition 5.1.2, $h \circ (g \circ f)$ and $(h \circ g) \circ f$ define equal functions. $\square$

For example, let X denote the set of married men and Y denote the set of all people. Let $w : X \to Y$ be the 'wife' function, $m : Y \to Y$ the 'mother' function and $f : Y \to Y$ the 'father' function. Then $m \circ w$ is the 'mother-in-law' function. By associativity, $f \circ (m \circ w) = (f \circ m) \circ w$; in other words, one's mother-in law's father is the same as one's wife's maternal grandfather.

Consider the functions

$$\mathbb{R} \xrightarrow{\;f\;} \mathbb{R} \xrightarrow{\;g\;} \mathbb{R} \xrightarrow{\;h\;} \mathbb{R}$$

where $f(x) = x + 1$, $g(x) = x^2$ and $h(x) = x - 1$. Then

$$g \circ f(x) \;=\; g(f(x)) \;=\; g(x + 1) \;=\; x^2 + 2x + 1$$

so

$$[h \circ (g \circ f)](x) \;\; = \;\; h(x^2 + 2x + 1) \;\; = \;\; (x^2 + 2x + 1) - 1 \;\; = \;\; x^2 + 2x.$$

Now

$$h \circ g(x) \;\; = \;\; h(g(x)) \;\; = \;\; h(x^2) \;\; = \;\; x^2 - 1$$

so

$$[(h \circ g) \circ f](x) \;\; = \;\; (h \circ g)(x + 1) \;\; = \;\; (x + 1)^2 - 1 \;\; = \;\; x^2 + 2x.$$

If X is any set, there is always a function from X to itself that leaves each element unchanged. This is called the *identity function* on X and is denoted by $1_X : X \to X$. It is defined by $1_X(x) = x$ for all $x \in X$.

5.3.4 Proposition.   If $f : X \to Y$ is any function and $1_X : X \to X$ and $1_Y : Y \to Y$ are the identity functions on X and Y respectively, then $f \circ 1_X = f$ and $1_Y \circ f = f$. In other words, composition with the identity leaves any function unchanged.

Proof.   The function $f \circ 1_X : X \to Y$ is defined by

$$f \circ 1_X(x) \;\; = \;\; f(1_X(x)) \;\; = \;\; f(x) \quad \text{for all } x \in X.$$

Therefore $f \circ 1_X = f$ and, similarly, $1_Y \circ f = f : X \to Y$. $\square$

5.4   INVERSE FUNCTIONS

A function $f : X \to Y$ is a rule that assigns to each point in X, a point in Y. If $g : Y \to X$ is a function that 'undoes' what f does, then g is called the inverse function to f. For example, the function $f : \mathbb{R} \to \mathbb{R}$ defined by $f(x) = x^3$, cubes every number. The function $g : \mathbb{R} \to \mathbb{R}$ defined by $g(x) = \sqrt[3]{x}$ takes the cube root of every number, or 'uncubes' the number, and hence g is the inverse function to f.

What is the precise meaning of 'undoes'? A function $g : Y \to X$ undoes the function $f : X \to Y$ if the composite $g \circ f : X \to X$ restores each point to its original position; that is, if $g \circ f$ is the identity function on X. If g is the inverse of f then f is the inverse of g. This suggests the following definition.

5.4.1 Definition.   If $f : X \to Y$ and $g : Y \to X$ are functions such that

$$g \circ f = 1_X \quad \text{and} \quad f \circ g = 1_Y$$

then g is called the *inverse* to f. We write this as $g = f^{-1}$.

The domain of the original function f becomes the codomain of its inverse f^{-1}, while the codomain of f becomes the domain of f^{-1}.

Note that the notation f^{-1} refers to the inverse of the function f, not to its reciprocal. If $f : \mathbb{R} \to \mathbb{R}$ is defined by $f(x) = x^3$ then $f^{-1} : \mathbb{R} \to \mathbb{R}$ is defined by $f^{-1}(x) = \sqrt[3]{x}$ and *not* by $f^{-1}(x) = \frac{1}{x^3}$.

If x is an element in the domain of the function f^{-1}, and $f^{-1}(x) = y$ then

$$x \;=\; 1_Y(x) \;=\; f \circ f^{-1}(x) \;=\; f(f^{-1}(x)) \;=\; f(y).$$

Similarly, if $x = f(y)$ then $f^{-1}(x) = y$. Hence $f^{-1}(x) = y$ if and only if $x = f(y)$.

Therefore, if the equation $y = f(x)$ defines a function that has an inverse, the formula for the inverse function, $y = f^{-1}(x)$, can be found by
  (i) interchanging x and y in the given equation and
  (ii) solving the resulting equation for y in terms of x.

There is no real necessity to interchange x and y. We could just as well solve $y = f(x)$ for x in terms of y to obtain the equation $x = f^{-1}(y)$. The reason many people like to interchange x and y is to keep x as the independent variable in the inverse function.

By no means do all functions have inverses. For example, if $f : \mathbb{R} \to \mathbb{R}$ is defined by $f(x) = x^2$ then $f(2) = 4$ and $f(-2) = 4$. This can have no inverse because there is no function that will 'undo' f by sending 4 to 2, and to -2. If we tried to solve the equation $y = x^2$ for x in terms of y, we would obtain $x = \pm\sqrt{y}$. This does not describe a function because the right side yields two values whenever y is positive, and no real value if y is negative.

5.4.2 Example.   Find, if possible, the inverse of the function $f : \mathbb{Z} \to \mathbb{Z}$ defined by $f(x) = x + 2$.

Solution.   Let $y = x + 2$. Interchanging x and y, we have $x = y + 2$ and, solving for y in terms of x, we have $y = x - 2$. The inverse function is therefore $f^{-1} : \mathbb{Z} \to \mathbb{Z}$ defined by $f^{-1}(x) = x - 2$.

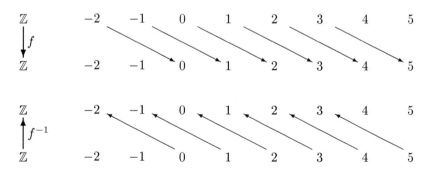

We check that $f(f^{-1}(x)) = f(x - 2) = x - 2 + 2 = x$ so that $f \circ f^{-1} = 1_{\mathbb{Z}}$. Similarly $f^{-1} \circ f = 1_{\mathbb{Z}}$.   □

5.4.3 Example.   Does the function $f : X \to Y$ have an inverse where $X = \{x_1, x_2, x_3\}$, $Y = \{y_1, y_2, y_3, y_4\}$, and $f(x_i) = y_i$, for $i = 1, 2, 3$?

Solution.   It is clear that if f did have an inverse, $g : Y \to X$, then g must send y_i to x_i for $i = 1, 2, 3$; but where should y_4 be sent to? Whatever the value of $g(y_4)$, $f \circ g(y_4)$ can never equal y_4, because y_4 is not in the image of f. Hence f cannot have an inverse.   □

There is a very close relationship between the graphs of a function $f : X \to Y$ and its inverse $f^{-1} : Y \to X$.

$$\begin{aligned} \text{Graph of } f \;&=\; \{(x, y) \in X \times Y \mid y = f(x)\}. \\ \text{Graph of } f^{-1} \;&=\; \{(y, x) \in Y \times X \mid x = f^{-1}(y)\} \\ &=\; \{(y, x) \in Y \times X \mid y = f(x)\}. \end{aligned}$$

The graph of f^{-1} is obtained from that of f by replacing (x, y) by (y, x); that is, by reflecting the graph in the line $y = x$.

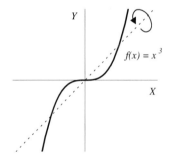

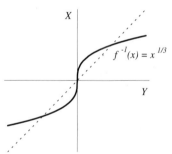

5.5 BIJECTIONS AND THE INVERSION THEOREM

We now lead up to the Inversion Theorem, which gives conditions for a function to have an inverse. We shall need to use the following important classes of functions.

5.5.1 Definitions.   A function $f : X \to Y$ is called *surjective* or *onto* whenever $f(X) = Y$; that is, whenever the image is equal to the whole of the codomain.

A function $f : X \to Y$ is called *injective* or *one-to-one* if $f(x_1) = f(x_2)$ implies that $x_1 = x_2$; that is, distinct elements in the domain must have distinct images.

A function $f : X \to Y$ is called *bijective* or a *one-to-one correspondence* if f is both injective and surjective.

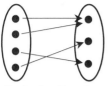 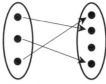 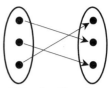

Surjective Function   Injective Function   Bijective Function

A function $f : X \rightarrow Y$ is surjective if, for each element y in the codomain, there is *at least* one element x in the domain such that $y = f(x)$.

A function $f : X \rightarrow Y$ is injective if, for each element y in the codomain, there is *at most* one element x in the domain such that $y = f(x)$.

A function $f : X \rightarrow Y$ is bijective if, for each element y in the codomain, there is *precisely* one element x in the domain, such that $y = f(x)$.

For any function, each element in the domain corresponds to precisely one element in the codomain. In a bijection, the reverse is also true and so there is a one-to-one correspondence between the points in the domain and points in the codomain. This correspondence allows us to define an inverse function.

5.5.2 Inversion Theorem. A function has an inverse if and only if the function is bijective.

Proof. Let $f : X \rightarrow Y$ be a function that has an inverse $f^{-1} : Y \rightarrow X$. Let $y \in Y$ and let $x = f^{-1}(y)$. Then $f(x) = f(f^{-1}(y)) = y$, so that y is in the image of f and hence f is surjective.

Now suppose $f(x_1) = f(x_2)$. Then $f^{-1}(f(x_1)) = f^{-1}(f(x_2))$ and $x_1 = x_2$. Hence f is injective and so f is bijective.

Conversely, suppose $f : X \rightarrow Y$ is bijective. Since f is surjective, for any $y \in Y$, there exists $x \in X$ with $f(x) = y$. Moreover, if x_1 is any element of X with $f(x_1) = y$ then, because f is injective, $x_1 = x$. Hence, for each $y \in Y$ there is a unique element $x \in X$ with $f(x) = y$. If we denote x by $g(y)$ then this defines a function $g : Y \rightarrow X$.

We shall now show that g is the inverse to f. We have $(f \circ g)(y) = f(g(y)) = f(x) = y$ for all $y \in Y$, so that $f \circ g = 1_Y$.

Also, if $x \in X$, $(g \circ f)(x) = g(f(x)) = g(y)$ say, where $y = f(x)$. By the definition of g, $g(y)$ is the unique element whose image, under f, is y. Since the image of x is y, it follows that $x = g(y)$ and so

$$(g \circ f)(x) \quad = \quad g(y) \quad = \quad x.$$

Therefore $g \circ f = 1_X$ and g is the inverse to f. $\square$

5.5.3 Example. Let $f : \{1, 2, 3, 4, 5\} \rightarrow \{A, B, C, D, E\}$ be the function such that $f(i)$ is the ith letter in 'DECAB'. Does this function have an inverse?

Solution. The function f is surjective because all the letters A, B, C, D and E occur in 'DECAB'. It is injective because all the letters of 'DECAB' are different. Hence f is bijective and does have an inverse. □

Suppose that each person in a telephone directory only has one telephone number. This directory then defines a bijective function from the set of listed subscribers to the set of listed numbers. Hence this function does have an inverse, but it is sometimes difficult for members of the general public to obtain a list of subscribers corresponding to each phone number. The telephone company often keeps this list secret, even though all the information is contained in the regular telephone directory.

A glance at the graph of a function is often sufficient to tell whether a function has an inverse or not.

- A function is injective if the horizontal line through each point of the codomain intersects the graph *at most* once.

- A function is surjective if the horizontal line through each point of the codomain intersects the graph *at least* once.

- A function is bijective if the horizontal line through each point of the codomain intersects the graph *precisely* once.

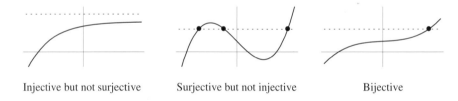

Injective but not surjective   Surjective but not injective   Bijective

5.5.4 Example.
Does the function $f : \mathbb{R} \longrightarrow \mathbb{R}$ defined by the formula $f(x) = x(x-1)(x-2)$ have an inverse?

Solution. It is clear that this function is not injective because $f(0) = f(1) = f(2)$. Hence it cannot have an inverse. □

5.5.5 Proposition.
Let $f : X \to Y$ and $g : Y \to Z$ be functions.

(i) If f and g are injections then $g \circ f$ is an injection.

(ii) If f and g are surjections then $g \circ f$ is a surjection.

(iii) If f and g are bijections then $g \circ f$ is a bijection.

Proof. *(i).*   Suppose that $g \circ f(x_1) = g \circ f(x_2)$. Then $g(y_1) = g(y_2)$ where $y_1 = f(x_1)$ and $y_2 = f(x_2)$. If g is an injection then $y_1 = y_2$; that is, $f(x_1) = f(x_2)$. If f is also an injection, $x_1 = x_2$ and it follows that $g \circ f$ is an injection.

(ii).   Let f and g be surjections and let $z \in Z$. Then there exists $y \in Y$ with $g(y) = z$ and there exists $x \in X$ with $f(x) = y$. Hence, $g \circ f(x) = g(f(x)) = g(y) = z$ and so $g \circ f$ is surjective.

(iii).   This follows from parts (i) and (ii).   □

5.6   CARDINALITY

You may have noticed that if $f : X \to Y$ is a bijection, whose domain, X, contains three elements say, then the codomain Y must also contain three elements. We will now use bijections to define the notion of sets having equal number of elements.

5.6.1   Definition.   If there exists a bijection from the set X to the set Y we write

$$\#X \;\; = \;\; \#Y$$

and we say that the sets X and Y have the same *cardinality*.

Let $\mathbb{P}_n$ denote the subset of $\mathbb{P}$ consisting of all positive integers less than or equal to n. Hence $\mathbb{P}_0 = \emptyset, \mathbb{P}_1 = \{1\}, \mathbb{P}_2 = \{1, 2\}, \mathbb{P}_3 = \{1, 2, 3\}$ and $\mathbb{P}_n = \{1, 2, 3, \dots, n\}$. If there exists a bijection between a set X and $\mathbb{P}_n$ we write

$$\#X \;\; = \;\; n$$

and say that the *number of elements* in X is n. If such a bijection exists for some integer n, we say that X is a *finite set*; if no such bijection exists, X is called an *infinite set*.

For example, $\#\{a, b\} = \#\{8, 5\}$ and these both have two elements. Furthermore, these two sets are finite, while $\mathbb{Z}$ is an infinite set. If $\#X = 0$, then there is a bijection between X and $\emptyset$, and it follows that X must be the empty set $\emptyset$; there is only one empty set.

This notion of the number of elements of a set agrees with our everyday idea of counting elements. A child, wishing to count five oranges, usually sets up a one-to-one correspondence or bijection between the oranges and a known set, such as the five fingers on a hand, or the words 'one', 'two', 'three', 'four', 'five'. Our definition does precisely the same, by setting up a one-to-one correspondence between a set and one of the known sets $\mathbb{P}_n$.

It is natural to extend this idea of sets with the same number of elements to include infinite sets, but, as we shall see later, our intuition often fails us when dealing with the cardinality of infinite sets.

5.6.2 Proposition.   If A and B are *disjoint* finite sets then

$$\#(A \cup B) \;=\; \#A + \#B.$$

Proof.   Suppose that $\#A = m$ and $\#B = n$ where $m \geq 0$ and $n \geq 0$. The there exist bijections $f : A \to \mathbb{P}_m$ and $g : B \to \mathbb{P}_n$. Construct the function $h : A \cup B \to \mathbb{P}_{m+n}$ by

$$h(x) \;=\; \begin{cases} f(x) & \text{if } x \in A \\ g(x) + m & \text{if } x \in B. \end{cases}$$

Since A and B are disjoint, this function is well defined and can be checked to be a bijection. Hence $\#(A \cup B) = m + n = \#A + \#B$. ▢

We now extend this result to sets which are not necessarily disjoint. We obtain the result one would expect, if one looks at the Venn diagram of two sets.

5.6.3 Theorem.   If A and B are any finite sets then

$$\#(A \cup B) \;=\; \#A + \#B - \#(A \cap B).$$

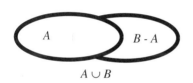

$A \cup B$

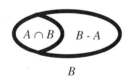

B

Proof.   As the previous proposition describes how to deal with the number of elements in the union of disjoint sets, we split $A \cup B$ into disjoint subsets. We can write

$$A \cup B \;=\; A \cup (B - A)$$

where the union is disjoint and $B - A$ denotes the set of elements in B that are not in A. Hence by Proposition 5.6.2

$$\#(A \cup B) \;=\; \#A + \#(B - A).$$

We can also write B as the disjoint union

$$B \;=\; (A \cap B) \cup (B - A)$$

so that $\#B = \#(A \cap B) + \#(B - A)$. Eliminating $\#(B - A)$, we obtain

$$\#(A \cup B) \;=\; \#A + \#B - \#(A \cap B). \quad ▢$$

5.6.4 Example.   In a survey of 100 students who smoked, 68 said they smoked cigarettes, 42 said they smoked marijuana while 7 said they smoked both. Are these figures consistent?

Solution. Let C be the set of students who smoked cigarettes and M be the set of students who smoked marijuana. Then, by Theorem 5.6.3,

$$\begin{aligned} \#(C \cup M) &= \#C + \#M - \#(C \cap M) \\ &= 68 + 42 - 7 \\ &= 103. \end{aligned}$$

Since this number is greater than the number of students in the survey, the figures must be inconsistent. $\qquad\square$

We shall now look at the cardinality of some infinite sets.

5.6.5 Theorem. $\#\mathbb{P} = \#\mathbb{Z}$.

Proof. We have to show that there is a bijection between the positive integers, $\mathbb{P}$, and all the integers, $\mathbb{Z}$. We can define such a bijection as follows.

$\mathbb{P}$	1	2	3	4	5	6	7	8	$\ldots$
$\downarrow f$	$\downarrow$	$\downarrow$	$\downarrow$	$\downarrow$	$\downarrow$	$\downarrow$	$\downarrow$	$\downarrow$	
$\mathbb{Z}$	0	1	-1	2	-2	3	-3	4	$\ldots$

The function $f : \mathbb{P} \to \mathbb{Z}$ is defined by

$$f(n) = \begin{cases} n/2 & \text{if } n \text{ is even} \\ -(n-1)/2 & \text{if } n \text{ is odd.} \end{cases}$$

This is a bijection because it has an inverse $f^{-1} : \mathbb{Z} \to \mathbb{P}$ defined by

$$f^{-1}(n) = \begin{cases} 2n & \text{if } n > 0 \\ 1 - 2n & \text{if } n \leq 0. \end{cases}$$

Therefore $\#\mathbb{P} = \#\mathbb{Z}$. $\qquad\square$

This result may seem surprising, because $\mathbb{P}$ is a proper subset of $\mathbb{Z}$, but still has the same cardinality (that is, the same number of elements) as $\mathbb{Z}$. Such a situation can never occur with finite sets, but it is a characteristic of infinite sets that there is always a proper subset of any infinite set which has the same cardinality as the whole set.

The following two results may be even more surprising.

5.6.6 Proposition. $\#(\mathbb{P} \times \mathbb{P}) = \#\mathbb{P}$

Proof. $\mathbb{P} \times \mathbb{P}$ is the set of all pairs of positive integers. We can write out all the elements of $\mathbb{P} \times \mathbb{P}$ in rows as follows.

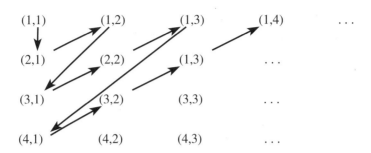

The sequence of arrows in the above diagram will eventually pass through every pair of positive integers precisely once, and we can use this fact to define a bijection

$$f : \mathbb{P} \times \mathbb{P} \longrightarrow \mathbb{P}$$

where $f(1,1) = 1, f(2,1) = 2, f(1,2) = 3, f(3,1) = 4$, etc. With a little work one can show that a formula for this function is

$$f(i,j) \;=\; \frac{(i+j-1)(i+j-2)}{2} + j.$$

This bijection shows that $\#(\mathbb{P} \times \mathbb{P}) = \#\mathbb{P}$. $\square$

5.6.7 Theorem. $\#\mathbb{Q} \;=\; \#\mathbb{P}.$

Proof.   A bijection from the rational numbers, $\mathbb{Q}$, to the positive integers, $\mathbb{P}$, can be constructed in a similar way to that of the previous proposition by consideration of the following diagram.

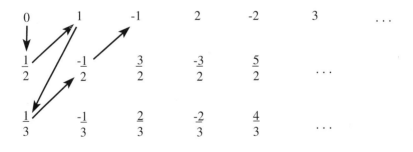

The last three examples might suggest that all infinite sets have the same cardinality. However, this is not the case. The following result shows that there is no bijection between $\mathbb{P}$ and the set of all real numbers $\mathbb{R}$.

5.6.8 Theorem. $\mathbb{P}$ and $\mathbb{R}$ do not have the same cardinality.

Proof. Suppose that there is a surjection $f : \mathbb{P} \to \mathbb{R}$. Write each element of $\mathbb{R}$ as an infinite decimal, and list the elements of $\mathbb{R}$ as follows.

$$
\begin{aligned}
f(1) &= & b_{1r} \ldots \ldots b_{12}b_{11}.a_{11}a_{12}a_{13}\ldots \\
f(2) &= & b_{2s} \ldots \ldots \ldots b_{22}b_{21}.a_{21}a_{22}a_{23}\ldots \\
f(3) &= & b_{3t} \ldots b_{32}b_{31}.a_{31}a_{32}a_{33}\ldots \\
&\vdots
\end{aligned}
$$

Since f is supposed to be surjection, all the elements of $\mathbb{R}$ must appear in the above list.

Construct the decimal $c = 0.c_1c_2c_3\ldots$ in the following way. Each digit is chosen from the digits 1 through 8 and $c_1 \neq a_{11}, c_2 \neq a_{22}, c_3 \neq a_{33}$ and, in general $c_r \neq a_{rr}$. Then c is a real number which does not contain a repeated sequence of zeros or nines and so has only one decimal expansion. Now $c \neq f(1)$ because they differ in the first decimal place; $c \neq f(2)$ because they differ in the second decimal place and, in general, $c \neq f(r)$ because they differ in the rth decimal place. Hence $c \notin f(\mathbb{P})$, which contradicts the assumption that f is a surjection.

Therefore there is no surjection from $\mathbb{P}$ to $\mathbb{R}$, and certainly no bijection from $\mathbb{P}$ to $\mathbb{R}$. $\qquad\square$

Since there is no surjection from $\mathbb{P}$ to $\mathbb{R}$, in some sense, $\mathbb{R}$ contains more elements than $\mathbb{P}$. In fact, this notion of sets of larger infinite cardinality can be made precise, and it can be shown that, for each set X, it is possible to construct a set of cardinality larger than X. (See Problem 101.)

Sets that have the same cardinality as $\mathbb{P}$ have the smallest infinite cardinality. Such sets are called *countable* because a one-to-one correspondence between $\mathbb{P}$ and the set has the effect of 'counting' the elements of the set.

5.7 INVERSE TRIGONOMETRIC FUNCTIONS

As an example of the use of the Inversion Theorem 5.5.2, we shall show that, by suitably restricting the domain and codomain of the trigonometric functions, it is possible to find inverse trigonometric functions.

Consider the graph of the sine function

$$\sin : \mathbb{R} \longrightarrow \mathbb{R}$$

where $\sin x$ is the sine of x radians.

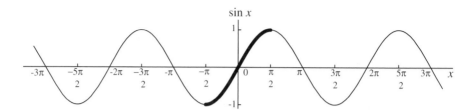

If we are given the sine of an angle and need to know the angle then we require an inverse function to the sine function. For example, if $\sin\theta = 1/2$, then θ could be $\pi/6$ or $5\pi/6$ or $13\pi/6$ or, in fact, one of an infinite number of values. It is clear from the above graph that the sine function is not bijective, and hence cannot have an inverse. However, if we restrict the domain of the sine function to the interval $[-\pi/2, \pi/2]$ and restrict the codomain to $[-1, 1]$, then the function will be a bijection because every horizontal line, through a point of the codomain $[-1, 1]$, will intersect that part of the graph above $[-\pi/2, \pi/2]$ precisely once.

5.7.1 Definition.   Denote the restricted sine function by

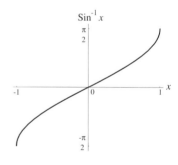

$$\text{Sin} : [-\pi/2, \pi/2] \longrightarrow [-1, 1]$$

and the *inverse sine function* by

$$\text{Sin}^{-1} : [-1, 1] \longrightarrow [-\pi/2, \pi/2].$$

An alternative notation for $\text{Sin}^{-1} x$ is Arcsin x.

Hence $y = \text{Sin}^{-1} x$ if and only if $x = \sin y$ and $-\pi/2 \le y \le \pi/2$.

For example, $\text{Sin}^{-1}(1/2) = \pi/6$, $\text{Sin}^{-1}(-1/2) = -\pi/6$ and $\text{Sin}^{-1}(1) = \pi/2$. (The notation $\text{Sin}^{-1} x$ is identical to that for an inverse function $f^{-1}(x)$ and does *not* refer to $\frac{1}{\text{Sin} x}$.)

We can define the inverse functions to the other trigonometric functions in a similar way.

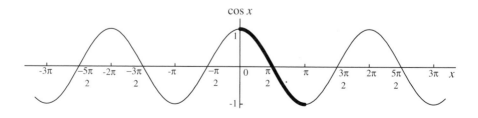

5.7.2 Definition. If the cosine function is restricted to

$$\text{Cos} : [0, \pi] \longrightarrow [-1, 1]$$

then the *inverse cosine function* is denoted by

$$\text{Cos}^{-1} : [-1, 1] \longrightarrow [0, \pi]$$

or by Arccos.

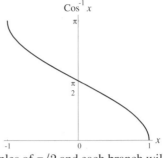

The tangent function has asymptotes at odd multiples of $\pi/2$ and each branch will have an inverse function. We normally use the branch through the origin to define the inverse.

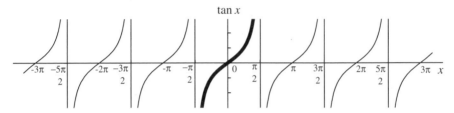

5.7.3 Definition. If the tangent function is restricted to

$$\text{Tan} : (-\pi/2, \pi/2) \longrightarrow \mathbb{R}$$

then the *inverse tangent function* is denoted by

$$\text{Tan}^{-1} : \mathbb{R} \longrightarrow (-\pi/2, \pi/2)$$

or by Arctan.

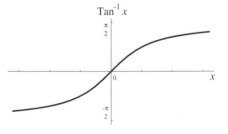

5.8 EXPONENTIAL AND LOG FUNCTIONS

A very important class of functions in the physical and biological sciences is that of the exponential function and its inverse, the logarithmic function.

A function, such as $f(x) = x^2$ is called a power function, whereas a function such as $g(x) = 2^x$, in which the independent variable appears as an exponent, is called an exponential function.

These functions occur in science whenever a rate of growth (or decay) of some quantity is proportional to its own size. For example, a colony of bacteria will start growing at an exponential rate, because each bacteria will divide after a certain time, and hence the rate of growth will depend on the size of the colony. Of course, after a while, the colony will run out of space and food, and will stop growing so rapidly; if this were not so, we would soon be overrun by bacteria.

An *exponential function* is a function of the form

$$f : \mathbb{R} \longrightarrow \mathbb{R} \quad \text{where } f(x) = b^x$$

for some fixed positive real number $b \neq 1$.

We have only defined what we mean by b^x, if x is a rational number. What does b^x mean if x is not rational? What is $2^{\sqrt{2}}$ for instance?

An irrational number can be approximated by the first n terms of its decimal expansion. Hence we would expect an irrational power to be approximated by rational powers obtained from successive terms of the decimal expansion. For example, we would hope that

$$2^{1.4} < 2^{\sqrt{2}} < 2^{1.5} \quad \text{since} \quad 1.4 < \sqrt{2} < 1.5$$
$$2^{1.41} < 2^{\sqrt{2}} < 2^{1.42} \quad \text{since} \quad 1.41 < \sqrt{2} < 1.42.$$

We shall not give a precise definition of irrational powers here, as it is too complicated, and it depends on the definition of the real numbers. But it can be shown, by using the properties of the real numbers, that for each $b > 0$, there is an exponential function $f : \mathbb{R} \to \mathbb{R}$, defined by $f(x) = b^x$, which has the following properties.

5.8.1 Properties of Exponents.

(i) $b^{m/n} = \sqrt[n]{b^m}$ for positive integers m and n.

(ii) $b^{-x} = \dfrac{1}{b^x}$

(iii) $b^0 = 1$

(iv) $b^x \cdot b^y = b^{x+y}$

(v) $\dfrac{b^x}{b^y} = b^{x-y}$

(vi) $(b^x)^y = b^{xy}$

(viia) If $b > 1$ then $b^x < b^y$ whenever $x < y$.

(viib) If $0 < b < 1$ then $b^x > b^y$ whenever $x < y$.

(viic) If $b = 1$ then $b^x = 1$ for all $x \in \mathbb{R}$.

The graphs of these exponential functions take the following forms when $b > 1$, and when $0 < b < 1$.

A real valued function, f, of a real variable is said to be *monotone increasing* if $f(x) > f(y)$ whenever $x > y$. The function, f, is called *monotone decreasing* if $f(x) < f(y)$ whenever $x > y$.

The exponential function $f(x) = b^x$ is monotone increasing, if $b > 1$. This means that the function increases as the independent variable increases and that the graph always slopes upward. It is this property that shows that $2^{\sqrt{2}}$ is sandwiched between $2^{1.41}$ and $2^{1.42}$.

If $0 < b < 1$, then the exponential function $f(x) = b^x$ is monotone decreasing and its graph always slopes downwards.

A radioactive substance is a material that emits subatomic particles and changes to another substance. If it is assumed that the probability of an individual atom disintegrating is unaffected by the number of other atoms present, then the amount of radioactive substance remaining decreases exponentially with time. This yields an example of a function of the form b^t where $0 < b < 1$.

The rate of decay of a substance is usually measured by its *half-life*. This is the length of time required for the radioactive substance to decay to half its original amount. For example, the isotope strontium 90 has a half-life of 28 years. If we started with one gram of strontium 90, there would be one half of a gram remaining after 28 years and one quarter of a gram after 56 years. In general, there would be $\left(\frac{1}{2}\right)^{t/28}$ grams remaining after t years.

Mass of radioactive substance

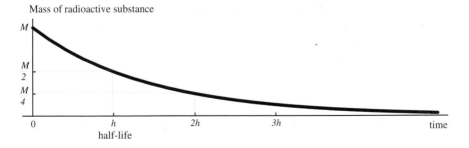

5.8.2 Example. Archaeologists use the isotope carbon 14 to date ancient remains. Carbon 14 occurs naturally in all living tissue and, while the plant or animal is alive, its carbon 14 content is maintained at a constant level. However, when the plant or animal dies, the carbon 14 is not replenished and decays with a half-life of 5700 years.

A piece of charcoal from an ancient campfire was discovered at an archaeological dig and was found to contain 25% of its original carbon 14. Estimate the age of the campfire.

Solution. If there was c_0 milligrams of carbon 14 in the charcoal when it was burnt, after t years the amount remaining would be

$$c = c_0 \left(\frac{1}{2}\right)^{t/5700}.$$

If the amount is remaining is $c_0/4$ then

$$\frac{c_0}{4} = c_0 \left(\frac{1}{2}\right)^{t/5700} \qquad \text{or} \qquad \left(\frac{1}{2}\right)^2 = \left(\frac{1}{2}\right)^{t/5700}.$$

Hence $2 = t/5700$ and $t = 11400$.

The campsite would therefore be approximately 11 thousand years old and would date from 9000 B.C. $\qquad\qquad \Box$

There is one exponential function that plays a very important role in mathematics. It is the function whose rate of growth is not only proportional to its size, but is actually equal to its size. That is, it is a solution to the differential equation

$$\frac{dy}{dx} = y.$$

It can be shown that all the solutions to this equation are of the form $y = ke^x$, where k is a constant that depends on the initial conditions, and e is a certain fixed irrational number, whose value to five places of decimals is 2.71828. The function

$$f(x) = e^x$$

is often referred to as *the* exponential function.

A monotone function (increasing or decreasing) is an injection. (See Problem 110.) Therefore, if we restrict the codomain of an exponential function to the positive real numbers, $\mathbb{R}_{>0}$, then $f : \mathbb{R} \to \mathbb{R}_{>0}$ is defined by $f(x) = b^x$ is a bijection, as long as $b \neq 1$.

5.8.3 Definition.

The inverse of this exponential function b^x is the *logarithmic function*

$$f^{-1} : \mathbb{R}_{>0} \to \mathbb{R}$$

where $f^{-1}(x)$ is denoted by $\log_b x$ and is called the *logarithm of x to the base b*.

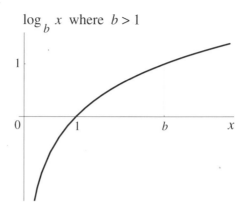

$\log_b x$ where $b > 1$

Hence $y = \log_b x$ if and only if $x = b^y$; that is, $\log_b x$ is the power that b has to be raised to in order to obtain the number x.

For example, $\log_{10} 1000 = 3$ because $1000 = 10^3$, $\log_3 81 = 4$ because $81 = 3^4$, $\log_2(1/32) = -5$ because $1/32 = 2^{-5}$ and $\log_{10} \sqrt{10} = 1/2$.

For any base b, $\log_b 1 = 0$, since $1 = b^0$, $\log_b b = 1$, since $b = b^1$ and $\log_b b^r = r$.

The logarithmic function has the following important properties that follow from the Properties of Exponents 5.8.1.

5.8.4 Proposition.

For $x, y \in \mathbb{R}_{>0}$ and $r \in \mathbb{R}$,

(i) $\log_b(xy) = \log_b x + \log_b y$

(ii) $\log_b \left(\dfrac{x}{y} \right) = \log_b x - \log_b y$

(iii) $\log_b(x^r) = r \log_b x$.

Proof. (i). Let $k = \log_b x, \ell = \log_b y$ and $m = \log_b(xy)$, so that $x = b^k, y = b^\ell$ and $xy = b^m$. Now $b^m = b^k b^\ell$ and it follows from 5.8.1 (iv) that $b^m = b^{k+\ell}$. Hence $m = k + \ell$, which proves (i).

(iii). Let $k = \log_b x$ again, so that $x = b^k$. Then, by 5.8.1 (vi), $x^r = (b^k)^r = b^{kr}$ and $\log_b(x^r) = kr = r \log_b x$.

(ii). Since $x/y = x \cdot y^{-1}$, part (ii) follows from parts (i) and (iii). □

Proposition 5.8.4 forms the basis for the method of calculation using 'log tables'. A *log table* is a list of values of logarithms of numbers to a given base. Any positive integer, other than 1, can be used as the base of a system of logarithms.

Logarithms to the base 10 are called *common logarithms*. These are very useful when dealing with numbers in scientific notation. The sun is about 149,000,000 kilometres from the earth and, in scientific notation, this would be written as 1.49×10^8

kilometres. A number in *scientific notation* consists of a real number between 1 and 10 followed by a multiplication sign and the appropriate integral power of 10. For example, the mass of the hydrogen atom is about 1.66×10^{-24} grams; it would be very inconvenient to write this number as a decimal.

The common logarithms for the numbers in the following table can be calculated once it is known that $\log_{10} 2.63$ is approximately 0.42.

Number x	In Scientific Notation	As a power of 10	$\log_{10} x$
263000	2.63×10^5	$10^{.42} \times 10^5 = 10^{5.42}$	5.42
26.3	2.63×10	$10^{.42} \times 10 = 10^{1.42}$	1.42
2.63	2.63	$10^{.42}$	.42
.263	2.63×10^{-1}	$10^{.42} \times 10^{-1} = 10^{.42-1}$	$.42 - 1$
.000263	2.63×10^{-4}	$10^{.42} \times 10^{-4} = 10^{.42-4}$	$.42 - 4$

Logarithms to the base e are called *natural logarithms* and these are often used in mathematics, because this base appears naturally in the calculus. In higher mathematics books, when no base is explicitly mentioned, it can be assumed that the logarithms are to the base e.

Logarithms to base 2 are often used in computer science, as machine numbers are usually represented in the binary system.

It is fairly easy to convert from one base to another, using the following result.

5.8.5 Theorem. $\log_a x = \log_a b \cdot \log_b x.$

Proof.   Let $k = \log_a b$ and $\ell = \log_b x$ so that $b = a^k$ and $x = b^\ell$. Now

$$x = b^\ell = (a^k)^\ell = a^{k\ell}$$

and so $\log_a x = k\ell$ and the theorem is true. $\qquad\square$

5.8.6 Corollary. $\log_a b = \dfrac{1}{\log_b a}.$

Proof.   This corollary follows from the above theorem by putting $x = a$ and using the fact that $\log_a a = 1$. $\qquad\square$

For example, to convert natural logarithms to common logarithms you just have to multiply by $\log_{10} e \approx .4343$ and, conversely, to convert common logarithms to natural logarithms you multiply by $\frac{1}{.4343} \approx 2.3026$.

In many calculus books, the natural logarithm is defined before the exponential function, by

$$\log_e x = \int_1^x \frac{dt}{t}.$$

It is then shown that this function is monotonic increasing and satisfies the properties given in Proposition 5.8.4. The inverse of this function is then defined to be the function e^x, which is shown to have the usual properties of an exponential.

5.9 PERMUTATIONS

Bijective functions appear in another disguise as permutations of a set.

5.9.1 Definition. Let S be a finite nonempty set. A *permutation* σ on S is a bijection $\sigma : S \to S$.

If $S = \{a, b, c, d\}$, then one permutation on S is defined by $\sigma(a) = b$, $\sigma(b) = d$, $\sigma(c) = a$ and $\sigma(d) = c$. We can think of the permutation σ as a rearrangement of the elements a, b, c, d, to form b, d, a, c. A convenient way of writing this permutation is

$$\sigma = \begin{pmatrix} a\ b\ c\ d \\ b\ d\ a\ c \end{pmatrix}$$

where the elements of S are written in the top row and their corresponding images, under σ, written below.

The set $\mathbb{P}_3 = \{1, 2, 3\}$ has six different permutations, namely

$$\sigma_1 = \begin{pmatrix} 1\ 2\ 3 \\ 1\ 2\ 3 \end{pmatrix} \qquad \sigma_2 = \begin{pmatrix} 1\ 2\ 3 \\ 2\ 3\ 1 \end{pmatrix} \qquad \sigma_3 = \begin{pmatrix} 1\ 2\ 3 \\ 3\ 1\ 2 \end{pmatrix}$$

$$\sigma_4 = \begin{pmatrix} 1\ 2\ 3 \\ 1\ 3\ 2 \end{pmatrix} \qquad \sigma_5 = \begin{pmatrix} 1\ 2\ 3 \\ 3\ 2\ 1 \end{pmatrix} \qquad \sigma_6 = \begin{pmatrix} 1\ 2\ 3 \\ 2\ 1\ 3 \end{pmatrix}.$$

The permutation σ_1 fixes all the elements and is called the *identity permutation*.

The set $\mathbb{P}_n = \{1, 2, 3, \ldots, n\}$ contains $n!$ permutations. There are n choices for the image of the element 1 and, once this has been chosen, this image cannot be the image of any other element; hence there are $(n-1)$ choices for the image of 2, and $(n-2)$ choices for the image of 3, etc. The total number of choices is therefore $n(n-1)(n-2) \cdots 2 \cdot 1 = n!$. Denote the set of permutations on $\mathbb{P}_n$ by $\mathcal{S}_n$.

If σ and τ are two permutations in $\mathcal{S}_n$, then $\tau : \mathbb{P}_n \to \mathbb{P}_n$ and $\sigma : \mathbb{P}_n \to \mathbb{P}_n$ are bijections and their composite $\sigma \circ \tau : \mathbb{P}_n \to \mathbb{P}_n$ can be defined. This composition has the following properties, that make the set $\mathcal{S}_n$, under the composition $\circ$, into what is called a *group*.

5.9.2 Proposition. If $\sigma, \tau \in \mathcal{S}_n$ then $\sigma \circ \tau \in \mathcal{S}_n$ and

(i) $\sigma \circ (\tau \circ \rho) = (\sigma \circ \tau) \circ \rho$ for all $\sigma, \tau, \rho \in \mathcal{S}_n$

(ii) there is an identity permutation $\iota \in \mathcal{S}_n$ such that $\iota \circ \sigma = \sigma \circ \iota = \sigma$ for all $\sigma \in \mathcal{S}_n$

(iii) for each permutation $\sigma \in \mathcal{S}_n$, there is an inverse permutation $\sigma^{-1} \in \mathcal{S}_n$ such that $\sigma \circ \sigma^{-1} = \sigma^{-1} \circ \sigma = \iota$.

Proof..   It follows from Proposition 5.5.5 that the composite $\sigma \circ \tau$ of two permutations σ and τ is also a permutation.

(i).   Associativity follows from the associativity of functions, Theorem 5.3.3.

(ii).   The identity permutation ι is the identity function on $\mathbb{P}_n$ and its properties follow from Proposition 5.3.4.

(iii).   Any permutation $\sigma : \mathbb{P}_n \to \mathbb{P}_n$ is a bijection and so has an inverse function $\sigma^{-1} : \mathbb{P}_n \to \mathbb{P}_n$ which is also a bijection. Hence σ^{-1} is also a permutation. $\square$

The composition of the elements $\sigma_1 = \iota, \sigma_2, \sigma_3, \sigma_4, \sigma_5$ and σ_6 in $\mathcal{S}_3$ are given by the following table in which $\sigma_i \circ \sigma_j$ is the element in the ith row and the jth column.

$\circ$	σ_1	σ_2	σ_3	σ_4	σ_5	σ_6
σ_1	σ_1	σ_2	σ_3	σ_4	σ_5	σ_6
σ_2	σ_2	σ_3	σ_1	σ_6	σ_4	σ_5
σ_3	σ_3	σ_1	σ_2	σ_5	σ_6	σ_4
σ_4	σ_4	σ_5	σ_6	σ_1	σ_2	σ_3
σ_5	σ_5	σ_6	σ_4	σ_3	σ_1	σ_2
σ_6	σ_6	σ_4	σ_5	σ_2	σ_3	σ_1

For example, $\sigma_3^2 = \sigma_2$, $\sigma_3^{-1} = \sigma_2$, $\sigma_2 \circ \sigma_6 = \sigma_5$ and $\sigma_6 \circ \sigma_2 = \sigma_4$. These last two relations show that this composition is not commutative. This should not be surprising as composition of functions is not commutative in general.

Exercise Set 5

1 - 4. *Which of the following are functions from $\{1, 2, 3\}$ to $\{a, b, c\}$?*

1. 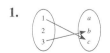   **2.** 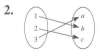   **3.**   **4.**

5 - 14. *For each of the following formulas, find the largest set $X \subseteq \mathbb{R}$ for which $f : X \to \mathbb{R}$ defines a real valued function of a real variable. Sketch the graph of each function and find the image $Y = f(X)$. State whether or not the function $f : X \to Y$ has an inverse $f^{-1} : Y \to X$ and give a formula for $f^{-1}(x)$ when the inverse exists.*

5. $f(x) = x^2 - 1$ **6.** $f(x) = \sqrt{x - 2}$

7. $f(x) = \dfrac{x}{x^2 + x}$ **8.** $f(x) = \dfrac{x}{x + 1}$

9. $f(x) = \sin 5x$ **10.** $f(x) = 5^x$

11. $f(x) = \log_{10}(3 - x)$ **12.** $f(x) = \sqrt[4]{2 - \log_3 x}$

13. $f(x) = \sqrt{\sin x}$ **14.** $f(x) = \mathrm{Sin}^{-1} 3x$

15 - 17. *Below are three diagrams defining functions f, g and h from $\mathbb{P}_5$ to itself.*

Draw similar diagrams for the following functions.

15. $f \circ g$ and $g \circ f$ **16.** $f \circ h$ and $h \circ g$

17. $g \circ h$, $f \circ (g \circ h)$ and $(f \circ g) \circ h$

18 - 23. *For each of the following formulas, specify subsets X and Y of $\mathbb{R}$ so $f : X \to Y$ is a bijective function. Find a formula for each inverse function.*

18. $f(x) = x^4$ **19.** $f(x) = \sqrt{3 - x}$

20. $f(x) = (\tan x)^2$ **21.** $f(x) = \dfrac{x + 2}{2x - 1}$

22. $f(x) = \sqrt{\log_e x}$ **23.** $f(x) = 3^{\sqrt{x}}$

24 - 28. *Which of the following functions are injections?*

24. The function that assigns to everybody their height, to the nearest millimetre.

25. The function that assigns to everybody their maternal grandfather.

26. The function that assigns to each ship at sea, its latitude and longitude.

27. The function that assigns to everybody their name.

28. The function that assigns to every worker their social security number (choose the lowest number if there are several).

29 - 31. *Draw the graph of each of the following functions.*

29. $f : \mathbb{P}_4 \longrightarrow \mathbb{P}_6$ defined by $f(n) = n$

30. $g : \mathbb{P}_6 \longrightarrow \mathbb{P}_6$ defined by $g(n) = \mathrm{GCD}(2, n)$

31. $h : \mathbb{P}_3 \longrightarrow \mathbb{P}_{10}$ defined by $h(n) = n^2 + 1$

32. Sketch the graph of the *greatest integer function* $f : \mathbb{R} \to \mathbb{R}$, where $f(x) = \lfloor x \rfloor$, the greatest integer less than or equal to x. What is the image of this function?

33. Let $f : \mathbb{R} \to \mathbb{R}$ and $g : \mathbb{R} \to \mathbb{R}$ be defined by $f(x) = x^2 - 1$ and $g(x) = x - 1$. Find formulas for $f \circ g$, $g \circ f$, $f \circ f$ and $g \circ f \circ g$.

34. Let $X = \mathbb{R} - \{0, 1\}$, the set of all real numbers except 0 and 1. Find all the possible functions obtained by taking composites of the two functions $f : X \to X$ and $g : X \to X$ where $f(x) = 1 - x$ and $g(x) = \frac{1}{x}$.

35 - 36. *Find inverses of each of the following bijective functions, f, from $\mathbb{Z}$ to itself.*

35. $f(n) = \begin{cases} n + 5 & \text{if } n \text{ is even} \\ n - 5 & \text{if } n \text{ is odd} \end{cases}$

36. $f(n) = \begin{cases} n + 4 & \text{if } n \equiv 0 \pmod{3} \\ -n - 3 & \text{if } n \equiv 1 \pmod{3} \\ n + 1 & \text{if } n \equiv 2 \pmod{3} \end{cases}$

37. If $f : X \to Y$ is a bijective function, prove that its inverse is unique.

38. Let $f : X \to Y$ and $g : Y \to Z$ be bijective functions. Prove that

$$(g \circ f)^{-1} = f^{-1} \circ g^{-1}.$$

39 - 42. *Determine which of the following functions are injective, surjective, and bijective. Find the inverses of those functions that have inverses.*

39. $f : \mathbb{R} \longrightarrow \mathbb{R}$ defined by $f(x) = (x - 2)^3$.
40. $g : \mathbb{R} - \{0\} \longrightarrow \mathbb{R}$ defined by $g(x) = \log_2 |x|$.
41. $h : \mathbb{Z} \longrightarrow \mathbb{Z}$ defined by $h(n) = n^3$.
42. $k : X \longrightarrow X$ where $k(n)$ is the greatest prime factor of n and $X = \mathbb{P} - \{1\}$, the set of integers greater than 1.

43. Let $f : X \to Y$ and $g : Y \to X$ be functions so that $g \circ f = 1_X$. Prove that f is injective and g is surjective. Need either be bijective?

44. (i) Prove that $\#A = \#A$ for every set A.
(ii) If $\#A = \#B$, prove that $\#B = \#A$.
(iii) If $\#A = \#B$ and $\#B = \#C$, prove that $\#A = \#C$.

45. If A, B and C are finite sets, show that

$$\#(A \cup B \cup C) = \#A + \#B + \#C - \#(A \cap B) - \#(A \cap C) - \#(B \cap C) + \#(A \cap B \cap C).$$

46. In a regiment returning from war, 70% of the men had lost an eye, 80% an arm and 85% a leg. What percentage, at least, must have lost all three? (Adapted from Lewis Carroll, "A Tangled Tale".)

47. Show that the set of even positive integers has the same cardinality as the set of all positive integers. Show that the set of odd positive integers also has the same cardinality.

48. Let $\mathcal{P}(X)$ denote the set of all subsets (including $\emptyset$ and X) of a set X. Write out the elements of $\mathcal{P}(\emptyset)$, $\mathcal{P}(\{a\})$ and $\mathcal{P}(\{r, s, t\})$. If $\#X = n$, a finite number, what is $\#\mathcal{P}(X)$? Prove your assertion.

49. Define the function $\mathrm{Sec}^{-1} x$, giving its domain and image.

50. Define the function $\mathrm{Cot}^{-1} x$, giving its domain and image.

51. Solve the equation $\mathrm{Sin}^{-1} x + \mathrm{Sin}^{-1} 1 = \pi$.

52. Solve the equation $\mathrm{Sin}^{-1} \frac{1}{2} + \mathrm{Sin}^{-1} \frac{\sqrt{3}}{2} = x$.

53. What is the relationship between $\mathrm{Cos}^{-1} x$ and $\mathrm{Sin}^{-1} x$ in the domain in which they are both defined.

54. Prove that the shaded segment of the circle has area

$$r^2 \mathrm{Cos}^{-1} \left(\frac{p}{r}\right) - p\sqrt{r^2 - p^2}.$$

55. Sketch the graph of $y = \dfrac{1}{10^x}$.

56. Sketch the graphs of $y = (1/2)^x$, $y = 2^x$ and $y = 3^x$ in the same diagram.

57. Sketch the graph of $y = \dfrac{2^x + 2^{-x}}{2}$.

58. Sketch the graph of $y = e^{-x^2}$. (This is a simple form of the normal probability curve in statistics.)

59 - 64. *Solve the following equations.*

59. $8 = \log_2 x$ 60. $2 = \log_x 10$
61. $\sqrt[x]{2} = e^2$ 62. $\log_e (\log_e x) = 5$
63. $10^{-3\log_{10} x} = 5$ 64. $5 = 2^{\log_e x}$

65. If $x > 0$, write x^x as a power of e.

66. If a piece of paper .2mm thick could be folded in half 20 times, approximately how thick would the resulting paper be? (Use the fact that $\log_{10} 2$ is approximately .3.)

67. An archaeologist claims that a bone he has discovered is seventeen thousand years old. If this were true, how much of the original amount of carbon 14 would you expect to remain in the bone?

68. The earth's population is now 6 billion and is increasing at the rate of 2% a year. If it continues at this rate, how long will it take to double? What would be the population in 100 years time? (Use the fact that $\log_{10} 2 \approx .3$ and $\log_{10} 1.02 \approx .0086$.)

69. When a ship docks, its rope is thrown to the quay and wound round a bollard and then held by a sailor. If θ is the angle that the rope turns through when wound round the bollard, then a sailor exerting a tension of M kilograms on the rope can hold a tension of T kilograms from the ship, where

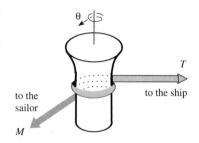

$$T = Me^{\mu\theta}.$$

The constant μ is the coefficient of friction between the rope and the bollard. How many times would the sailor have to wrap the rope around the bollard to hold a tension of 160 tonnes, if $\mu = .5$ and the sailor could exert a tension of 20 kilograms? (e^3 is approximately 20.)

70. If $1000 is placed in a savings bank at 10% interest, compounded daily, how much will be in the account after one year?

71 - 72. *For each of the following functional equations satisfied by the function $f : \mathbb{R} \to \mathbb{R}$, find*

> *(i) $f(0)$*
>
> *(ii) $f(-x)$ in terms of $f(x)$*
>
> *(iii) $f(n)$ where $n \in \mathbb{P}$*
>
> *(iv) $f(n)$ where $n \in \mathbb{Z}$*
>
> *(v) $f(r)$ where $r \in \mathbb{Q}$.*

71. $f(x + y) = f(x) + f(y)$ and $f(1) = a$.
72. $f(x + y) = f(x) \cdot f(y)$ and $f(1) = b$.

73. Give one example of a function $f : \mathbb{R} \to \mathbb{R}$ satisfying $f(x + y) = f(x) \cdot f(y)$ with $f(1) = 2$.

74. Give two examples of functions $f : \mathbb{R} \to \mathbb{R}$ satisfying $f(x + y) = f(x) \cdot f(y)$.

75. Solve the functional equation

$$f(xy) = f(x) + f(y)$$

when f is a function from $\mathbb{R}$ to $\mathbb{R}$.

76. If $f(x+y) = f(x) \cdot f(y)$ and f is a bijection, show that its inverse satisfies the functional equation

$$f^{-1}(xy) = f^{-1}(x) + f^{-1}(y).$$

77. If X is a finite set, show that the following conditions on a function $f : X \to X$ are equivalent.

(i) f is an injection.

(ii) f is a surjection.

(iii) f is a bijection.

78 - 85. If $\rho = \left(\begin{smallmatrix} 1 & 2 & 3 & 4 \\ 2 & 1 & 4 & 3 \end{smallmatrix}\right)$, $\sigma = \left(\begin{smallmatrix} 1 & 2 & 3 & 4 \\ 2 & 3 & 4 & 1 \end{smallmatrix}\right)$ and $\tau = \left(\begin{smallmatrix} 1 & 2 & 3 & 4 \\ 3 & 2 & 4 & 1 \end{smallmatrix}\right)$ are permutations of the set $\mathbb{P}_4 = \{1, 2, 3, 4\}$, find the following permutations.

78. $\rho \circ \sigma$

79. $\sigma \circ \rho$

80. $\rho^2 = \rho \circ \rho$

81. $(\rho \circ \sigma) \circ \tau$

82. ρ^{-1}

83. τ^{-1}

84. $\rho^{-1} \circ \tau^{-1}$

85. $(\tau \circ \rho)^{-1}$

86. If S is a finite set with more than two elements, show that there are permutations σ and τ of S such that $\sigma \circ \tau \neq \tau \circ \sigma$.

Problem Set 5

87. Find all real functions f, of a real variable, of the form

$$f(x) = \frac{ax + b}{cx + d} \quad \text{where } a, b, c, d \in \mathbb{R}$$

such that $f(f(x)) = x$ for all x except when $cx + d = 0$.

88. Find a function $f : \mathbb{R} \to \mathbb{R}$, different from those of the previous example, for which $f \circ f = 1_{\mathbb{R}}$.

*89 - 92. In Section 2.3 we introduced the idea of a 'relation'. Just as the concept of a function $f : X \to Y$ was made precise in 5.2.4 by defining it to be a special subset of $X \times Y$, we can give a precise definition of a relation. A **relation**, R between the set X and the set Y is any subset of $X \times Y$. If (x, y) is in this subset, we say that x is related to y and we write xRy. If (x, y) is not in the subset, then x is not related to y and we write $x \not{R} y$. A function from X to Y is therefore a special kind of relation between X and Y.*

89. What are all the elements of the subset $\mathbb{P}_4 \times \mathbb{P}_4$ that define the relation 'greater than'?

90. Which subset of $\mathbb{P}_6 \times \mathbb{P}_6$ defines the relation 'divides'? Is this relation a function?

91. Sketch the subset of $\mathbb{R} \times \mathbb{R}$ that defines the 'equals' relation. Do the same for the 'less than or equals' relation. Are either of these relations functions?

92. Sketch the subset of $\mathbb{R} \times \mathbb{R}$ that defines the relation R where xRy if and only if $x^2 + y^2 = 4$. Is this relation a function?

93. If the telephone directory defines a bijection from the set of listed subscribers to the set of listed numbers, how would you find the inverse of a given number?

94. Let ℓ and m be lines and P a point in a plane. We try to define a function f, from the points of ℓ to the points of m, by taking any point X on ℓ and letting the line PX intersect m in the point $f(X)$. Under what geometric conditions will f be a bijection?

95. Does the function $f : \mathbb{R} \to \mathbb{R}$ defined by $f(x) = x^3 + x + 1$ have an inverse? If so, can you find an equation for the inverse function?

96. How many functions are there from $\mathbb{P}_r$ to $\mathbb{P}_n$?

97. How many injections are there from $\mathbb{P}_r$ to $\mathbb{P}_n$?

98. How would you tackle the problem of finding the number of surjections from $\mathbb{P}_r$ to $\mathbb{P}_n$?

99. Prove that the function $f : X \to Y$ is injective if and only if it satisfies the following condition. 'For any set T, and functions $g : T \to X$ and $h : T \to X$, $f \circ g = f \circ h$ implies that $g = h$.'

100. Prove that the function $f : X \to Y$ is surjective if and only if it satisfies the following condition. 'For any set Z, and functions $g : Y \to Z$ and $h : Y \to Z$, $g \circ f = h \circ f$ implies $g = h$.'

101. If X is any set, finite or infinite, and $P(X)$ is the set of all subsets of X, then show that there is no surjection from X to $P(X)$. (This shows that the cardinality of $P(X)$ is always larger than that of X. This gives a method for constructing infinite sets of larger and larger cardinality. Starting with the set $\mathbb{P}$, we obtain $P(\mathbb{P}), P(P(\mathbb{P}))$, etc. each of which has larger cardinality than the previous set. It can be shown that $\#P(\mathbb{P}) = \#\mathbb{R}$. However, it is an extremely difficult problem to determine whether there is an infinite set whose cardinality is strictly greater than $\mathbb{P}$ but strictly less than $\mathbb{R}$. The *continuum hypothesis* states that there is no such set. Many interesting conclusions can be derived from this hypothesis, but it has been shown that the continuum hypothesis cannot be proven and it cannot be disproven!)

102 - 105. Define addition of infinite cardinals by $\#A + \#B = \#(A \cup B)$, if $A \cap B = \emptyset$, and multiplication by $\#A \cdot \#B = \#(A \times B)$. For finite sets, these definitions agree with the usual notions of addition and multiplication.

102. Show that $\#\mathbb{P} \cdot \#\mathbb{P} = \#\mathbb{P}$.   **103.** Show that $\#\mathbb{P} + \#\mathbb{P} = \#\mathbb{P}$.

104. Show that $\#\mathbb{P} + \#\mathbb{P}_n = \#\mathbb{P}$.   **105.** Show that $\#\mathbb{R} + \#\mathbb{P} = \#\mathbb{R}$.

106. *(For discussion)* A man takes an hour walk. After half an hour two mosquitoes land on him and he immediately manages to kill one of them. After three quarters of an hour, two more mosquitoes land on him and he kills one of the three on him. In general, at time $(1 - \frac{1}{2^n})$ hours, two mosquitoes land on him. He kills one of those on him leaving n still alive. How many mosquitoes will be on him when he finishes his walk?

107. A man wishes to invest the same amount of money each year and to have $1000 after 10 years. How much will he have to invest each year, if his money earns 10% compounded annually?

108. A mortgage of $20,000 is to be paid off in 10 years by equal payments at the end of each year. If the interest rate is 10% compounded annually, what payments must be made each year?

109. If b is a real number greater than 1, show that b^x is a monotone increasing function, for $x \in \mathbb{Q}$, by proving

(i) $b^m > b^n$ if $m > n$ and $m, n \in \mathbb{P}$
(ii) $b^m > b^n$ if $m > n$ and $m, n \in \mathbb{Z}$
(iii) $a^m > b^m$ if $a > b > 1$ and $m \in \mathbb{P}$
(iv) $a^m > b^m$ if $a > b > 1$ and m is a positive rational
(v) $b^m > b^n$ if $m > n$ and $m, n \in \mathbb{Q}$.

110. Prove that if $f : X \to Y$ is a monotone increasing function then f is an injection. If f is an injective real valued function of a real variable, show that it need not be monotone increasing or monotone decreasing.

111. It can be shown that the value of the infinite series

$$\sum_{r=0}^{\infty} \frac{1}{r!} = e.$$

(i) Prove that, if $m > n \geq 1$, then

$$\frac{1}{(n+1)!} + \frac{1}{(n+2)!} + \cdots + \frac{1}{m!} < \frac{1}{n!}.$$

(ii) Calculate e, correct to 4 decimal places, using the above infinite sum.

112. Use the following idea to prove that e is irrational. Suppose that $e = p/q$ where $p, q \in \mathbb{P}$. Multiply the equation

$$\frac{p}{q} = \sum_{r=0}^{\infty} \frac{1}{r!}$$

by q and use the fact that

$$\left[\frac{1}{(q+1)} + \frac{1}{(q+1)(q+2)} + \cdots \right] \leq \left[\frac{1}{3} + \frac{1}{3 \cdot 3} + \cdots \right] = \frac{1}{2}.$$

113 - 116. *A permutation that interchanges just two elements i and j is called a* **transposition** *and is often denoted by* (ij).

113. What is the inverse of the transposition (ij)?

114. Write the permutation $\begin{pmatrix} 1\,2\,3\,4 \\ 3\,4\,1\,2 \end{pmatrix}$ as a product of transpositions.

115. Write the permutation $\begin{pmatrix} 1\,2\,3 \\ 2\,3\,1 \end{pmatrix}$ as a product of transpositions.

116. Write the permutation $\begin{pmatrix} 1\,2\,3\,4 \\ 2\,3\,4\,1 \end{pmatrix}$ as a product of transpositions.

117. Let p be a prime and r be a positive integer coprime to $p - 1$. Prove that $f : \mathbb{Z}_p \to \mathbb{Z}_p$, defined by $f[x] = [x^r]$, is a bijection.

118. For which values of $k \in \mathbb{Z}_7$ is $f_k : \mathbb{Z}_7 \to \mathbb{Z}_7$, defined by $f_k([x]) = [x^4 + kx]$, a bijection? Find the inverse function, f_k^{-1}, for each bijection.

119. If a and b are fixed integers, when is the function $f : \mathbb{Z} \times \mathbb{Z} \to \mathbb{Z}$, defined by $f(x, y) = ax + by$, a surjection?

Chapter 6

An Introduction to Cryptography

6.1 CRYPTOGRAPHY

Cryptography is the study of sending messages in a secret or hidden form, so that only those people authorized to receive the message will be able to read it. "Crypto" is derived from the Greek word which means "hidden." *Cryptanalysis*, on the other hand, is the science of breaking cryptographic writings. Cryptography and cryptanalysis are collectively referred to as *cryptology*.

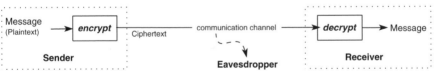

An early user of cryptography was Julius Caesar. Messages sent to his troops were disguised by the following simple method. A letter of the alphabet is replaced by another letter of the alphabet, which is 3 letters say, to the right in the natural ordering (we are assuming here that the letters of the alphabet are on a circle, so that A follows Z). Hence the word

        ATTACK   would become   DWWDFN.

The message being sent, in this case "ATTACK", is usually referred to as the *plaintext* and the *encrypted* message, "DWWDFN", is referred to as the *ciphertext*. The above cipher is commonly referred to as a *Caesar cipher* and is, of course, very easily *broken*. That is, the plaintext can be deduced from the ciphertext without knowing how the replacement of letters was done.

147

You might like to try your hand at cryptanalyzing the following piece of ciphertext. A standard practice is to suppress blanks in the plaintext and block the ciphertext into a fixed number of characters.

```
PDAEZ   AWXAD   EJZPD   EOXKK   GEOPD   WPWHH   PDAQO
ABQHP   KLEYO   EJWYK   HHACA   WHCAX   NWYKQ   NOASE
HHBKH   HKSBN   KIPDA   MQAOP   PKOKH   RALKH   UJKIE
WHAMQ   WPEKJ   OKRAN   RWNEK   QOJQI   XANOU   OPAIO
```

In a Caesar cipher we apply the same shift to each letter in the plaintext message. We could complicate the situation a bit more by using more than one translation and applying them in some systematic fashion. In order to describe this method let's assign each letter of the alphabet the integers 1 through 26 respectively. So A will be 1, B will be 2 and so on. Select a word, say MATH, as the *key* for the cipher. Suppose the plaintext of the message is

THE TIME HAS COME.

To put this into a ciphertext (or to encipher it), we will add the key word letter by letter to the plaintext (repeating the key word as often as necessary) and reduce modulo 26. For example,

```
THE   TIME   HAS   COME   ⇐   Plaintext
MAT   HMAT   HMA   THMA   ⇐   Key
GIY   BVNY   PNT   WWZF   ⇐   Ciphertext
```

The ciphertext is formed as follows:

$$T + M = 20 + 13 = 33 \equiv 7 \pmod{26}$$

and since G is 7 we have that

$$T + M = G.$$

The ciphertext would likely be transmitted as

GIYBV NYPNT WWZF

so that the length of the individual words in the plaintext would not be given away by the ciphertext. Notice that every fourth letter of the plaintext is being translated by the same amount. That is, every fourth letter is being acted upon by the same Caesar cipher and, in total, four distinct Caesar ciphers are being combined here.

In order for two people to communicate using a Caesar cipher they must both know the key. If either party divulges it, the cipher scheme becomes useless. We would then say that the cipher scheme has been *compromised*. Of course, it may be possible for an opponent to break the scheme without either of the legitimate users giving away the key. An eavesdropping opponent might be able to deduce the key by simply looking at enough ciphertext. When the key has few letters in it this is quite likely, and hence, very long keys are needed. A further way to reduce this problem is to change the keys regularly. This poses problems for legitimate users since they must somehow have a mechanism to exchange very long keys securely.

The Caesar cipher is a special case of what is called a *substitution cipher*. To describe a substitution cipher we let $\mathcal{A}$ be the set of letters of the alphabet and we let

$$f : \mathcal{A} \longrightarrow \mathcal{A}$$

be a permutation on $\mathcal{A}$. If we associate the letters of the alphabet with the integers $1, 2, \ldots, 26$ (or to be more precise, the congruence classes $[1], [2], \ldots, [26]$) then the permutation describing the Caesar cipher is

$$f(x) \equiv x + 3 \pmod{26}.$$

There are 25 simple Caesar ciphers (plus one trivial one) and altogether 26! different permutations that could be used as substitution ciphers. One type of substitution cipher that makes use of some of the algebraic ideas developed earlier in the book is as follows. Suppose we select an integer a such that the GCD$(a, 26) = 1$. Then define

$$f(x) \equiv ax \pmod{26}.$$

It is not difficult to check that this function permutes the congruence classes of the integers modulo 26. We made use of this fact in the proof of Fermat's Little Theorem.

6.2 PRIVATE KEY CRYPTOGRAPHY

A *private key system* is a method for data encryption (and decryption) that requires the parties who communicate to share a common key. The substitution ciphers of the previous section are examples of private key systems. It may be useful to illustrate one more example of a private key system.

Let's assume that our data consists of binary strings; that is, sequences of 0's and 1's. This is how data is commonly represented in computers and telecommunication networks. Our method of encryption will be as follows.

A positive integer n is selected. A key will be a sequence of n 0's and 1's. Hence there will be 2^n possible keys. We will assume that the data to be encrypted is a sequence whose length is a multiple of n. (This is not a severe restriction since we can always pad out a data sequence by adding 0's to the end of it.) Partition the data sequence into blocks of length n. We will encipher each block of data by adding the key to each block of data term by term using addition modulo 2 so that the resulting ciphertext term is also a 0 or a 1. We illustrate this with an example.

6.2.1 Example. Encrypt the data sequence (or plaintext)

$$0\ 1\ 1\ 1\ 0\ 0\ 1\ 0\ 0\ 0\ 0\ 1\ 1\ 0\ 1\ 0\ 1\ 0\ 1\ 0\ 0$$

using blocks of length $n = 7$ and the key 1 0 1 1 0 1 1.

Solution. Partition the data sequence into the three sequences

$$M_1 = 0111001 \qquad M_2 = 0000110 \qquad M_3 = 1010100.$$

Add the key $K = 1011011$ to M_1, using addition modulo 2 (*not* addition of binary numbers), to get the ciphertext C_1 as follows:

$$
\begin{aligned}
M_1 &= 0111001 \\
K &= 1011011 \\
C_1 &= 1100010.
\end{aligned}
$$

Do the same for M_2 and M_3 to get the ciphertext 110001010111010001111. □

To decrypt the ciphertext we need only add the key to blocks of the ciphertext and the message is recovered.

In practice the number n would be selected to be much larger, for otherwise a cryptanalyst could simply try all possible keys and see which one gives a meaningful sequence. In the example above there would be only $2^7 = 128$ keys to try, which would be a very easy task for a computer to do.

Private key systems have advantages and disadvantages. One very practical advantage is that they can be designed and built to handle very large volumes of data very quickly. For example, some of the commercially successful private key schemes will handle in the range of 100 million bits (0's or 1's) per second. Perhaps the biggest disadvantage of these systems is the fact that two users of the scheme must somehow exchange a common key in a secure fashion before any data is encrypted. These keys should also be changed relatively often for other cryptographic reasons. To illustrate why this as a problem consider a network of 500 terminals, where each terminal may want to communicate with each other terminal in private, using a common private key scheme. Each pair of terminals should use a different key, which requires the exchange, in some secure way, of $\binom{500}{2} = \frac{(500)(499)}{2} = 124,750$ keys. If this exchange needs to be done once a day, or even once a month, then we have a major problem to overcome. In the next section we will show how to surmount this difficulty.

6.3 PUBLIC KEY CRYPTOGRAPHY

In 1976, a radically new idea was introduced into cryptography. Very simply, and in general terms, the idea was as follows. Suppose that we could find a method for data encryption and decryption where the key for encryption was different from the key for decryption, and that the knowledge of one of these keys would not allow one to find the other. Why is this of interest? To answer this, suppose that two people A and B wish to communicate in private, and that A has produced an encryption key k_1 and a decryption key k_2. A sends B the encryption key k_1. B can now encrypt data using this key k_1 and send it to A who decrypts it using the key k_2. An opponent might intercept the transmission of the key k_1 and hence would be able to send encrypted messages to A. However the point is that only A can decrypt them. If A wants to send messages to B, then B will also have to construct an encryption key ℓ_1 and a decryption key ℓ_2 and then send A the key ℓ_1. Hence we no longer care whether or not opponents intercept the encryption keys, and we might just as well make them public knowledge. Hence, the term *public key cryptosystem* has been used to describe this method. If it were possible to realize such a scheme then our problem of managing keys is greatly reduced. Referring back to our 500 terminal network, if each terminal (or user) produces a public encryption key and a private decryption key, then all the encryption keys can be placed in a central public file accessible to all members of the network. If terminal A wishes to communicate with another terminal B, then A simply looks up B's encryption key in the public file, encrypts the data and sends it to B. Only B knows the secret decrypting key, and hence only B can recover the original data. This has reduced the number of keys to be transmitted in the system from 124,750 to 500.

Conceptually, the idea of a public key system is very attractive, but is it possible to realize it? The answer is a resounding yes! Several ways to realize public key schemes give rise to what we consider are the most exciting applications of classical algebra to be developed in recent years.

6.4 THE RSA SCHEME

In 1977, shortly after the idea of a public key system was proposed, three mathematicians, Ron Rivest, Adi Shamir and Len Adleman, gave a concrete example as to how such a method could be realized. In honour of its discoverers the method is commonly referred to as the *RSA scheme*. We proceed to describe how it works.

We are going to think of our data as being integers. If our data is simply English text then we might let

$$\text{blank} \leftrightarrow 00, \quad \text{A} \leftrightarrow 01, \quad \text{B} \leftrightarrow 02, \quad \text{C} \leftrightarrow 03, \quad \ldots \quad \text{Z} \leftrightarrow 26$$

and a piece of text such as MATH would be thought of as the integer 13012008.

A user, called Ursula, who wishes to participate in the network must first produce two keys; one public key for encryption and one private key for decryption. To use the RSA scheme, Ursula begins by selecting two large prime numbers p and q, and then multiplies them together to obtain the integer $n = pq$. If we let $\phi(n) = (p-1)(q-1)$, then Ursula also selects an integer $e > 1$ such that $\text{GCD}(e, \phi(n)) = 1$. In practice this is relatively easy to do since a randomly selected e will have a fairly high probability of being coprime to $\phi(n)$, if n is large enough. This integer e will turn out to be part of the encryption key. Ursula now solves the linear Diophantine equation

$$ed \equiv 1 \pmod{\phi(n)}$$

for d. Recall from Theorem 2.5.4, that since $\text{GCD}(e, \phi(n)) = 1$, there is precisely one congruence class modulo $\phi(n)$ which satisfies this congruence and, hence, exactly one integer between 0 and $\phi(n)$ which satisfies it. Take d to be the integer in this range. Ursula now makes the integers e and n public knowledge and can destroy p and q, if she desires. (We will see a little later on that there may be reasons to keep p and q.) The pair of integers (e, n) is Ursula's *public key* that is used for encryption. The pair of integers (d, n) is her *private key* that she uses for decryption. She must keep d secret and not divulge it to anybody.

Now suppose that Sue is in the network and wants to send a message M to Ursula. Recall that messages are integers. We restrict our messages even further by requiring that they be in the range 0 to $n - 1$. This is not a severe restriction as the following example illustrates.

If $n = 12319$, and we want to send the message 'MATH' which is 13012008 then we would form two messages, one being 'MA' and the other 'TH' to get two integers 1301 and 2008 respectively, which have fewer than five digits. So in general we simply block off the digits of the entire message into messages which are smaller than n.

To encrypt the message M, the sender Sue looks up Ursula's public encryption key (e, n). Sue now exponentiates M to the power e to get M^e and divides by n to get a remainder C. This can be expressed as

$$M^e \;=\; qn + C \quad \text{where } 0 \le C < n$$

for some integer quotient q. In congruence notation this is

$$M^e \equiv C \pmod{n} \quad \text{where } 0 \le C < n.$$

The sender Sue takes C as the ciphertext to transmit to Ursula.

Decryption is the inverse of encryption. Ursula decrypts the received ciphertext C in the same way that Sue encrypted the message, except that Ursula uses her private key (d, n). Ursula computes C^d and divides it by n to get a remaider R. As above this can be expressed as

$$C^d \equiv R \pmod{n} \quad \text{where } 0 \le R < n.$$

We claim that this decrypted message R is the same as the original message M.

6.4.1 Theorem.   Let p and q be distinct primes, $n = pq$, and e and d positive integers such that $ed \equiv 1 \pmod{(p-1)(q-1)}$. If $0 \le M < n$ and

$$\begin{aligned} M^e &\equiv C \pmod{n} \\ C^d &\equiv R \pmod{n} \quad \text{where } 0 \le R < n \end{aligned}$$

then $R = M$.

Proof. The proof is a nice application of Fermat's Little Theorem 2.4.3 and the Chinese Remainder Theorem 2.6.1. Since $ed \equiv 1 \pmod{(p-1)(q-1)}$, there exists a positive integer k such that

$$ed = 1 + k(p-1)(q-1).$$

Therefore

$$
\begin{aligned}
R &\equiv C^d \pmod{n} \\
&\equiv (M^e)^d \pmod{n} \\
&\equiv M^{ed} \pmod{n} \\
&\equiv M^{1+k(p-1)(q-1)} \pmod{n} \\
&\equiv M M^{k(p-1)(q-1)} \pmod{n}.
\end{aligned}
$$

Since $p|n$, this congruence implies that

$$R \equiv M M^{k(p-1)(q-1)} \pmod{p}.$$

Now consider the two cases $p \nmid M$, and $p|M$.

Case 1. If $p \nmid M$, Fermat's Little Theorem 2.4.3 implies that

$$M^{p-1} \equiv 1 \pmod{p}.$$

Hence

$$M^{k(p-1)(q-1)} \equiv (M^{p-1})^{k(q-1)} \equiv 1^{k(q-1)} \equiv 1 \pmod{p}.$$

Multiplying both sides of this congruence by M gives

$$M M^{k(p-1)(q-1)} \equiv M \pmod{p}.$$

Case 2. If $p|M$ then $M \equiv 0 \pmod{p}$. Hence

$$
\begin{aligned}
M M^{k(p-1)(q-1)} &\equiv 0 \pmod{p} \\
M M^{k(p-1)(q-1)} &\equiv M \pmod{p}.
\end{aligned}
$$

In both Case 1 and Case 2 we have

$$R \equiv M M^{k(p-1)(q-1)} \equiv M \pmod{p}.$$

Since $q|n$, an analogous argument shows that

$$R \equiv M \pmod{q}.$$

We therefore have the two simultaneous congruences

$$
\begin{aligned}
R &\equiv M \pmod{p} \\
R &\equiv M \pmod{q}.
\end{aligned}
$$

Since p and q are distinct primes, $\text{GCD}(p, q) = 1$ and the Chinese Remainder Theorem 2.6.6 implies that the simultaneous congruences are equivalent to the congruence

$$R \;\equiv\; M \quad (\text{mod } n).$$

where $n = pq$. Now R and M are both integers between 0 and $n-1$ and are congruent modulo n; hence $R = M$. $\square$

Encryption, using the public key (e, n), can be considered as the function

$$f : \mathbb{Z}_n \longrightarrow \mathbb{Z}_n \quad \text{defined by} \quad f([M]) = [M^e]$$

and decryption, using the private key (d, n), can be considered as the function

$$g : \mathbb{Z}_n \longrightarrow \mathbb{Z}_n \quad \text{defined by} \quad g([C]) = [C^d].$$

The above theorem shows that f and g are inverse functions.

Note also, that if $n = pq$, where p and q are distinct primes, then $\phi(n) = (p-1)(q-1)$ is the Euler ϕ-function defined in Problem 105 of Chapter 1. The above theorem essentially includes a proof of the Euler-Fermat Theorem of Problem 77 of Chapter 2, namely

$$M^{\phi(n)} \;\equiv\; 1 \quad (\text{mod } n).$$

Let us summarize the RSA system described above.

SELECTING THE PUBLIC AND PRIVATE KEYS

1. Select large prime numbers p and q and form $n = pq$.

2. Select an integer $e > 1$ such that $\text{GCD}(e, (p-1)(q-1)) = 1$.

3. Solve the congruence

$$ed \equiv 1 \quad (\text{mod } (p-1)(q-1))$$

   for an integer d where $1 < d < (p-1)(q-1)$.

4. The public encryption key is (e, n).

5. The private decryption key is (d, n).

SENDING MESSAGES TO A USER

1. Look up the user's public key (e, n).

2. Make sure that the message M is an integer such that $0 \leq M < n$.

3. Compute

$$M^e \equiv C \pmod{n} \quad \text{where } 0 \leq C < n.$$

4. Transmit the integer C.

DECRYPTING RECEIVED MESSAGES

1. Use your private key (d, n).

2. Receive the integer C, where $0 \leq C < n$.

3. Compute
$$C^d \equiv R \pmod{n} \quad \text{where } 0 \leq R < n.$$

4. R is the original message.

6.4.2 Example. Find a set of keys in the RSA system using the primes $p = 631$ and $q = 409$.

Solution. The product is $n = pq = 258079$ and $\phi(n) = (p - 1)(q - 1) = 257040$. Selecting $e = 11$, we check that $\text{GCD}(e, \phi(n)) = 1$. Solving

$$11d \equiv 1 \pmod{257040}$$

gives $d = 163571$.

Hence the public key is the integer pair $(e, n) = (11, 258079)$ and the private key is the integer pair $(d, n) = (163571, 258079)$. $\qquad\square$

6.4.3 Example. Send the message 'MATHEMATICS' to the user with public key $(e, n) = (11, 258079)$, using the RSA system.

Solution. If we group the letters of the message in threes, then each group gives rise to an integer that is smaller than n and hence is suitable as a message block for the RSA system. In order that each block has three letters in it, we add a blank to the last block. The blocks and their associated integers are:

$$
\begin{aligned}
\texttt{MAT} &\longleftrightarrow 130120 = M_1 \\
\texttt{HEM} &\longleftrightarrow 080513 = M_2 \\
\texttt{ATI} &\longleftrightarrow 012009 = M_3 \\
\texttt{CS\_} &\longleftrightarrow 031900 = M_4
\end{aligned}
$$

We now encrypt the message blocks individually using the public key.

$$
\begin{aligned}
M_1^{11} &\equiv 042477 \pmod{258079} \\
M_2^{11} &\equiv 213941 \pmod{258079} \\
M_3^{11} &\equiv 195725 \pmod{258079} \\
M_4^{11} &\equiv 051122 \pmod{258079}.
\end{aligned}
$$

Hence the ciphertext is   042477   213941   195725   051122.   □

6.4.4 Example. Decrypt the ciphertext $C = 042477$ using the RSA system with the private key $(d, n) = (163571, 258079)$.

Solution. We have to compute $C^d \pmod{n}$. Using a computer algebra system such as Maple, we find

$$
C^d = 042477^{163571} \equiv 130120 \pmod{258079}.
$$

Hence the integer message must be 130120. This corresponds to the letters 'MAT' in the first block of the message from Example 6.4.3.

Later in this section we give an algorithm for exponentiation in $\mathbb{Z}_n$ using large exponents.   □

We claimed at the beginning of this section that the RSA system is a public key cryptosystem. We will be justified in saying this if we can be convinced that a knowledge of the public integers e and n does not reveal the integer d, that is used in the private key. An opponent knows the public key (e, n), so knows the integer n, that is the product of two large primes p and q. If it were possible to determine p and q from n, then it would be a simple matter to compute d from e. (After all Ursula was able to deduce d given e, p and q.)

The security of the RSA system relies on the fact that it is very difficult to factor a large integer into its prime factors. A factoring algorithm, such as the sieve of Eratosthenes given in Theorem 1.5.6, where we divide by all the primes up to $\sqrt{n}$, is hopelessly inadequate when the integer n is large.

In practice, the primes p and q are chosen to be about 100 decimal digits, so that n is about a 200 digit number. At present, nobody knows how to factor such a large number. Let us do a few calculations to get a feeling for the magnitude of the numbers involved.

Suppose that we are given $n = pq$, where p and q are both primes with about 100 decimal digits each, so that n is approximately 10^{200}. How long would the sieve of Eratosthenes take to factor n? There is a famous theorem, called the Prime Number Theorem, which gives a very good approximation to the number of prime numbers in the interval from 1 to x. It says that there are about $x/\log_e x$ primes in this interval. Hence there are about $\sqrt{n}/\log_e \sqrt{n}$ primes from 1 to $\sqrt{n}$. The sieve of Eratosthenes would require us to do about $\sqrt{n}/\log_e \sqrt{n}$ divisions to find the prime factors of n. If n is approximately 10^{200}, which we write as $n \approx 10^{200}$, then $\sqrt{n} \approx 10^{100}$, and the number of divisions is about $10^{100}/(100\log_e 10) \approx 0.4 \times 10^{98}$. There are less than 4×10^7 seconds in a year, so if we could do one billion divisions every second, we could do at most 4×10^{16} divisions per year of computing. Hence, it would take us more than 10^{81} years to factor n. Since the solar system is only expected to last another 10^{10} or so years, we can forget about this approach to factoring n.

There are better algorithms known for factoring integers than simply dividing by all primes less than $\sqrt{n}$. But when n is about 10^{200} these are still quite infeasible for finding the factors of n. The reason for choosing n as the product of two primes is that integers of this type are among the hardest to factor.

It is believed that as long as n cannot be factored, then it is impossible to find the private decrypting key d from a knowledge of n. Under this assumption, the RSA system is a public key scheme. The reason we say "believed" is that no proof of this fact has as yet been given. The problem has been studied by many outstanding mathematicians around the world.

Even though we cannot factor 200 digit numbers, there are methods for determining whether a 200 digit number is composite of not. There are also efficient methods for finding very large prime numbers. For example, in 1999, Nayan Hajratwala found a record new prime,

$$2^{6972593} - 1$$

with his PC. Such a prime of the form $2^p - 1$ is called a Mersenne Prime, and this largest known prime has over 2 million digits. Hajratwala was one of the 12,000 net users searching for large primes using free software from the Great Internet Mersenne Prime Search, a service run by George Woltman and Scott Kurowski.

In order for the RSA scheme be secure, the keys must be very large integers. This poses problems as far as computations are concerned. How can we compute M^e and M^d modulo n, when the numbers have 200 digits? Could you calculate 42477^{163571} or even 130120^{11}, modulo 258079, on your calculator? You could calculate M^{11} by computing $M, M^2, M^3, \ldots, M^{10}, M^{11}$ modulo n, but this would be impossible, even for a computer, if the exponent e had 200 digits.

It is possible to perform these exponentiations using the *square and multiply algorithm*. For example, suppose the exponent is $e = 331$. First find the binary representation of e as

$$e = (101001011)_2 = 2^8 + 2^6 + 2^3 + 2^1 + 2^0$$

Then, using the law of exponents, we have

$$M^e = M^{2^8} M^{2^6} M^{2^3} M^{2^1} M^{2^0}.$$

We can compute M, M^2, M^{2^2}, M^{2^3}, M^{2^4}, M^{2^5}, M^{2^6}, M^{2^7}, M^{2^8} (mod n) by successively squaring the previous term, since

$$M^{2^3} = M^8 = (M^4)^2, \quad M^{2^4} = M^{16} = (M^8)^2, \quad \ldots, M^{2^8} = (M^{2^7})^2.$$

We can then multiply the appropriate terms together to obtain M^e modulo n. For $e = 331$, this method would use 12 multiplications to compute M^{331} modulo n.

**THE SQUARE AND MULTIPLY ALGORITHM FOR
EXPONENTIATION**

1. To compute M^e modulo n for large e, first write e in binary as

$$e = (r_t \ldots r_2 r_1 r_0)_2 \quad \text{where each } r_i = 0 \text{ or } 1.$$

2. Compute M, M^2, M^4, M^8, ..., $M^{2^{t-1}}$, M^{2^t} (mod n) by squaring the previous term in the sequence.

3. Then multiply the appropriate terms together, modulo n, to obtain

$$M^e = \prod_{r_i=1} M^{2^i}.$$

Step 2 requires t modular multiplications and step 3 will take at most t modular multiplications. Therefore M^e can be computed in at most $2t$ modular multiplications, where $t = \log_2(e)$. For a 200 digit integer e this requires about 1400 multiplications. Computer chips have been designed and built to do precisely what we have described. It takes about 0.1 second to compute M^e modulo n, for $n \approx 10^{200}$.

6.4.5 Example.   Use the square and multiply algorithm to compute

$$130120^{11} \quad (\text{mod } 258079).$$

Solution.   The binary representation of the exponent is $11 = (1011)_2 = 8 + 2 + 1$. Hence $M^{11} = M^8 M^2 M$. Now calculate the powers of M. Since the modulus is

258079 and $258079^2 \approx 6.7 \times 10^{10}$, you can only do this on your calculator if it is accurate to 11 places.

$$
\begin{aligned}
M &\equiv 130120 \pmod{258079} \\
M^2 &\equiv 199684 \pmod{258079} \\
M^4 \equiv (M^2)^2 &\equiv 236277 \pmod{258079} \\
\equiv (M^4)^2 &\equiv 203765 \pmod{258079} \\
M^{11} &\equiv M^8 M^2 M \pmod{258079} \\
&\equiv M^8(4518) \pmod{258079} \\
&\equiv 42477 \pmod{258079}
\end{aligned}
$$

$\square$

At the beginning of this section we indicated that Ursula might not want to destroy the primes p and q. In our discussion above we did not use the primes p and q after the keys were selected. However p and q can be used to significantly speed up the decryption. To decrypt the ciphertext C, Ursula must compute $C^d \pmod{n}$. Since $n = pq$ and $\text{GCD}(p, q) = 1$, Ursula can compute the congruences

$$
\begin{aligned}
C^d &\pmod{p} \\
C^d &\pmod{q}
\end{aligned}
$$

and recombine them, using the Chinese Remainder Theorem, to obtain $C^d \pmod{pq}$. Note that this only works for decryption, because the person encrypting the message does not know the primes p and q, but only knows their product n.

6.4.6 Example.   Decrypt the second block, 213941, of the ciphertext sent in Example 6.4.3 by computing

$$213941^{163571} \pmod{258079}$$

using the Chinese Remainder Theorem.

Solution.   We know that $n = 258079$ factors as $n = pq = (631)(409)$, so we shall compute the exponential modulo 631 and 409 and then use the Chinese Remainder Theorem.

Now $213941 \equiv 32 \pmod{631}$. Since Fermat's Little Theorem 2.4.3 implies that $a^{630} \equiv 1 \pmod{631}$ and $a^{630+k} \equiv a^k \pmod{631}$, we only need to know the exponent modulo 630. Now $163571 \equiv 401 \pmod{630}$, so

$$
\begin{aligned}
213941^{163571} &\equiv 32^{401} \pmod{631} \\
&\equiv 376 \pmod{631}
\end{aligned}
$$

where the computation can be done by the square and multiply algorithm on any calculator.

Similarly, since $213941 \equiv 34 \pmod{409}$ and $163571 \equiv 371 \pmod{408}$,

$$213941^{163571} \equiv 34^{371} \pmod{409}$$
$$\equiv 349 \pmod{409}.$$

If $x = 213941^{163571}$ then

$$x \equiv 376 \pmod{631}$$
$$x \equiv 349 \pmod{409}.$$

The Chinese Remainder Theorem guarantees these congruences have a unique solution modulo n and it can be computed to be $x \equiv 080513 \pmod{258079}$. This is the second block of the original message corresponding to the letters 'HEM'. $\square$

Fermat's Little Theorem 2.4.3 can be used in conjunction with the square and multiply algorithm to test whether a large number is prime. Fermat's Little Theorem says that if p is prime and a is not divisible by p then $a^{p-1} \equiv 1 \pmod{p}$. Hence, if q were some number and you could show that $a^{q-1} \not\equiv 1 \pmod{q}$ for some particular a, then this would prove that q was not prime, even though you had no factorization of q.

For example, let us compute 2^{322} modulo 323. We have

$$2^8 \equiv 256, \qquad 2^{16} \equiv 256^2 \equiv 290, \qquad 2^{32} \equiv 290^2 \equiv 120,$$
$$2^{64} \equiv 120^2 \equiv 188, \qquad 2^{128} \equiv 188^2 \equiv 137, \qquad 2^{256} \equiv 137^2 \equiv 35 \pmod{323}.$$

Hence $\quad 2^{322} \equiv 2^{256} \cdot 2^{64} \cdot 2^2 \equiv 35 \cdot 188 \cdot 4 \equiv 157 \not\equiv 1 \pmod{323}$, and so we have shown that 323 is composite without factoring it. Note that $18^{322} \equiv 1 \pmod{323}$, but this tells us nothing about the primality of 323. There are a few composite numbers q for which $a^{q-1} \equiv 1 \pmod{q}$ for all a coprime to q.

One of the truly remarkable features of the public key system is its ability to allow a user to sign a message electronically by providing a *digital signature*. Suppose that Ursula is in a network and she wants to authorize her stockbroker Sue to buy 100000 shares of Dome Petroleum. Let u be Ursula's encryption function defined on strings of integers and based on her public key (e, n). Ursula is the only person who can compute the inverse function u^{-1} because it requires her private key (d, n). Let M represent the message to be sent. Ursula uses her private key to compute $u^{-1}(M)$ and transmits this to Sue. Sue knows that this is a transmission from Ursula, so she looks up Ursula's public key and computes $u(u^{-1}(M))$. If the result is not gibberish, then this proves that the message must have been sent by Ursula, since she is the only person who can produce u^{-1}.

Notice that under this scenario, the RSA scheme has not been used for secrecy. A person intercepting the message $u^{-1}(M)$ could look up u and compute $u(u^{-1}(M))$. If Ursula would like to send the message M privately, then she would use Sue's encryption function s, based on Sue's public key (e', n'). Ursula would send $C = s(u^{-1}(M))$ to Sue. Sue would then compute $u(s^{-1}(C)) = u(s^{-1}(s(u^{-1}(M))))$ to obtain M. Digital signatures are one of the most attractive features of this system.

Exercise Set 6

1. The following is known to be a simple substitution cipher. Break the code.

```
PCTPG  ANJHT  GDURG  NEIDV  GPEWN  LPHYJ  AXJHR  PTHPG
BTHHP  VTHHT  CIIDW  XHIGD  DEHLT  GTSXH  VJXHT  SQNIW
TUDAA  DLXCV  HXBEA  TBTIW  DS
```

2. The following is known to be a simple substitution cipher with a key length of 3. The following table may be of some help in cryptanalyzing the cipher. It gives the frequency distribution of letters in an English passage of 100,000 characters.

Letter	A	B	C	D	E	F	G	H	I	J	K	L	M
%	8.0	1.5	3.0	4.0	13.0	2.0	1.5	6.0	6.5	0.5	0.4	3.5	3.0

Letter	N	O	P	Q	R	S	T	U	V	W	X	Y	Z
%	7.0	8.0	2.0	0.2	6.5	6.0	9.0	3.0	1.0	1.5	0.5	2.0	0.2

```
VRMGX  LGKDQ  EZVYA  QVDGD  PGQMP  OZCVI  NQMDB  IKMWT
ZWNIV  QWQCV  MSEIV  SWPVQ  GCIVD  PGRMC  BBQPB  JOJTK
VERWH  WIVRM  OKBKM  AEKTN  OLEVI  UCQEK  TCVOG  LZCMT
CCAKM  INKTI  OJTKM  PMWOZ  IUCMU  WWUDW  HDPGK  TIOJT
KLKCK  QFMTO  LRBQQ  BBQDP  GXQPO  BGOVV  RKGXB  WBGCB
WWXLC  LWWDM  KQPVO  MPRCP  NZGNQ  VGIUZ  ZQFMF  DPCDI
RBMES  AGCWN  EBKYV  VYBJO  OGXMT  KTRYT  AXWOS  INOYW
KBKYV  YKAKW  XQCAK  LTGKV  FDPKC  EQBSN  OIFDW  VRMFO
DGVWR  WMPDW  HGPCD  QUUVQ  GVCCU  QNMTX  INQMD  BI
```

3 - 6. *For each of the following values of p, q and e, find the public key (e, n) and the associated private key (d, n).*

3. $p = 17$, $q = 19$, $e = 25$ 4. $p = 59$, $q = 67$, $e = 1003$
5. $p = 97$, $q = 107$, $e = 5$ 6. $p = 211$, $q = 241$, $e = 65$

7 - 10. *For each of the following public keys (e, n) determine the associated private key (d, n).*

7. $(e, n) = (5, 7663)$ 8. $(e, n) = (197, 6283)$
9. $(e, n) = (1277, 47083)$ 10. $(e, n) = (100937, 295927)$

11. Given $n = pq, p > q$ and $\phi(n) = (p - 1)(q - 1)$ prove that

$$p + q = n - \phi(n) + 1 \quad \text{and} \quad p - q = \sqrt{(p + q)^2 - 4n}.$$

12 - 15. *Each integer n is the product of two primes p and q and $\phi(n) = (p-1)(q-1)$. Determine the prime factors p and q.*

12. $n = 19837$, $\phi(n) = 19516$ 13. $n = 6887$, $\phi(n) = 6720$
14. $n = 71531$, $\phi(n) = 70992$ 15. $n = 2751121$, $\phi(n) = 2747700$

16. (a) Prove that the encryption function $f : \mathbb{Z}_n \to \mathbb{Z}_n$, for the RSA system defined by $f[x] = [x^e]$, is a bijection.

(b) Find the permutation of $\mathbb{Z}_{15}$ defined by the bijection $f : \mathbb{Z}_{15} \to \mathbb{Z}_{15}$ with $f[x] = [x^7]$.

17 - 20. Encrypt each message M using the public key (e, n).

17. $M = 47,\ (e, n) = (5, 119)$ **18.** $M = 10,\ (e, n) = (7, 143)$

19. $M = 2425,\ (e, n) = (17, 28459)$ **20.** $M = 21421,\ (e, n) = (13, 101617)$

21 - 24. Decrypt each received ciphertext C using the private key (d, n).

21. $C = 32,\ (d, n) = (77, 119)$ **22.** $C = 99,\ (d, n) = (103, 143)$

23. $C = 7415,\ (d, n) = (263, 13261)$ **24.** $C = 1701,\ (d, n) = (519, 2773)$

25 - 26. Find each congruence class by the square and multiply algorithm.

25. 873^{193} $(\mathrm{mod}\ 1000)$ **26.** 567^{81} $(\mathrm{mod}\ 1024)$

27 - 30. Encrypt each message M using the public key (e, n) and the square and multiply algorithm.

27. $M = 1240,\ (e, n) = (17, 4757)$ **28.** $M = 2041,\ (e, n) = (13, 3599)$

29. $M = 2607,\ (e, n) = (21, 12193)$ **30.** $M = 1425,\ (e, n) = (19, 12091)$

31 - 33. For each the exponent e, determine the number of modular multiplications to encrypt a message using the square and multiply algorithm.

31. $e = 92487$ **32.** $e = 1247683$

33. $e = 524289$ **34.** $e = 46321$

35 - 37. Use the Chinese Remainder Theorem to decrypt each received ciphertext C using the private key (d, n) where $n = pq$.

35. $C = 762,\ d = 899,\ p = 31,\ q = 37$

36. $C = 1120,\ d = 5051,\ p = 79,\ q = 131$

37. $C = 113261,\ d = 9809,\ p = 367,\ q = 401$

38. Let $(e, n) = (1837, 9379)$ be the public encryption keys for an RSA system and let $(d, n) = (5, 9379)$ be the corresponding private decryption key. Decode the following received message blocks, where the plaintext has been grouped into message blocks of two letters per block, using the equivalence A $\leftrightarrow$ 01, etc. You will find it useful to take advantage of the prime factorization of n as $83 \cdot 113$.

$$2485 \quad 1169 \quad 1981 \quad 2897$$

39. Let (e, n) be the public encryption keys for an RSA system. Suppose that it takes 10^{-4} seconds to do one modular multiplication and that the number of ones in the binary representation of e is 200. Determine the amount of time required to encrypt a message.

40. Anne has a public key $(e_A, n_A) = (7, 8453)$ and private key $(d_A, n_A) = (7087, 8453)$. Bill has public key $(e_B, n_B) = (1837, 9379)$ and private key $(d_B, n_B) = (5, 9379)$. Anne sends to Bill a signed message encrypted under Bill's public key. The ciphertext comes in two enciphered blocks.

$$5752 \quad 7155.$$

Find the message sent by Anne.

41. Suppose that Anne's encryption function is a based on the public key (e_A, n_A) and her decryption function is a^{-1} based on the private key (d_A, n_A). Bill's encryption function is b based on the public key (e_B, n_B) and his decryption function is b^{-1} based on the private key (d_B, n_B). Suppose also that Anne wants to send a digitally signed message M in private to Bill, by sending him $b(a^{-1}(M))$. Anne would first compute $M^{d_A} \equiv C \pmod{n_A}$ with $0 \leq C < n_A - 1$. Anne then computes $C^{e_B} \pmod{n_B}$ provided C is such that $0 \leq C < n_B - 1$. This will be true if $n_A < n_B$. If $n_A > n_B$, this may be false and complications arise. Describe several ways to overcome this problem.

Problem Set 6

42. Which elements are fixed under the function

$$f : \mathbb{Z}_{77} \to \mathbb{Z}_{77} \quad \text{defined by} \quad f[x] = [x^7] ?$$

That is, for which $[x] \in \mathbb{Z}_{77}$ is $f[x] = [x]$?

43. Two people A and B communicate using an RSA system for privacy. An opponent somehow knows that the messages being passed between the two are limited to a set of 100 messages. Describe a method by which the opponent can read the messages passing between A and B without ever having to factor n. Can you devise a way for A and B to alter their RSA system slightly so as to avoid such an attack?

44. Suppose that an opponent discovers a nonzero message M that is not relatively prime to the modulus $n = pq$ of an RSA system.

    (i) Show that the opponent can factor n and, hence, break the system.

    (ii) If the opponent selects a message at random, determine the probability that the message M is not relatively prime to n.

    (iii) If both p and q are larger than 10^{100} show that the probability in (ii) is less than 10^{-99}.

45. Select a prime number p and an integer k, $0 \leq k < p$. We would like to distribute some information to s people ($s < p$) so that if any two of the s people combine their information they can deduce the secret number k, but no person alone can do so. Select a polynomial $f(x) = ax + k \in \mathbb{Z}_p[x]$ with $a \neq 0$. Compute pairs $(i, f(i))$, $1 \leq i \leq s$, and distribute these to the s people. Prove that this scheme has the desired properties.

46. Select a prime number p and an integer k, $0 \leq k < p$. We would like to distribute some information to s people ($s < p$) so that if any three of the s people combine their information they can deduce the secret number k, but any fewer than three can not. Select a polynomial $f(x) = ax^2 + bx + k \in \mathbb{Z}_p[x]$ with $a \neq 0$. Compute pairs $(i, f(i))$, $1 \leq i \leq s$, and distribute these to the s people. Prove that this scheme has the desired properties.

47.   (i) Generalize the previous two problems so that any t of the s people have enough information to deduce a secret number k, but any fewer than t can not.

    (ii) Six people receive the information pairs $(1,10)$, $(2,6)$, $(3,1)$, $(4,1)$, $(5,1)$, $(6,7)$ generated in this way using $p = 11$. It is known that any four of the six have enough information to deduce the secret integer k. Find k.

48.   (i) Let $n = pq$, where p and q are primes. Prove that if $p - q$ is known then n can be factored. (Exercise 11 will help.)

    (ii) Describe a way to break an RSA system with modulus $n = pq$ if $p-q$ is not too large. (This problem illustrates an important point. When constructing an RSA system one must pick the primes so that their difference is large.)

49. Use the algorithm developed in the previous problem to break the RSA system having modulus $n = 26,850,099,599$.

50. Jane announces that her public RSA key pair is $(2743, 9797)$. Determine Jane's private key, and decode the message 3940 which is sent to her.

51. Compute 8^{132} and 9^{132} modulo 133. Do these calculations tell you anything about the primality of 133?

Chapter 7

Complex Numbers

We now come to the final extension of our number system. The real number system allowed us to find roots of any *positive* number. The complex number system will be constructed from the real numbers so as to contain the roots of *any* number, positive or negative. In fact, any polynomial equation of the form

$$a_n x^n + a_{n-1} x^{n-1} + \cdots + a_1 x + a_0 = 0$$

will have a solution in the complex numbers. This result is known as the Fundamental Theorem of Algebra.

Taking the positive integers, $\mathbb{P}$, as a starting point, our number system was built up by first introducing zero and the negative integers, to obtain all the integers $\mathbb{Z}$. Because of the inability to solve some equations of the form $ax = b$ in $\mathbb{Z}$, the integers were extended to the rational number system, $\mathbb{Q}$. Every linear equation can be solved in $\mathbb{Q}$, but many quadratic and higher order equations cannot. The real number system, $\mathbb{R}$, enabled us to solve equations of the form $x^n = a$ for positive a, and now the complex number system, $\mathbb{C}$, will allow us to solve such equations for negative a. Since any polynomial equation, even with complex coefficients, has a solution in the complex numbers, there will be no need, and no obvious way, to extend our number system any further.

7.1 QUADRATIC EQUATIONS

Before we construct the complex numbers, we shall derive the well known formula for solving quadratic equations with real coefficients.

7.1.1 Quadratic Formula. If $a, b, c \in \mathbb{R}, a \neq 0$ and $b^2 - 4ac \geq 0$ then the quadratic equation

$$ax^2 + bx + c = 0$$

165

has the solution

$$x = \frac{-b \pm \sqrt{b^2 - 4ac}}{2a}.$$

Proof.   Since $a \neq 0$ we can divide by it to obtain

$$x^2 + \frac{b}{a}x + \frac{c}{a} = 0.$$

Now *complete the square* in x; that is, add a constant to the terms containing x so that they become the square of a linear expression in x. We have

$$x^2 + \frac{b}{a}x + \left(\frac{b}{2a}\right)^2 - \left(\frac{b}{2a}\right)^2 + \frac{c}{a} = 0$$

$$\left(x + \frac{b}{2a}\right)^2 - \frac{b^2}{4a^2} + \frac{c}{a} = 0$$

$$\left(x + \frac{b}{2a}\right)^2 = \frac{b^2 - 4ac}{4a^2}.$$

If $b^2 - 4ac \geq 0$, the right hand side is positive and has a real square root. Hence

$$x + \frac{b}{2a} = \pm\sqrt{\frac{b^2 - 4ac}{4a^2}} = \pm\frac{\sqrt{b^2 - 4ac}}{2a}.$$

The solution to the quadratic is therefore

$$x = \frac{-b \pm \sqrt{b^2 - 4ac}}{2a}. \qquad \Box$$

If $b^2 - 4ac > 0$, then there are two distinct solutions to the quadratic equation. If $b^2 - 4ac = 0$ then there is just one solution. If $b^2 - 4ac < 0$ then there is no real solution.

However, if the complex numbers allow us to find square roots of negative numbers, then the above result shows that we will also be able to solve the quadratic equation when $b^2 - 4ac < 0$. In fact, the quadratic formula holds even if a, b and c are complex.

7.2   COMPLEX NUMBERS

We shall initially define a complex number as a pair of real numbers. This is rather analogous to our Definition 4.1.1 of a rational number as a pair of integers. However, in the case of complex numbers, we have no need to pass to any equivalence class.

After we have defined addition and multiplication and developed a few properties, we shall obtain a more convenient form for the expression of complex numbers.

7.2.1 Definition.   A *complex number* is an ordered pair of real numbers $z = (x, y) \in \mathbb{R} \times \mathbb{R}$. The set of all complex numbers is denoted by $\mathbb{C}$.

Addition and multiplication are defined by

$$(x_1, y_1) + (x_2, y_2) = (x_1 + x_2, y_1 + y_2)$$
$$(x_1, y_1) \cdot (x_2, y_2) = (x_1 x_2 - y_1 y_2, x_1 y_2 + x_2 y_1).$$

The subset $\tilde{\mathbb{R}} = \{(x, 0) \in \mathbb{C} \mid x \in \mathbb{R}\}$ of the complex numbers, consisting of pairs whose second element is zero, is in one-to-one correspondence with the set of real numbers $\mathbb{R}$; the element $(x, 0)$ in $\tilde{\mathbb{R}}$ corresponds to x in $\mathbb{R}$. Moreover, addition and multiplication in $\tilde{\mathbb{R}}$ are given by

$$(x_1, 0) + (x_2, 0) = (x_1 + x_2, 0)$$
$$(x_1, 0) \cdot (x_2, 0) = (x_1 x_2, 0)$$

which corresponds to the addition and multiplication in $\mathbb{R}$. This shows that the elements of $\tilde{\mathbb{R}}$ behave just like those of $\mathbb{R}$. We shall therefore identify the complex number $(x, 0)$ with the real number x. This means that $\mathbb{R} \subset \mathbb{C}$ and the complex number system is now an extension of the real number system.

Let us now look at the complex number $(0, 1)$. This is not a real number, because its second element is not zero. When we square this element, we obtain

$$(0, 1)^2 = (0, 1) \cdot (0, 1) = (-1, 0)$$

which is the real number -1. Hence $(0, 1)$ is one square root of -1; another square root of -1 is $(0, -1)$.

If a is any positive real number

$$(0, \sqrt{a})^2 = (-a, 0) = -a$$

and we have achieved our objective of extending the number system to include square roots of negative numbers.

Define the symbol i to be the complex number $(0, 1)$. That is, $i = (0, 1) \in \mathbb{C}$ and i has the property that $i^2 = -1$. Any complex number can be written in terms of real numbers and the complex number i as follows.

$$(x, y) = (x, 0) + (0, y) = (x, 0) + (0, 1) \cdot (y, 0)$$
$$= x + iy.$$

This is the most convenient way of writing a complex number. The set of all complex numbers can therefore be written as

$$\mathbb{C} = \{x + iy \mid x, y \in \mathbb{R}\}.$$

A complex number z will normally be written as

$$z \;=\; x + iy \qquad \text{where } x, y \in \mathbb{R}.$$

This is called the *standard form* for z. The number x is called the *real part* of z and the number y is called the *imaginary part* of z. For example, the real part of the complex number $5 - 4i$ is 5 while the imaginary part is -4. If the real part of a complex number is zero, then that complex number is called *purely imaginary*. For example, $0 + 2i = 2i$ is purely imaginary. The complex number $3 + 0i$, whose imaginary part is zero, is just the real number 3.

7.2.2 Addition and Multiplication of Complex Numbers.

$$
\begin{aligned}
(x_1 + iy_1) + (x_2 + iy_2) &= (x_1 + x_2) + i(y_1 + y_2) \\
(x_1 + iy_1) \cdot (x_2 + iy_2) &= (x_1 x_2 - y_1 y_2) + i(x_1 y_2 + x_2 y_1).
\end{aligned}
$$

These operations can be treated just as the usual addition and multiplication of algebraic expressions, where i is handled as an algebraic symbol with the property that whenever i^2 occurs, it is replaced by -1. For example,

$$
\begin{aligned}
(5 + 4i) + (3 + i) &= (5 + 3) + (4 + 1)i = 8 + 5i \\
(5 + 4i) \cdot (3 + i) &= 5 \cdot 3 + 4 \cdot 3i + 5 \cdot 1i + 4i^2 = 15 + 17i - 4 = 11 + 17i \\
(2 - 3i) \cdot \left(\frac{1}{2}i\right) &= i - \frac{3}{2}i^2 = \frac{3}{2} + i \\
(1 + i)^2 &= 1 + 2i + i^2 = 1 + 2i - 1 = 2i.
\end{aligned}
$$

7.2.3 Example.

Let $z = 4 + i$ and $w = -3 + 2i$ be complex numbers. Find (i) $z + w$, (ii) $z - w$, (iii) $z^2 w$, (iv) the real and imaginary parts of w^4.

Solution. (i). $z + w \;=\; (4 + i) + (-3 + 2i) \;=\; 1 + 3i.$

(ii). $z - w \;=\; (4 + i) - (-3 + 2i) \;=\; 7 - i.$

(iii).

$$
\begin{aligned}
z^2 w &= (4 + i)^2(-3 + 2i) = (16 + 8i + i^2)(-3 + 2i) \\
&= (15 + 8i)(-3 + 2i) = -45 - 24i + 30i + 16i^2 \\
&= -61 + 6i.
\end{aligned}
$$

(iv).

$$
\begin{aligned}
w^4 &= (-3 + 2i)^4 \\
&= (-3)^4 + 4(-3)^3(2i) + \frac{4 \cdot 3}{1 \cdot 2}(-3)^2(2i)^2 + 4(-3)(2i)^3 + (2i)^4 \\
&= 81 - 216i + 216i^2 - 96i^3 + 16i^4 = 81 - 216i - 216 + 96i + 16 \\
&= -119 - 120i.
\end{aligned}
$$

The real part of w^4 is therefore -119 and the imaginary part -120. $\square$

Notice in the above calculation that, since $i^2 = -1$.

$$i^4 \ = \ (i^2)^2 \ = \ (-1)^2 \ = \ +1.$$

In fact all the different powers of i are as follows.

7.2.4 Proposition.

$$i^n \ = \ \begin{cases} 1 & \text{if } n \equiv 0 \pmod 4 \\ i & \text{if } n \equiv 1 \pmod 4 \\ -1 & \text{if } n \equiv 2 \pmod 4 \\ -i & \text{if } n \equiv 3 \pmod 4 \end{cases}$$

Proof. We shall first show that $i^n = i^m$ if $n \equiv m \pmod 4$. If $m = n + 4k$ where $k \in \mathbb{Z}$ then

$$i^m \ = \ i^{n+4k} \ = \ i^n \cdot i^{4k} \ = \ i^n (i^4)^k \ = \ i^n \cdot i^k \ = \ i^n.$$

The result now follows because $i^0 = 1$, $i^1 = i$, $i^2 = -1$ and $i^3 = i \cdot i^2 = -i$. $\square$

7.2.5 Example. Calculate $(2 + i)^6$.

Solution. By the Binomial Theorem

$$\begin{aligned} (2+i)^6 \ &= \ 2^6 + 6 \cdot 2^5 i + \frac{6 \cdot 5}{1 \cdot 2} \cdot 2^4 i^2 + \frac{6 \cdot 5 \cdot 4}{1 \cdot 2 \cdot 3} \cdot 2^3 i^3 + \frac{6 \cdot 5}{1 \cdot 2} \cdot 2^2 i^4 + 6 \cdot 2 i^5 + i^6 \\ &= \ 64 + 192i - 240 - 160i + 60 + 12i - 1 \\ &= \ -117 + 44i. \end{aligned}$$

$\square$

The operations on complex numbers have the following properties we would expect of an addition and multiplication.

7.2.6 Proposition. Let $z, w, t \in \mathbb{C}$ and let $z = x + iy$ and $w = u + iv$ where $x, y, u, v \in \mathbb{R}$. Then

(i) $z = w$ if and only if $x = u$ and $y = v$; in other words two complex numbers are equal if and only if their real parts are equal and their imaginary parts are equal

(ii) $(z + w) + t = z + (w + t)$ (*Associativity of Addition*)

(iii) $z + w = w + z$ (*Commutativity of Addition*)

(iv) the number $0 = 0 + i0 \in \mathbb{C}$ is such that $0 + z = z$ (*Existence of a Zero*)

(v) the number $-z = -x - iy \in \mathbb{C}$ is such that $z + (-z) = 0$ (*Existence of Negatives*)

(vi) $(z \cdot w) \cdot t = z \cdot (w \cdot t)$ (*Associativity of Multiplication*)

(vii) $z \cdot w = w \cdot z$ (*Commutativity of Multiplication*)

(viii) the number $1 = 1 + i0 \in \mathbb{C}$ is such that $1 \cdot z = z$ (*Existence of a Unit*)

(ix) if $z \neq 0$, the element

$$z^{-1} = \frac{1}{z} = \frac{x - iy}{x^2 + y^2}$$

is the inverse of z and satisfies $z \cdot z^{-1} = 1$ (*Existence of Inverses*)

(x) $z \cdot (w + t) = z \cdot w + z \cdot t$ (*Distributive Law*)

Proof. *(i).*   The complex numbers $z = x + iy$ and $w = u + iv$ represent the ordered pairs (x, y) and (u, v) respectively. These two ordered pairs are equal if and only if their first elements are equal and their second elements are equal; that is $z = w$ if and only if $x = u$ and $y = v$.

(ii) - (x).   All these parts of the proposition can be proved by calculating each expression directly, using 7.2.2. We shall just perform this calculation for one of the parts and leave the remainder for the reader.

(ix).   The complex number $z = x + iy$ is zero if and only if $x = 0$ and $y = 0$. Hence, if $z \neq 0$ then either x or y is nonzero and $x^2 + y^2 > 0$. Therefore

$$\frac{x - iy}{x^2 + y^2} = \frac{x}{x^2 + y^2} - \frac{iy}{x^2 + y^2} \in \mathbb{C}$$

$$\left(\frac{x - iy}{x^2 + y^2} \right) (x + iy) = \frac{x^2 + xyi - xyi + y^2}{x^2 + y^2} = 1.$$

Hence the complex number $\dfrac{x - iy}{x^2 + y^2}$ is the inverse of $x + iy$. $\square$

The above properties (ii) - (x) show that the complex number system forms a *field*. Other examples of fields that we have encountered are $\mathbb{Q}$, $\mathbb{R}$ and $\mathbb{Z}_p$, when p is a prime.

One property of the real numbers that does not carry over to the complex numbers is the order relation, which is the ability to say that one number is bigger than another. If we could compare the sizes of complex numbers then either $i > 0$ or $i < 0$. However the properties of any ordering would imply that $i^2 > 0$, and so $-1 > 0$. This contradicts our order relation in $\mathbb{R}$, and shows that there is no order relation in $\mathbb{C}$. It is therefore nonsense to talk about inequalities of complex numbers. (However, we can talk about inequalities involving the real or imaginary parts of complex numbers and, as the next section will show, moduli of complex numbers. This is because, for any complex number, its real part, its imaginary part and its modulus are all real numbers.) The breakdown of the complex numbers into different subsets is illustrated in the following diagram.

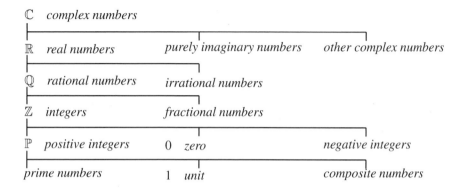

7.3 PROPERTIES OF COMPLEX NUMBERS

If $x + iy$ is any complex number then $(x + iy)(x - iy) = x^2 + y^2$, which is always a real number. This relationship is very useful in finding inverses of complex numbers.

7.3.1 Definition.   The *complex conjugate* of $z = x + iy$ is the complex number

$$\overline{z} \; = \; x - iy.$$

The *modulus* or *absolute value* of the complex number $z = x + iy$ is the nonnegative real number

$$|z| \; = \; \sqrt{x^2 + y^2}.$$

If z is the real number $x + i0$, then this modulus $|z| = \sqrt{x^2} = |x|$, the usual absolute value of the real number x.

The simplest way to calculate the inverse $1/z$ of any complex number is to multiply numerator and denominator by its conjugate $\overline{z}$. For example, the inverse of $4 + 5i$ is

$$\frac{1}{4 + 5i} \; = \; \frac{4 - 5i}{(4 + 5i)(4 - 5i)} \; = \; \frac{4 - 5i}{16 + 25} \; = \; \frac{4}{41} - \frac{5i}{41}.$$

The same method can be used to rid any denominator of complex numbers.

7.3.2 Example.   Calculate $\dfrac{5 + 6i}{(7 - i)(-i)}$.

Solution.

$$\frac{5+6i}{(7-i)(-i)} = \frac{5+6i}{-1-7i} = \frac{(5+6i)(-1+7i)}{(-1-7i)(-1+7i)} = \frac{-5+35i-6i+42i^2}{1+49}$$
$$= \frac{-47+29i}{50} = \frac{-47}{50} + \frac{29}{50}i. \qquad \square$$

7.3.3 Proposition.   If z and w are complex numbers, then

  (i) $\overline{z+w} = \overline{z} + \overline{w}$

  (ii) $\overline{zw} = \overline{z}\,\overline{w}$

  (iii) $\overline{\overline{z}} = z$

  (iv) $z\overline{z} = |z|^2$

  (v) $z + \overline{z}$ is twice the real part of z

  (vi) $z - \overline{z}$ is $2i$ times the imaginary part of z.

Proof.   Let $z = x + iy$ and $w = u + iv$, where $x, y, u, v \in \mathbb{R}$.

$$
\begin{array}{rll}
(i) \quad \overline{z+w} &= \overline{(x+u+i(y+v))} &= x+u-i(y+v) \\
&= x-iy+u-iv &= \overline{z}+\overline{w}. \\
(ii) \quad \overline{zw} &= \overline{(xu-yv+i(xv+yu))} &= xu-yv-i(xv+yu) \\
&= (x-iy)(u-iv) &= \overline{z}\,\overline{w}. \\
(iii) \quad \overline{\overline{z}} &= \overline{x-iy} = x+iy &= z. \\
(iv) \quad z\overline{z} &= (x+iy)(x-iy) = x^2+y^2 &= |z|^2. \\
(v) \quad z+\overline{z} &= x+iy+x-iy &= 2x. \\
(vi) \quad z-\overline{z} &= x+iy-(x-iy) &= 2iy.
\end{array}
$$

$\qquad \square$

7.3.4 Corollary.   If z is a nonzero complex number then $\dfrac{1}{z} = \dfrac{\overline{z}}{|z|^2}$.

Proof.   This follows directly from part (iv) of the preceding result. $\square$

7.3.5 Proposition.   If z and w are complex numbers, then

  (i) $|z| = 0$ if and only if $z = 0$

  (ii) $|\overline{z}| = |z|$

  (iii) $|zw| = |z||w|$

  (iv) $|z+w| \leq |z| + |w|$.   (*Triangle Inequality*)

Proof. Let $z = x + iy$ and $w = u + iv$, where $x, y, u, v \in \mathbb{R}$.

(i). $|z| = \sqrt{x^2 + y^2}$, which is zero if and only if $x^2 + y^2 = 0$. This happens if and only if $x = y = 0$.

(ii). $|\bar{z}| = |x - iy| = \sqrt{x^2 + (-y)^2} = \sqrt{x^2 + y^2} = |z|$.

(iii). By Proposition 7.3.3

$$|zw|^2 = (zw)(\overline{zw}) = zw\bar{z}\,\bar{w} = (z\bar{z})(w\bar{w}) = |z|^2|w|^2 = (|z||w|)^2$$

Since the modulus is a nonnegative real number it follows that $|zw| = |z||w|$.

(iv). By Proposition 7.3.3,

$$|z + w|^2 = (z + w)(\overline{z + w}) = (z + w)(\bar{z} + \bar{w}) = z\bar{z} + z\bar{w} + \bar{z}w + w\bar{w}$$
$$= |z|^2 + |w|^2 + (z\bar{w} + \bar{z}\,\bar{w}).$$

Hence $(|z| + |w|)^2 - |z + w|^2 = 2|z||w| - (z\bar{w} + \bar{z}\,\bar{w}) = 2|z\bar{w}| - (z\bar{w} + (\overline{z\bar{w}}))$. By Proposition 7.3.3(v), $z\bar{w} + (\overline{z\bar{w}})$ is twice the real part of $z\bar{w}$ and this is always less than or equal to twice the modulus of $z\bar{w}$. Therefore

$$(|z| + |w|)^2 \geq |z + w|^2$$

and, since the moduli are nonnegative real numbers,

$$|z| + |w| \geq |z + w|. \qquad \square$$

The modulus provides a crude method for comparing sizes of complex numbers. But note that many different complex numbers have the same modulus. For example,

$$1 = |1| = |-1| = |i| = |-i| = \left|\frac{1}{\sqrt{2}} + \frac{i}{\sqrt{2}}\right| = \left|\frac{1}{2} - \frac{\sqrt{3}i}{2}\right|.$$

The Quadratic Formula 7.1.1 solves the quadratic equation

$$ax^2 + bx + c = 0$$

with real coefficients, when $b^2 - 4ac \geq 0$. If $b^2 - 4ac < 0$, put $b^2 - 4ac = -d$ where $d > 0$, then $i\sqrt{d}$ and $-i\sqrt{d}$ are both complex numbers whose square is $b^2 - 4ac$. The Quadratic Formula can still be used to yield the two complex solutions

$$x = \frac{-b + \sqrt{b^2 - 4ac}}{2a} = \frac{-b \pm i\sqrt{d}}{2a}$$
$$= \frac{-b}{2a} + \frac{i\sqrt{d}}{2a} \quad \text{or} \quad \frac{-b}{2a} - \frac{i\sqrt{d}}{2a}.$$

Notice that these two solutions are complex conjugates of each other.

Hence, if $a, b, c \in \mathbb{R}$, the quadratic equation

$$ax^2 + bx + c \;=\; 0$$

has the following types of solutions depending on the value of the *discriminant* $\Delta = b^2 - 4ac$.

- If $\Delta > 0$, there are two real and distinct solutions.
- If $\Delta = 0$, there is one real solution.
- If $\Delta < 0$, there are two complex conjugate solutions.

7.3.6 Example.   Solve the equation $2x^2 - 3x + 5 = 0$ for $x \in \mathbb{C}$.

Solution.   By the Quadratic Formula we have

$$x \;=\; \frac{3 \pm \sqrt{9 - 40}}{4} \;=\; \frac{3 \pm \sqrt{-31}}{4} \;=\; \frac{3 \pm i\sqrt{31}}{4}. \qquad \square$$

7.3.7 Example.   Solve the equation $x^2 = -1$.

Solution.   We can either solve this by the Quadratic Formula to obtain

$$x \;=\; \pm\sqrt{-1} \;=\; \pm i$$

or we can factor $x^2 + 1$ as $(x + i)(x - i)$ and obtain the same solutions. $\qquad \square$

7.4   THE ARGAND DIAGRAM

The real numbers have a geometric representation as points of a number line. We shall now give a geometric interpretation of the complex numbers, and of its various operations such as addition and multiplication.

Recall that complex numbers were initially defined as ordered pairs of real numbers; in other words, as elements of $\mathbb{R}^2 = \mathbb{R} \times \mathbb{R}$. The points of $\mathbb{R}^2$ can naturally be interpreted as points of a plane. This allows us to associate to each complex number a point on a plane.

Choose rectangular coordinates in the plane and label one axis the *real axis* and the other the *imaginary axis*. The geometric representation of the complex number $z = x + iy$ is the point (x, y) in the plane, whose coordinate along the real axis is the real part of z and whose coordinate along the imaginary axis is the imaginary part of z.

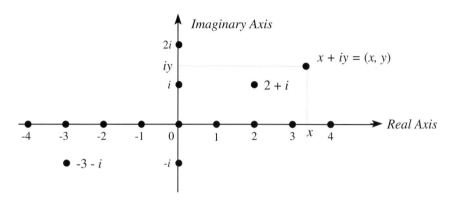

This defines a one-to-one correspondence between the complex numbers, $\mathbb{C}$, and the plane. Such a representation is called an *Argand diagram* or a *complex plane*.

The points on the real axis correspond to all the real numbers $x + 0i$. Hence the real axis is a copy of the usual real number line. The points on the imaginary axis correspond to the purely imaginary numbers $0 + iy$.

If $z = x + iy$ and $w = v + iv$ are two complex numbers, their sum is the complex number

$$z + w = (x + u) + i(y + v).$$

In the Argand diagram, the point $z + w$ corresponds to the fourth vertex of the parallelogram, whose other vertices are the points $z, 0$ and w.

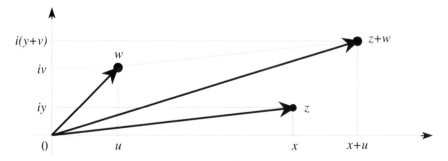

This addition is precisely the 'parallelogram law of addition' for vectors. Because of this equivalence with vectors, we sometimes draw a directed arrow from the origin 0 to the point corresponding to a complex number. The vector $z + w$ is the diagonal of the parallelogram $z, 0, w, z + w$.

The modulus $|z| = \sqrt{x^2 + y^2}$ of a complex number $z = x + iy$ is just the distance of the point z from the origin in the Argand diagram. This is the length of the vector from 0 to z. The distance from the point w to z is $|z - w|$.

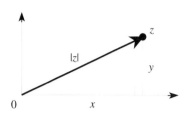
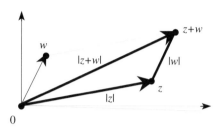

The Triangle Inequality in Proposition 7.3.5(iv)

$$|z + w| \leq |z| + |w|$$

now has a simple geometric interpretation. In the parallelogram $z, 0, w, z + w$, the distance from 0 to w is $|w|$ and this is the same as the distance from z to $z + w$. Hence, the sides of the triangle with vertices $z, 0$ and $z + w$ have lengths $|z|, |z + w|$ and $|w|$. The inequality $|z + w| \leq |z| + |w|$ expresses the fact that the length of one side of a triangle cannot exceed the sum of the lengths of the other two sides.

7.4.1 Example.   When does the equality $|z + w| = |z| + |w|$ hold?

Solution.   From the above discussion of the triangle $z, 0, z+w$ in the Argand diagram, it follows that $|z + w| = |z| + |w|$ if and only if z lies on the line segment from 0 to $z + w$ (and lies between 0 and $z + w$). This happens if and only if the parallelogram $z, 0, w, z + w$ collapses and w and z lie on a line through the origin and are both on the same side of the origin. Hence either w or z is zero or there exists a positive real number k such that $w = kz$.

Therefore

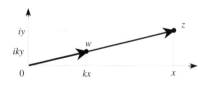

$$|z + w| = |z| + |w|$$

if and only if $z = 0$ or $w = 0$ or $w = kz$ for some positive real number k. □

7.4.2 Example.   Sketch the points in the Argand diagram that have modulus 1.

Solution.   If $z = x + iy$ and $|z| = 1$ then $\sqrt{x^2 + y^2} = 1$ and $x^2 + y^2 = 1$. Therefore all the points with modulus 1 lie on a circle radius 1 and centre the origin. This shows that there are an infinite number of points with modulus 1; among them are the points $1, -1, i, -i, \frac{1}{\sqrt{2}} + \frac{i}{\sqrt{2}}$ and $\frac{1}{2} - \frac{\sqrt{3}i}{2}$.

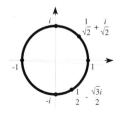

In the Argand diagram, the complex conjugate, $\overline{z} = x - iy$, is just the reflection of the number $z = x + iy$ in the real axis.

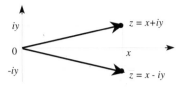

7.4.3 Example.
If $z = 2 + i$, plot the points z, $\overline{z}$ and iz in the Argand diagram.

Solution. If $z = 2 + i$ then

$$\overline{z} = 2 - i$$

and

$$iz = 2i + i^2$$
$$= -1 + 2i.$$

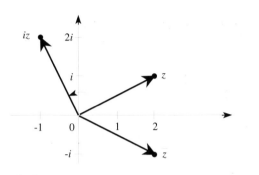

It should be noted that multiplication by i has the effect of rotating the complex number counter clockwise through an angle $\pi/2$. This fact is true for all complex numbers, because if $z = x + iy$ then $iz = -y + ix$, and the fact that z and iz are at right angles can be seen from the diagram. However, to interpret multiplication of complex numbers in general, we shall need to represent points in the Argand diagram by polar coordinates.

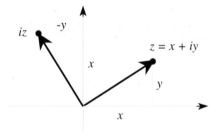

7.5 POLAR REPRESENTATION

The pair of real numbers (x, y), in the rectangular *Cartesian coordinate system system*, corresponds to the point P in the plane, where the projection of OP onto the two axes are x and y. The *polar coordinate system* is another way of associating to each point in the plane, a pair of real numbers. To form the polar coordinate system, we start with the origin 0 and take the x-axis as polar axis. A point P has polar coordinates (r, θ) if r is the distance from 0 to P and θ is the angle, in radians measured counterclockwise, between the polar axis and the line OP.

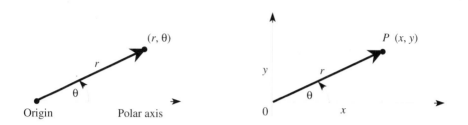

For example, the point with Cartesian coordinates $(1,1)$ has polar coordinates $(\sqrt{2}, \pi/4)$. The point with Cartesian coordinates $(-3,0)$ has polar coordinates $(3, \pi)$.

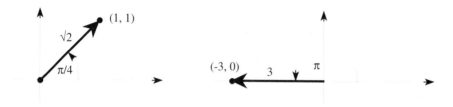

If (r, θ) are the polar coordinates of a point, then r is always a positive or zero real number, while θ can be any real number, positive or negative (a negative angle is measured clockwise). However, unlike the Cartesian coordinate system, there is not a one-to-one correspondence between polar coordinates and the points in the plane. For example, the point with polar coordinates $(\sqrt{2}, \pi/4)$ is also represented by the polar coordinates $(\sqrt{2}, 9\pi/4)$ and by $(\sqrt{2}, -7\pi/4)$.

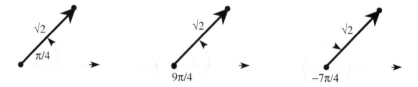

We can always add any integer multiple of 2π to an angle. Hence (r, θ) and $(r, \theta + 2k\pi)$ always represent the same point for all $k \in \mathbb{Z}$. Furthermore, the polar coordinates $(0, \theta)$ represent the origin for all real values of the angle θ.

By applying trigonometry to the right-angled triangle in the accompanying diagram, we can convert the polar coordinates (r, θ) into the Cartesian coordinates (x, y) by means of the following relations.

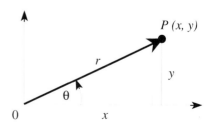

7.5.1 Convert from Polar to Cartesian Coordinates.

$$x = r \cos \theta$$
$$y = r \sin \theta$$

Conversely, a point whose Cartesian coordinates are (x, y) has the polar coordinates (r, θ) where

$$r = \sqrt{x^2 + y^2}$$

and θ is an angle such that

$$\cos \theta = \frac{x}{r}, \quad \sin \theta = \frac{y}{r} \quad \text{and} \quad \tan \theta = \frac{y}{x}.$$

If $r = 0$ then θ can be any angle. There is a slight complication in finding the exact angle θ; it is either $\text{Tan}^{-1}(y/x)$ or $\pi + \text{Tan}^{-1}(y/x)$, depending on the signs of x and y. The safest way to find the angle is to plot the required point in a diagram to see which quadrant it lies in. Then θ can be found once $\text{Tan}^{-1}(y/x)$ or $\text{Sin}^{-1}(y/r)$ is known.

Let $z = x + iy$ be any complex number and let (r, θ) be the polar coordinates of the point whose Cartesian coordinates are (x, y). Then the complex number z can be written in the form $z = r \cos \theta + ir \sin \theta$.

7.5.2 Definition.   The *polar form* of the complex number z is

$$z = r(\cos \theta + i \sin \theta).$$

The real number r is just the modulus of the complex number z. The angle θ is called the *argument* or *amplitude* of z. The expression $\cos \theta + i \sin \theta$ is often abbreviated to cis θ, so that the polar form becomes $z = r$ cis θ.

7.5.3 Example.   Convert the complex numbers i, $-1 + i$, $\sqrt{3} - 3i$ and -4 to polar form.

Solution.   Since $|i| = 1$ and the argument of i is $\frac{\pi}{2}$ it follows that the polar form is

$$i = 1\left(\cos \frac{\pi}{2} + i \sin \frac{\pi}{2}\right).$$

Now $|-1 + i| = \sqrt{1^2 + 1^2} = \sqrt{2}$ and it is seen from the diagram that the argument of $-1 + i$ is $\frac{3\pi}{4}$. Hence

$$-1 + i = \sqrt{2}\left(\cos \frac{3\pi}{4} + i \sin \frac{3\pi}{4}\right).$$

We have $|\sqrt{3} - 3i| = \sqrt{3 + 9} = \sqrt{12} = 2\sqrt{3}$. If θ is the argument of $\sqrt{3} - 3i$, then $\sin \theta = \frac{-3}{2\sqrt{3}} = -\frac{\sqrt{3}}{2}$. It is well known that $\text{Sin}^{-1} \frac{\sqrt{3}}{2} = \frac{\pi}{3}$ (see the Appendix if it is not well known to you) and hence it follows from the diagram that $\theta = -\frac{\pi}{3}$ or $\frac{5\pi}{3}$. Therefore

$$\sqrt{3} - 3i = \sqrt{3}\left(\cos\frac{5\pi}{3} + i\sin\frac{5\pi}{3}\right).$$

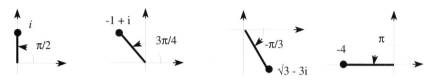

Since $|-4| = 4$ and the argument of -4 is π,

$$-4 = 4(\cos\pi + i\sin\pi). \qquad \square$$

One reason for converting complex numbers into polar form is that multiplication then takes on a rather elementary form.

7.5.4 Theorem.   If $z_1 = r_1(\cos\theta_1 + i\sin\theta_1)$ and $z_2 = r_2(\cos\theta_2 + i\sin\theta_2)$ are two complex numbers in polar form, then

$$z_1 z_1 = r_1 r_2[\cos(\theta_1 + \theta_2) + i\sin(\theta_1 + \theta_2)].$$

Proof.
$$\begin{aligned}
z_1 z_2 &= r_1(\cos\theta_1 + i\sin\theta_1) \cdot r_2(\cos\theta_2 + i\sin\theta_2) \\
&= r_1 r_2[\cos\theta_1\cos\theta_2 - \sin\theta_1\sin\theta_2 + i(\cos\theta_1\sin\theta_2 + \sin\theta_1\cos\theta_2)] \\
&= r_1 r_2[\cos(\theta_1 + \theta_2) + i\sin(\theta_1 + \theta_2)]
\end{aligned}$$

using the formulas for the sine and cosine of the sum of two angles. $\square$

Hence, to multiply two complex numbers, we multiply their moduli and *add* their arguments.

If the complex number z has modulus 1 and argument θ then multiplication by z corresponds to a rotation through an angle θ. In particular, multiplication by i corresponds to a rotation through an angle $\frac{\pi}{2}$.

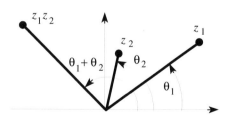

7.5.5 Example.   Multiply the complex number $z_1 = 2\left(\cos\frac{\pi}{4} + i\sin\frac{\pi}{4}\right)$ by the complex number $z_2 = \frac{1}{\sqrt{2}}\left(\cos\frac{7\pi}{6} + i\sin\frac{7\pi}{6}\right)$.

Solution.

$$z_1 z_2 = 2 \cdot \frac{1}{\sqrt{2}} \left[\cos \left(\frac{\pi}{4} + \frac{7\pi}{6} \right) + i \sin \left(\frac{\pi}{4} + \frac{7\pi}{6} \right) \right]$$

$$= \sqrt{2} \left(\cos \frac{17\pi}{12} + i \sin \frac{17\pi}{12} \right).$$ $\square$

7.6 DE MOIVRE'S THEOREM

The previous section showed that the result of multiplying two complex numbers of unit modulus together, is another number of unit modulus, whose argument is the sum of their arguments. By repeatedly applying this result we obtain the following important theorem.

7.6.1 De Moivre's Theorem. For any real number θ and any integer n,

$$(\cos \theta + i \sin \theta)^n = \cos n\theta + i \sin n\theta.$$

Proof. We shall prove the three cases (i) $n > 0$, (ii) $n = 0$ and (iii) $n < 0$, separately.

(i). We shall use induction to prove the result when $n > 0$.
  If $n = 1$, the result is clearly true.
  Now suppose that the result is true for $n = k$, where $k \in \mathbb{P}$. Then

$$\begin{aligned}
(\cos \theta + i \sin \theta)^{k+1} &= (\cos \theta + i \sin \theta)^k (\cos \theta + i \sin \theta) \\
&= (\cos k\theta + i \sin k\theta)(\cos \theta + i \sin \theta) \\
&= \cos(k+1)\theta + i \sin(k+1)\theta, \quad \text{by Theorem 7.5.4.}
\end{aligned}$$

Hence the result is true for $n = k + 1$, if it is true for $n = k$. It follows from Mathematical Induction that the theorem is true for all $n \in \mathbb{P}$.

(ii). If $n = 0$, $(\cos \theta + i \sin \theta)^0 = 1$, by the standard convention that $z^0 = 1$ for every nonzero number z. Note that $\cos \theta + i \sin \theta$ cannot be zero, because it always has modulus 1. Hence the result is true if $n = 0$ since

$$\cos 0\theta + i \sin 0\theta = 1 + i0 = 1.$$

(iii). Suppose that n is a negative integer, say $n = -m$ where $m \in \mathbb{P}$. Then

$$\begin{aligned}
(\cos \theta + i \sin \theta)^n &= (\cos \theta + i \sin \theta)^{-m} \\
&= \frac{1}{(\cos \theta + i \sin \theta)^m} \\
&= \frac{1}{(\cos m\theta + i \sin m\theta)}, \quad \text{by part (i)}
\end{aligned}$$

$$
\begin{aligned}
&= \quad \cos m\theta - i \sin m\theta, \qquad \text{by Corollary 7.3.4}\\
&= \quad \cos(-m\theta) + i \sin(-m\theta)\\
&= \quad \cos n\theta + i \sin n\theta.
\end{aligned}
$$

$\Box$

7.6.2 Corollary.   If $z = r(\cos \theta + i \sin \theta)$ then, for any integer n,

$$
z^n \;=\; r^n(\cos n\theta + i \sin n\theta).
$$

Proof.   This follows immediately from the previous theorem. $\Box$

7.6.3 Example.   Calculate $(\sqrt{3} + i)^{11}$.

Solution.   We could expand this by the Binomial Theorem. However it is easier to convert the number to polar form and use De Moivre's Theorem.

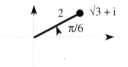   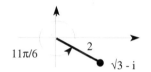

We have

$$
\sqrt{3} + i \;=\; 2\left(\cos \frac{\pi}{6} + i \sin \frac{\pi}{6}\right)
$$

and so

$$
\begin{aligned}
(\sqrt{3} + 1)^{11} &\;=\; 2^{11}\left(\cos \frac{11\pi}{6} + i \sin \frac{11\pi}{6}\right)\\
&\;=\; 2^{11}(\sqrt{3} - i)/2\\
&\;=\; 1024\sqrt{3} - 1024i.
\end{aligned}
$$

$\Box$

7.6.4 Example.   Show that

$$
\begin{aligned}
\cos 3\theta &= 4\cos^3 \theta - 3\cos \theta\\
\sin 3\theta &= 3\sin \theta - 4\sin^3 \theta.
\end{aligned}
$$

Solution.   By De Moivre's Theorem

$$
\cos 3\theta + i \sin 3\theta \;=\; (\cos \theta + i \sin \theta)^3
$$

and by the Binomial Theorem

$$
(\cos \theta + i \sin \theta)^3 \;=\; \cos^3 \theta + 3i \cos^2 \theta \sin \theta - 3 \cos \theta \sin^2 \theta - i \sin^3 \theta.
$$

Hence

$$\cos 3\theta + i \sin 3\theta = \cos^3 \theta - 3 \cos \theta \sin^2 \theta + i(3 \cos^2 \theta \sin \theta - \sin^3 \theta)$$

and, by Proposition 7.2.6(i), two complex numbers are equal if and only if their real parts are equal and their imaginary parts are equal. Therefore, equating real parts we have

$$\cos 3\theta = \cos^3 \theta - 3 \cos \theta \sin^2 \theta$$

and equating imaginary parts we have

$$\sin 3\theta = 3 \cos^2 \theta \sin \theta - \sin^3 \theta.$$

By using the relation $\sin^2 \theta + \cos^2 \theta = 1$, which is true for all θ, we obtain

$$\cos 3\theta = \cos^3 \theta - 3 \cos \theta (1 - \cos^2 \theta) = 4 \cos^3 \theta - 3 \cos \theta$$
$$\sin 3\theta = 3(1 - \sin^2 \theta) \sin \theta - \sin^3 \theta = 3 \sin \theta - 4 \sin^3 \theta. \qquad \square$$

The multiplication of complex numbers of unit modulus by adding their arguments is reminiscent of the multiplication of powers by adding their exponents. This can be utilized in the following way. A knowledge of elementary calculus will show that the real exponential function $y = e^{kx}$ is a solution to the differential equation $\frac{dy}{dx} = ky$ with the initial condition that $y = 1$ when $x = 0$. Assuming that we can differentiate complex functions by differentiating their real and imaginary parts, we have

$$\frac{d}{d\theta}(\cos \theta + i \sin \theta) = -\sin \theta + i \cos \theta = i(\cos \theta + i \sin \theta)$$

and $\cos \theta + i \sin \theta = 1$ when $\theta = 0$. Hence it is plausible to define the *complex exponential function* by

$$e^{i\theta} = \cos \theta + i \sin \theta.$$

This complex exponential obeys the usual laws of exponents because

$$e^{i\theta} \cdot e^{i\phi} = e^{i(\theta+\phi)} \qquad \text{by Theorem 7.5.4}$$
$$(e^{i\theta})^n = e^{in\theta} \qquad \text{by De Moivre's Theorem.}$$

The polar form of a complex number z can now be written as

$$z = re^{i\theta}$$

where $r = |z|$ and θ is the argument of z.

Since $e^{i\pi} = \cos \pi + i \sin \pi = -1 + i0$, we obtain the famous equation due to Euler that connects the numbers π, e, i, 1 and 0, namely

$$e^{i\pi} + 1 = 0.$$

We have so far only defined the complex exponential function with purely imaginary exponents. However, if $z = x + iy$ we can define

$$e^z \;=\; e^{x+iy} \;=\; e^x \cdot e^{iy} \;=\; e^x(\cos y + i \sin y)$$

The equation $e^{i\theta} = \cos\theta + i\sin\theta$ expresses the exponential function in terms of trigonometric functions. We can use this to express the trigonometric functions in terms of exponential functions as follows. Since

$$e^{-i\theta} \;=\; \cos(-\theta) + i\sin(-\theta) \;=\; \cos\theta - i\sin\theta$$

by adding and subtracting the equations

$$\begin{aligned}
e^{i\theta} &= \cos\theta + i\sin\theta \\
e^{-i\theta} &= \cos\theta - i\sin\theta
\end{aligned}$$

we obtain the formula for the cosine

$$\cos\theta \;=\; \frac{e^{i\theta} + e^{-i\theta}}{2}$$

and for the sine

$$\sin\theta \;=\; \frac{e^{i\theta} - e^{-i\theta}}{2i}.$$

7.7   ROOTS OF COMPLEX NUMBERS

Our reason for introducing complex numbers was to be able to find the roots of any number. We have already shown that complex numbers can be used to find the square roots of any negative real number. Using De Moivre's Theorem, we shall now show how to find the nth roots of any number, positive, negative or complex; in other words, we will show how to solve the equation

$$z^n \;=\; a \quad \text{for any } a \in \mathbb{C}.$$

7.7.1 Example.   Find all the complex fourth roots of -16.

Solution.   We have to solve the equation $z^4 = -16$. Let $z = r(\cos\theta + i\sin\theta)$ so that $z^4 = r^4(\cos 4\theta + i\sin 4\theta)$. In polar form, $-16 = 16(\cos\pi + i\sin\pi)$. Hence, if $z^4 = -16$ then

$$r^4(\cos 4\theta + i\sin 4\theta) \;=\; 16(\cos\pi + i\sin\pi).$$

This equation is an equality between two complex numbers. Therefore their moduli must be equal and their arguments must define the same angle. Hence $r^4 = 16$ and, since the modulus is a nonnegative real number, $r = 2$. The arguments 4θ and π will define the same angle if and only if they differ by an integer multiple of 2π. Therefore

$$4\theta = \pi + 2k\pi \qquad \text{where } k \in \mathbb{Z}$$
$$\theta = \frac{\pi}{4} + k\frac{\pi}{2}.$$

The solutions to the equation $z^4 = -16$ are

$$z = 2\left[\cos\left(\frac{\pi}{4} + k\frac{\pi}{2}\right) + i\sin\left(\frac{\pi}{4} + k\frac{\pi}{2}\right)\right] \qquad \text{where } k \in \mathbb{Z}.$$

When $k = 0$, this gives $z = 2(\cos\frac{\pi}{4} + i\sin\frac{\pi}{4}) = 2(\frac{1}{\sqrt{2}} + \frac{i}{\sqrt{2}}) = \sqrt{2} + i\sqrt{2}$.

When $k = 1$, $z = 2(\cos\frac{3\pi}{4} + i\sin\frac{3\pi}{4}) = 2(\frac{-1}{\sqrt{2}} + \frac{i}{\sqrt{2}}) = -\sqrt{2} + i\sqrt{2}$.

When $k = 2$, $z = 2(\cos\frac{5\pi}{4} + i\sin\frac{5\pi}{4}) = 2(\frac{-1}{\sqrt{2}} - \frac{i}{\sqrt{2}}) = -\sqrt{2} - i\sqrt{2}$.

When $k = 3$, $z = 2(\cos\frac{7\pi}{4} + i\sin\frac{7\pi}{4}) = 2(\frac{1}{\sqrt{2}} - \frac{i}{\sqrt{2}}) = \sqrt{2} - i\sqrt{2}$.

When $k = 4$, $z = 2(\cos\frac{9\pi}{4} + i\sin\frac{9\pi}{4}) = 2(\cos\frac{\pi}{4} + i\sin\frac{\pi}{4})$ and this gives the same value as was obtained by putting $k = 0$.

In fact, there are only four different fourth roots because $(\frac{\pi}{4} + k\frac{\pi}{2})$ and $(\frac{\pi}{4} + \ell\frac{\pi}{2})$ define the same angle if

$$k \equiv \ell \pmod 4.$$

Hence the fourth roots of -16 are $\sqrt{2} + i\sqrt{2}$, $-\sqrt{2} + i\sqrt{2}$, $-\sqrt{2} - i\sqrt{2}$ and $\sqrt{2} - i\sqrt{2}$.

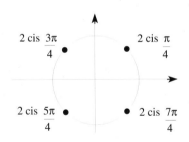

The method used in the above example can be used in general to prove the following result.

7.7.2 Theorem. If $r(\cos\theta + i\sin\theta)$ is the polar form of a complex number, then all its complex nth roots are

$$\sqrt[n]{r}\left[\cos\left(\frac{\theta + 2k\pi}{n}\right) + i\sin\left(\frac{\theta + 2k\pi}{n}\right)\right] \qquad \text{for } k = 0, 1, 2, 3, \ldots, n - 1.$$

The modulus $\sqrt[n]{r}$ is the unique real nonnegative nth root of r.

This result shows that any nonzero complex (or real) number has exactly n different complex nth roots.

Proof.   Let $w = s(\cos\phi + i\sin\phi)$ be an nth root of $r(\cos\theta + i\sin\theta)$. Then

$$w^n \;=\; s^n(\cos n\phi + i\sin n\phi) \;=\; r(\cos\theta + i\sin\theta).$$

Equating moduli, we obtain $s^n = r$ and $s = \sqrt[n]{r}$. The arguments must define the same angle and hence must differ by an integral multiple of 2π; therefore $n\phi = \theta + 2k\pi$ and $\phi = (\theta + 2k\pi)/n$, where $k \in \mathbb{Z}$. Hence the nth roots of $r(\cos\theta + i\sin\theta)$ are

$$\sqrt[n]{r}\left[\cos\left(\frac{\theta + 2k\pi}{n}\right) + i\sin\left(\frac{\theta + 2k\pi}{n}\right)\right] \qquad \text{for } k \in \mathbb{Z}.$$

The integers k_1 and k_2 will give the same solution

$$
\begin{array}{llll}
\text{iff} & \dfrac{\theta + 2k_1\pi}{n} - \dfrac{\theta + 2k_2\pi}{n} = 2\ell\pi & \text{for some } \ell \in \mathbb{Z} \\[3mm]
\text{iff} & \dfrac{2\pi(k_1 - k_2)}{n} = 2\ell\pi & \text{for some } \ell \in \mathbb{Z} \\[3mm]
\text{iff} & k_1 - k_2 = n\ell & \text{for some } \ell \in \mathbb{Z} \\[2mm]
\text{iff} & k_1 \equiv k_2 \pmod{n}. &
\end{array}
$$

Hence, if $r \neq 0$, the number $r(\cos\theta + i\sin\theta)$ has exactly n distinct complex nth roots, namely when $k = 0, 1, 2, 3, \ldots, n-1$. $\square$

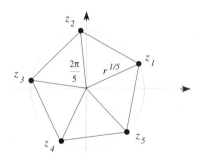

Note that all the nth roots have the same modulus and so, in the Argand diagram, they all lie on a circle centre the origin, radius $\sqrt[n]{r}$. All their arguments differ by multiples of $2\pi/n$ from each other and so the n different nth roots lie at the vertices of a regular n-gon, whose centre is the origin.

This diagram illustrates a typical example of the five fifth roots z_1, z_2, z_3, z_4 and z_5 of a complex number.

It is clear that if we could find one nth root of a complex number, the other $n-1$ could easily be sketched in the Argand diagram.

Theorem 7.7.2 can be viewed as an extension of De Moivre's Theorem to rational exponents. It is true that *one* of the values of $[r(\cos\theta + i\sin\theta)]^{1/n}$ is

$$r^{1/n}\left(\cos\frac{\theta}{n} + i\sin\frac{\theta}{n}\right).$$

It is also straightforward to show that *one* of the values of $[r(\cos\theta + i\sin\theta)]^{p/q}$ is

$$r^{p/q}\left(\cos\frac{p\theta}{q} + i\sin\frac{p\theta}{q}\right).$$

7.7.3 Example. Find all the sixth roots of unity.

Solution. We have to solve the equation $z^6 = 1$. We can write 1, in polar form, as $1(\cos 0 + i \sin 0)$. Hence, by Theorem 7.7.2, the sixth roots of unity are

$$
z_k = \sqrt[6]{1}\left(\cos\frac{2k\pi}{6} + i\sin\frac{2k\pi}{6}\right)
$$
$$
= \cos\frac{k\pi}{3} + i\sin\frac{k\pi}{3} \qquad \text{for } k = 0, 1, 2, 3, 4, 5.
$$

The different roots are

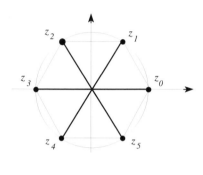

$$
\begin{aligned}
z_0 &= \cos 0 + i\sin 0 &&= 1 \\
z_1 &= \cos\frac{\pi}{3} + i\sin\frac{\pi}{3} &&= \frac{1}{2} + \frac{\sqrt{3}i}{2} \\
z_2 &= \cos\frac{2\pi}{3} + i\sin\frac{2\pi}{3} &&= \frac{-1}{2} + \frac{\sqrt{3}i}{2} \\
z_3 &= \cos \pi + i\sin \pi &&= -1 \\
z_4 &= \cos\frac{4\pi}{3} + i\sin\frac{4\pi}{3} &&= \frac{-1}{2} - \frac{\sqrt{3}i}{2} \\
z_5 &= \cos\frac{5\pi}{3} + i\sin\frac{5\pi}{3} &&= \frac{1}{2} - \frac{\sqrt{3}i}{2}.
\end{aligned}
$$

Hence the six sixth roots of unity are ± 1 and $\dfrac{\pm 1}{2} \pm \dfrac{\sqrt{3}i}{2}$. $\quad\square$

7.7.4 Example. Find all the square roots of $-2i$.

Solution. In polar form

$$
-2i = 2\left(\cos\frac{3\pi}{2} + i\sin\frac{3\pi}{2}\right).
$$

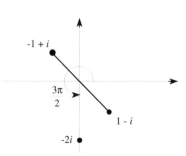

Hence by Theorem 7.7.2, its square roots are

$$
\sqrt{2}\left[\cos\left(\frac{3\pi}{4} + k\pi\right) + i\sin\left(\frac{3\pi}{4} + k\pi\right)\right]
$$

for $k = 0$ and 1. That is,

$$
\begin{aligned}
\sqrt{2}\left(\cos\frac{3\pi}{4} + i\sin\frac{3\pi}{4}\right) &= \sqrt{2}\left(-\frac{1}{\sqrt{2}} + \frac{i}{\sqrt{2}}\right) &&= -1 + i \\
\sqrt{2}\left(\cos\frac{7\pi}{4} + i\sin\frac{7\pi}{4}\right) &= \sqrt{2}\left(\frac{1}{\sqrt{2}} - \frac{i}{\sqrt{2}}\right) &&= 1 - i
\end{aligned}
$$

The two square roots of $-2i$ are therefore $\pm(1 - i)$. $\quad\square$

7.7.5 Example.   Solve the quadratic equation

$$iz^2 - 2(1+i)z + 1 \;=\; 0 \quad \text{for } z \in \mathbb{C}.$$

Solution.   The proof of the Quadratic Formula 7.1.1 will still be valid if the coefficients of the quadratic equation are complex. Therefore we can use the formula to solve our quadratic equation to obtain

$$
\begin{aligned}
z &= \frac{2(1+i) \pm [4(1+i)^2 - 4i]^{1/2}}{2i} \\
  &= \frac{1+i \pm [(1+i)^2 - i]^{1/2}}{i}
\end{aligned}
$$

where $\pm[(1+i)^2 - i]^{1/2}$ are the two complex square roots of $[(1+i)^2 - i]$. Now

$$
\begin{aligned}
(1+i)^2 - i &= 2i - i \;=\; i \\
&= \cos\frac{\pi}{2} + i\sin\frac{\pi}{2}.
\end{aligned}
$$

Hence, the two square roots of i are

$$
\begin{aligned}
\cos\frac{\pi}{4} + i\sin\frac{\pi}{4} &= \frac{1}{\sqrt{2}} + \frac{i}{\sqrt{2}} \\
\cos\frac{5\pi}{4} + i\sin\frac{5\pi}{4} &= -\frac{1}{\sqrt{2}} - \frac{i}{\sqrt{2}}.
\end{aligned}
$$

Therefore the solutions to the quadratic equation are

$$
z \;=\; \frac{1+i \pm \left(\frac{1+i}{\sqrt{2}}\right)}{i} \;=\; \left(\frac{1+i}{i}\right)\left(1 \pm \frac{1}{\sqrt{2}}\right) \;=\; (-i+1)\left(\frac{2 \pm \sqrt{2}}{2}\right).
$$

The two solutions are $\dfrac{(2+\sqrt{2})(1-i)}{2}$ and $\dfrac{(2-\sqrt{2})(1-i)}{2}$.   □

7.7.6 Example.   Solve the equation

$$z^6 - z^3 - 2 \;=\; 0 \quad \text{for } z \in \mathbb{C}.$$

Solution.   The above equation of the sixth degree is a quadratic in z^3, which factors as

$$(z^3 - 2)(z^3 + 1) \;=\; 0$$

Hence $z^3 = 2$ or -1.

The cube roots of $2 = 2(\cos 0 + i \sin 0)$ are

$$\sqrt[3]{2}(\cos 0 + i \sin 0) = \sqrt[3]{2}$$

$$\sqrt[3]{2}\left(\cos\frac{2\pi}{3} + i\sin\frac{2\pi}{3}\right) = \sqrt[3]{2}\left(\frac{-1}{2} + \frac{\sqrt{3}i}{2}\right)$$

$$\sqrt[3]{2}\left(\cos\frac{4\pi}{3} + i\sin\frac{4\pi}{3}\right) = \sqrt[3]{2}\left(\frac{-1}{2} - \frac{\sqrt{3}i}{2}\right).$$

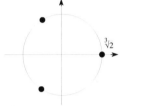
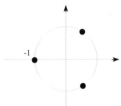

The cube roots of $-1 = 1(\cos \pi + i \sin \pi)$ are

$$\cos\frac{\pi}{3} + i\sin\frac{\pi}{3} = \frac{1}{2} + \frac{\sqrt{3}i}{2}$$

$$\cos\frac{3\pi}{3} + i\sin\frac{3\pi}{3} = -1$$

$$\cos\frac{5\pi}{3} + i\sin\frac{5\pi}{3} = \frac{1}{2} - \frac{\sqrt{3}i}{2}.$$

Hence the six solutions to the equation $z^6 - z^3 - 2 = 0$ are

$$z = -1, \quad \sqrt[3]{2}, \quad \frac{\sqrt[3]{2}(-1 \pm \sqrt{3}i)}{2} \quad \text{and} \quad \frac{1 \pm \sqrt{3}i}{2}. \qquad \square$$

7.8 THE FUNDAMENTAL THEOREM OF ALGEBRA

The complex number system allows us to solve all quadratic equations of the form

$$a_2 z^2 + a_1 z + a_0 = 0$$

where the coefficients a_0, a_1 and a_2 can be real or complex, and also to solve equations of the form

$$z^n - a_0 = 0$$

where a_0 is real or complex. However, far more is true. Every polynomial equation with real or complex coefficients has a solution in the complex numbers. This result is so important that it is called the Fundamental Theorem of Algebra. The theorem only tells us that a solution *exists*. It does not tell us how to find the exact solution. In Chapter 8 we will investigate various methods for finding solutions to polynomial equations.

The first proof of this Fundamental Theorem of Algebra was given by Gauss in his doctoral thesis in 1799. However, none of the known proofs are easy, and they all require the use of concepts outside the realm of pure algebra. We now give an intuitive proof using concepts from topology. (Topology is a branch of mathematics often known as 'rubber-sheet geometry'. The reason for this name should soon become clear.)

7.8.1 Fundamental Theorem of Algebra.   Every equation of the form

$$a_n z^n + a_{n-1} z^{n-1} + \cdots + a_2 z^2 + a_1 z + a_0 = 0$$

where $a_n, a_{n-1}, \ldots, a_2, a_1, a_0 \in \mathbb{C}, n \geq 1$ and $a_n \neq 0$, has at least one solution in the complex numbers.

Sketch Proof.   Since $a_n \neq 0$, we can divide by it, so that the coefficient of the highest power of z is 1. Let

$$f(z) = z^n + b_{n-1} z^{n-1} + \cdots + b_1 z + b_0$$

where $b_i = a_i / a_n$. This defines a function

$$f : \mathbb{C} \longrightarrow \mathbb{C}$$

from the Argand diagram to the Argand diagram. To show that the original equation has a solution, we have to show that there exists a complex number α such that $f(\alpha) = 0$; in other words, we have to show that the origin of the Argand diagram lies in the image of the function f. We shall look at the image under f of the different circles centred at the origin in the domain; that is, the images of the complex numbers of a fixed modulus.

When the modulus of z is large, we shall show that the function $f(z)$ is dominated by its first term z^n. Let

$$g : \mathbb{C} \longrightarrow \mathbb{C}$$

be this function defined by the first term, so that $g(z) = z^n$. Then, for any complex number $z = r(\cos \theta + i \sin \theta)$,

$$g(z) = r^n (\cos \theta + i \sin \theta)^n = r^n (\cos n\theta + i \sin n\theta)$$

by De Moivre's Theorem.

Denote the circle of radius r by

$$\Gamma_r = \{z \mid |z| = r\}.$$

Therefore, if $z \in \Gamma_r$, $|z| = r$, $|g(z)| = |z^n| = r^n$ and furthermore, as z travels once round the circle Γ_r, $g(z) = z^n$ will travel n complete times around the circle of radius r^n.

Let us see how close $f(z)$ and $g(z)$ are for points on the circle Γ_r. If $z \in \Gamma_r$,

$$
\begin{aligned}
|f(z) - g(z)| &= |f(z) - z^n| = |b_{n-1}z^{n-1} + \cdots + b_1 z + b_0| \\
&= |z|^n \cdot \left| \frac{b_{n-1}}{z} + \cdots + \frac{b_1}{z^{n-1}} + \frac{b_0}{z^n} \right| \qquad \text{by Proposition 7.3.5(iii)} \\
&\leq |z|^n \left[\left| \frac{b_{n-1}}{z} \right| + \cdots + \left| \frac{b_1}{z^{n-1}} \right| + \left| \frac{b_0}{z^n} \right| \right] \qquad \text{by Proposition 7.3.5(iv)} \\
&< r^n \left[\frac{1}{2n} + \cdots + \frac{1}{2n} + \frac{1}{2n} \right]
\end{aligned}
$$

if r is larger than the fixed real number

$$
R = \max\{2n|b_{n-1}|, (2n|b_{n-2}|)^{1/2}, \ldots, (2n|b_0|)^{1/n}\}.
$$

Hence, if $z \in \Gamma_r$, where $r > R$, then

$$
|f(z) - g(z)| < \frac{r^n}{2}.
$$

The points $f(z)$ and $g(z)$ are therefore within $r^n/2$ of each other in the Argand diagram, whenever z lies on the circle Γ_r. Since $g(z)$ always lies on the circle of radius r^n, it follows that

$$
\frac{r^n}{2} < |f(z)| < \frac{3r^n}{2} \qquad \text{whenever } z \in \Gamma_r \text{ and } r > R.
$$

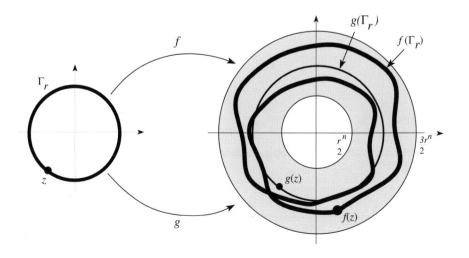

Hence, if $r > R$, the image of Γ_r under f will be a curve wrapped n times around the origin and lying inside an annulus of outer radius $3r^n/2$ and inner radius $r^n/2$.

It can be shown that the function f is continuous and so the image $f(\Gamma_r)$ is a continuous curve.

Now let r get smaller and smaller so that the circle Γ_r shrinks continuously towards the origin. Its image $f(\Gamma_r)$ must shrink continuously to the point $f(0) = b_0$. We can visualize this by imagining the curve $f(\Gamma_r)$ to be an elastic band in the Argand diagram. This elastic band is initially wrapped n times round the origin and this must be contracted onto the point b_0, without breaking the band. At some point the band $f(\Gamma_r)$ must pass through the origin. Hence the origin lies in the image of f and there exists a complex number α such that $f(\alpha) = 0$. $\qquad\square$

From the above argument, it can be seen that the solution α and, in fact all solutions, have modulus less than R.

7.8.2 Example. Let $f : \mathbb{C} \to \mathbb{C}$ be defined by $f(z) = z^2 + z + \frac{1}{2}$. Sketch the images, under f, of the circles $|z| = 1$ and $|z| = \frac{1}{2}$.

Solution.

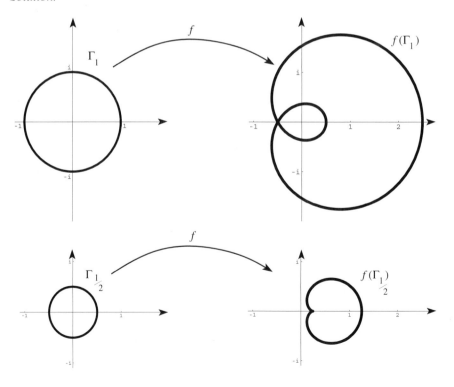

Table of Approximate Values			
θ		$f(e^{i\theta})$	$f(e^{i\theta}/2)$
0	0°	2.5	1.25
$\pi/6$	30°	1.9+1.4i	1.1+.5i
$\pi/3$	60°	.5+1.7i	.6+.6i

Any point on the circle $|z| = 1$ can be written as $e^{i\theta} = \cos\theta + i\sin\theta$ and any point on $|z| = \frac{1}{2}$ can be written as $e^{i\theta}/2 = (\cos\theta + i\sin\theta)/2$. It follows from De Moivre's Theorem that

$$f(e^{i\theta}) = (\cos 2\theta + \cos\theta + 1/2) + i(\sin 2\theta + \sin\theta)$$
$$f\left(\frac{e^{i\theta}}{2}\right) = \left(\frac{\cos 2\theta}{4} + \frac{\cos\theta}{2} + \frac{1}{2}\right) + i\left(\frac{\sin 2\theta}{4} + \frac{\sin\theta}{2}\right).$$

We see that as r decreases from 1 to $\frac{1}{2}$, $f(\Gamma_r)$ shrinks continuously and hence must pass through the origin for some $\frac{1}{2} < r < 1$. Therefore $f(z)$ has a root with modulus between $\frac{1}{2}$ and 1. Of course, in this example, we can solve the equation $z^2 + z + \frac{1}{2} = 0$ by the Quadratic Formula to obtain the two roots $z = (-1 \pm i)/2$, which have moduli $1/\sqrt{2} \approx .71$. $\qquad\qquad\square$

Exercise Set 7

1 - 22. Express each of the following complex numbers in the standard form $x + iy$, where $x, y \in \mathbb{R}$.

1. $(1 + i\sqrt{2}) + (1 - i\sqrt{2})$ **2.** $(1 + i\sqrt{2}) - (1 - i\sqrt{2})$

3. $(7 + 6i) - (4 - 5i)$ **4.** $5i + (2 - 3i)$

5. $(1 + i\sqrt{2})(1 - i\sqrt{2})$ **6.** $(2 + 3i)^2$

7. $(4 - i)(3 + i)$ **8.** $(\sqrt{2} - i\sqrt{3})(\sqrt{2} + i\sqrt{3})$

9. $(3 - i)(1 + i)^2$ **10.** $(4 - i)(3 - i)(2 - i)$

11. $\dfrac{1}{2 + i}$ **12.** $\dfrac{i}{3 - \sqrt{2}i}$

13. $\dfrac{7 - i}{4 + 3i}$ **14.** $\dfrac{1}{\sqrt{2}i}$

15. $\dfrac{1 + i}{1 - i}$ **16.** $\dfrac{1 + i\sqrt{2}}{1 - i\sqrt{2}}$

17. $1 + i + i^2 + i^3$ **18.** $\dfrac{1}{i^{65}}$

19. $(2 - i)^3$ **20.** $(\sqrt{5} - i\sqrt{3})^4$

21. $\dfrac{1}{(1 - 2i)(2 - i)}$ **22.** $\dfrac{(\sqrt{2} - i)^2}{(\sqrt{2} + i)(1 - \sqrt{2}i)}$

23 - 26. What are the real and imaginary parts of the following complex numbers?

23. $4 - 7i$ **24.** $-10 + \sqrt{2}i$
25. -3 **26.** $(6 - i)^2$

27 - 32. What is the complex conjugate and modulus of each of the following numbers?

27. $3 - 2i$ **28.** $1 + i\sqrt{5}$
29. $-i$ **30.** 2
31. $2 + \frac{i}{\sqrt{2}}$ **32.** $-\sqrt{3} - i\sqrt{7}$

33 - 37. Plot the following points in the Argand diagram.

33. $z = -i$, $w = 1 + i$, $z + w$, $2z$ and $3w$
34. $z = 1 - i$, $w = 2 + i$, $2z$, $z + w$, $z - w$ and $z - 2w$
35. $z = 2i$, z^2, z^3 and $1/z$
36. $z = 1 + i$, z^2, z^3, z^4 and $1/z$
37. $z = 3 + i$, iz, $i^2 z$, $i^3 z$ and $i^4 z$

38 - 41. Find polar coordinates for each of the following points that are given in Cartesian form.

38. $(2, 2)$ **39.** $(1, -1)$
40. $(-\sqrt{3}, 1)$ **41.** $(-1, -\sqrt{3})$

42 - 45. Each of the following pairs of numbers gives the polar coordinates of a point in the plane. Express each point in Cartesian coordinates.

42. $(1, \pi/2)$ **43.** $(\sqrt{3}, 3\pi/4)$
44. $(7, 7\pi/6)$ **45.** $(1, -2\pi/3)$

46 - 51. Express each of the following complex numbers in their polar form.

46. $-1 + i$ **47.** -8
48. $\sqrt{3} - i$ **49.** $-2i$
50. 5 **51.** $\frac{1}{\sqrt{3}} + \frac{i}{\sqrt{3}}$

52 - 55 Express each of the following numbers $r\mathrm{cis}\,\theta = r(\cos\theta + i\sin\theta)$ in the standard form $x + iy$ where $x, y \in \mathbb{R}$.

52. $\mathrm{cis}\,(3\pi/2)$ **53.** $4\,\mathrm{cis}\,2\pi$
54. $\sqrt{3}\,\mathrm{cis}\,(4\pi/3)$ **55.** $2\,\mathrm{cis}\,(-3\pi/4)$

56 - 59. *Find the modulus and argument of each of the following complex numbers.*

56. $2 - 2i$ **57.** $-3i$

58. $\sqrt{2} + (3 - \sqrt{5})i$ **59.** $(1 + i)^{30}$

60. Show that $(1 + i^{2n})(1 + i^n)$ is either 0 or 4 for $n \in \mathbb{P}$. Describe the values of n that yield the various answers.

61. Solve the equation $\bar{z} = z^2$ for $z \in \mathbb{C}$.

62 - 65. *Express the following complex numbers in standard form.*

62. $(1 - i)^6$ **63.** $\left(\dfrac{\sqrt{3}}{2} + \dfrac{i}{2} \right)^{25}$

64. $(1 - \sqrt{3}i)^8$ **65.** $\dfrac{1}{(-1 - \sqrt{3}i)^{10}}$

66. Use De Moivre's Theorem to show that

$$\begin{aligned} \cos 2\theta &= 2\cos^2 \theta - 1 \\ \sin 2\theta &= 2\sin\theta \cos\theta. \end{aligned}$$

67. (a) Use De Moivre's Theorem to show that

$$\begin{aligned} \cos 4\theta &= 8\cos^4 \theta - 8\cos^2 \theta + 1 \\ \sin 4\theta &= 4\cos\theta(\sin\theta - 2\sin^3 \theta). \end{aligned}$$

(b) Calculate $\cos 4\theta$ if $\theta = \mathrm{Cos}^{-1}(1/\sqrt{3})$.

68. Find expressions for $\cos 5\theta$ and $\sin 5\theta$ in terms of $\cos\theta$ and $\sin\theta$. Calculate $\cos 5\theta$ if $\cos\theta = 0.1$.

69. Prove that $(1 + i)^n = 2^{\frac{n}{2}} \left(\cos\dfrac{n\pi}{4} + i\sin\dfrac{n\pi}{4} \right)$.

70. Find all the cube roots of unity.

71. Find all the fourth roots of unity.

72 - 83. *Solve each of the following equations for* **z** $\in \mathbb{C}$ *and plot your solutions on the Argand diagram.*

72. $z^3 = \dfrac{1 - i\sqrt{3}}{8}$ **73.** $z^4 + 1 = 0$

74. $z^3 = 9i$ **75.** $z^4 + 1 + i\sqrt{3} = 0$

76. $z^8 = 16$ **77.** $z^2 = i$

78. $2z^2 + 5 = 0$ **79.** $7z^2 - z + 4 = 0$

80. $z^2 - 5z + 6 = 0$ **81.** $4z^2 + iz - 1 = 0$

82. $z^2 - (2 + 2i)z - 1 + 2i = 0$ **83.** $iz^3 + 1 + i = 0$

84. If $\alpha \in \mathbb{C}$ is a solution to the equation $ax^2 + bx + c = 0$, where $a, b, c \in \mathbb{R}$, show that the complex conjugate $\overline{\alpha}$ is also a solution.

85. By substitution and calculation, show that each of the numbers $-1/2$, $1 + i\sqrt{5}$ and $1 - i\sqrt{5}$ are solutions to the equation

$$2z^3 - 3z^2 + 10z + 6 \;=\; 0.$$

86.   (i) If $x_1, x_2 \in \mathbb{R}$ and $x_1^3 = x_2^3$, does it follow that $x_1 = x_2$?
    (ii) If $z_1, z_2 \in \mathbb{C}$ and $z_1^3 = z_2^3$, does it follow that $z_1 = z_2$?

87. If $c + id = (a + ib)^n$ show that $c^2 + d^2 = (a^2 + b^2)^n$.

88. Find one value of $\sqrt[5]{\dfrac{1 - i}{\sqrt{3} + i}}$.

89 - 92 Plot the solutions to the following equations in the Argand diagram.

89. $z^5 = 1$ **90**. $z^4 = 16i$
91. $z^{16} + z = 0$ **92**. $z^2 = 2 - \sqrt{5}i$

93 - 103. Shade each of the following regions of the Argand diagram.

93. Real part of z less than or equal to 2
94. Imaginary part of z equal to -1
95. Imaginary part of z greater than -1
96. $|z| = 3$ **97**. $z\overline{z} = 9$
98. $|z - i| = 1$ **99**. $|z + 3i| \leq 2$
100. $z - \overline{z} = 1$ **101**. $(z + \overline{z})^2 = |z|^2 + |z - \overline{z}|^2$
102. $|z| \geq |\overline{z}|$ **103**. $2 < |z + 1| < 3$

104. Prove that, for all $z_1, z_2 \in \mathbb{C}$

$$|z_1 - z_2| \geq |z_1| - |z_2|.$$

What is the geometric interpretation of this inequality, and when does this equality hold?

105 - 108. Write the following numbers in the exponential form e^{x+iy}.

105. $-2i$ **106**. $-1 + i$
107. 3 **108**. $(\sqrt{3} - i)^{100}$

Problem Set 7

109.   (i) If $z = r \text{ cis } \theta$ and $w = s \text{ cis } \phi$ prove directly that

$$\frac{z}{w} = \frac{r}{s} \text{ cis } (\theta - \phi).$$

   (ii) Find $\dfrac{\sqrt{3} - 3i}{\sqrt{2} + \sqrt{6}i}$ using this result.

110. If $z, w \in \mathbb{C}$, prove that

$$|1 - z\overline{w}|^2 - |z - w|^2 = (1 - |z|^2)(1 - |w|^2).$$

111. If $z, w \in \mathbb{C}$, prove that

$$|z + w|^2 + |z - w|^2 = 2|z|^2 + 2|w|^2.$$

What is the geometric interpretation of this equality?

112. Shade the region of the Argand diagram for which

$$|z - 1| + |z + 1| \leq 4.$$

113. Shade the region of the Argand diagram for which $\dfrac{iz - 1}{z - i}$ is real.

114 - 115. Shade the following regions of the Argand diagram.

114. $\left\{ \left| \dfrac{1}{z} \right| \; z \in \mathbb{C}, |z| = 1 \right\}$ **115.** $\{1 - z \mid z \in \mathbb{C}, |z| = 1\}$

116. Prove that the sum of the fifth roots of unity is zero. Can you generalize this result?

117. Let $z_1, z_2, z_3 \in \mathbb{C}$ be such that $z_1 + z_2 + z_3 = 0$ and $|z_1| = |z_2| = |z_3| = 1$. Show that these numbers correspond to points in the Argand diagram which are the vertices of an equilateral triangle.

118. Show that the three points z_1, z_2, z_3 form an equilateral triangle in the Argand diagram if and only if

$$z_1^2 + z_2^2 + z_3^2 = z_1 z_2 + z_2 z_3 + z_3 z_1.$$

119. Find all $z \in \mathbb{C}$ for which $\overline{z} = z^{n-1}$.

120. What is wrong with the following argument?

$$-1 \; = \; \sqrt{-1}\sqrt{-1} \; = \; \sqrt{-1}\sqrt{\frac{1}{-1}} \; = \; \frac{\sqrt{-1}}{\sqrt{-1}} \; = \; 1$$

121.   (i) Prove that

$$\tan nt \; = \; \frac{\binom{n}{1}\tan t - \binom{n}{3}\tan^3 t + \binom{n}{5}\tan^5 t - \cdots}{1 - \binom{n}{2}\tan^2 t + \binom{n}{4}\tan^4 t - \cdots}$$

   (ii) Calculate $\tan 5t$ if $t = \mathrm{Tan}^{-1}\sqrt{2}$.

122. Find all the values of $(1 + i)^{2/3}$.

123. Let ω be a complex cube root of unity, where $\omega \neq 1$. If b is one solution to $z^3 = a$, show that the other two solutions are $b\omega$ and $b\omega^2$.

124.   (i) If $z \in \mathbb{C}$, prove by induction that $z^n + \dfrac{1}{z^n}$ can be written as a polynomial

   in $w = z + \dfrac{1}{z}$.
   (ii) Prove that $\cos n\theta$ can be written as a polynomial in $\cos\theta$.
   (iii) Is a similar result true for $\sin n\theta$?

125. If θ is not a multiple of 2π, show that

$$\sin\theta + \sin 2\theta + \sin 3\theta + \cdots + \sin n\theta \; = \; \sin\frac{(n+1)\theta}{2} \cdot \sin\frac{n\theta}{2} \Big/ \sin\frac{\theta}{2}$$

$$1 + \cos\theta + \cos 2\theta + \cdots + \cos n\theta \; = \; \sin\frac{(n+1)\theta}{2} \cdot \cos\frac{n\theta}{2} \Big/ \sin\frac{\theta}{2}\,.$$

126 - 130. *Find all the solutions to the following equations for $z \in \mathbb{C}$.*

126. $z^4 - 3z^2 + 4 = 0$ **127**. $z^4 - 30z^2 + 289 = 0$
128. $z^8 + z^4 + 1 = 0$ **129**. $z^4 + iz^2 + 2 = 0$
130. $(z + 1)^n + (z - 2)^n = 0$

131. If you know how to integrate exponential functions, evaluate the integrals

$$U \; = \; \int e^{ax}\cos bx \, dx \quad \text{and} \quad V \; = \; \int e^{ax}\sin bx \, dx$$

by computing

$$U + iV = \int e^{(a+ib)x} \, dx.$$

(Assume that the usual integration formulas hold when the constants are complex numbers.)

132. (i) If $z, w \in \mathbb{C}$, when is $\dfrac{z}{w}$ real?

(ii) If z_1, z_2, $z_3 \in \mathbb{C}$, what is the argument of $\dfrac{z_3 - z_1}{z_3 - z_2}$?

(iii) Prove that the four complex numbers z_1, z_2, z_3, z_4 lie on a circle, or on a straight line, in the Argand diagram if and only if $\dfrac{(z_3 - z_1)(z_4 - z_2)}{(z_3 - z_2)(z_4 - z_1)}$ is real.

133. Let $H = \{z \in \mathbb{C} \mid \text{real part of } z \text{ is positive}\}$ and $D = \{z \in \mathbb{C} \mid |z| < 1\}$. Show that $f : H \to D$ is a bijection when $f(z) = \dfrac{z - 1}{z + 1}$.

134. Sketch the image of the two circles $|z| = 1$ and $|z| = 2$ under the function $f : \mathbb{C} \to \mathbb{C}$ defined by $f(z) = z^3 + z + 1$. What can you say about the complex solutions to the equation $z^3 + z + 1 = 0$?

135. Sketch the image of the circle $|z| = 2$ under the function $f : \mathbb{C} \to \mathbb{C}$ defined by $f(z) = z^4 - 3z + 1$.

136. *(For discussion)*

(i) Is the complex function $f : \mathbb{C} \to \mathbb{C}$, defined by $f(z) = e^z$, a bijection?

(ii) How would you define $\mathrm{Log}_e z$ for $z \in \mathbb{C}$?

(iii) What is $\mathrm{Log}_e i$?

(iv) What is i^i?

137. Use the fact that $\theta = 2\pi/5$ satisfies the equation $\cos 2\theta = \cos 3\theta$ to calculate $\cos(2\pi/5)$.

138. Find all the complex solutions to

$$z^9 + z^6 + z^3 + 1 \;=\; 0.$$

Chapter 8

Polynomial Equations

In this chapter we discuss various methods for finding solutions to equations of the form

$$a_n x^n + a_{n-1} x^{n-1} + \cdots + a_1 x + a_0 \;=\; 0.$$

Such equations are called polynomial equations and they form the most basic type of equation in mathematics.

There is no systematic method for solving all such equations. However, they can be solved in many special cases. We already know how to find all the complex solutions to equations of the form $a_2 x^2 + a_1 x + a_0 = 0$ and of the form $a_n x^n + a_0 = 0$.

Even if we cannot find an exact solution, we can often find the number of solutions and their approximate values.

Before we begin to actually solve polynomial equations, we must examine the polynomial expressions contained in the equations.

8.1   POLYNOMIALS AND FACTORING

Let $\mathbb{F}$ be a field, such as the rational numbers $\mathbb{Q}$, the real numbers $\mathbb{R}$, the complex numbers $\mathbb{C}$, or $\mathbb{Z}_p$, the integers modulo a prime p. An expression of the form

$$a_n x^n + a_{n-1} x^{n-1} + \cdots + a_1 x + a_0$$

where $a_0, a_1, \ldots, a_n \in \mathbb{F}$ and $n \geq 0$ is called a *polynomial in x with coefficients from $\mathbb{F}$*. If $a_n \neq 0$, then the above polynomial is said to have *degree n*. The degree of a polynomial is the highest power of x that has a nonzero coefficient. If all the coefficients are zero, the polynomial is called the *zero polynomial* and its degree is not defined.

For example, $2x^3 - \sqrt{3}x + 1$ is a polynomial in x of degree 3 with coefficients from $\mathbb{R}$ and $5z - 1 + i$ is a linear polynomial in z (that is, of degree 1) with coefficients from $\mathbb{C}$.

Polynomial of low degree are assigned the names given in the following table.

Degree	Name	General Example	
Undefined	Zero polynomial	0	
0	Constant polynomial	a_0	$(a_0 \neq 0)$
1	Linear polynomial	$a_1 x + a_0$	$(a_1 \neq 0)$
2	Quadratic polynomial	$a_2 x^2 + a_1 x + a_0$	$(a_2 \neq 0)$
3	Cubic polynomial	$a_3 x^3 + a_2 x^2 + a_1 x + a_0$	$(a_3 \neq 0)$
4	Quartic polynomial	$a_4 x^4 + a_3 x^3 + a_2 x^2 + a_1 x + a_0$	$(a_4 \neq 0)$
5	Quintic polynomial	$a_5 x^5 + a_4 x^4 + a_3 x^3 + a_2 x^2 + a_1 x + a_0$	$(a_5 \neq 0)$

The *set of all polynomials in x with coefficients from* $\mathbb{F}$ is denoted by

$$\mathbb{F}[x] \;=\; \{a_n x^n + \cdots + a_1 x + a_0 \mid a_i \in \mathbb{F}, n \geq 0\}.$$

A typical element in $\mathbb{F}[x]$ will often be denoted by $f(x)$, so that

$$f(x) \;=\; a_n x^n + \cdots + a_1 x + a_0.$$

Two polynomials

$$f(x) \;=\; a_n x^n + \cdots + a_1 x + a_0$$
$$g(x) \;=\; b_m x^n + \cdots + b_1 x + b_0$$

in $\mathbb{F}[x]$ are *equal* if they have the same degree and $a_i = b_i$ for all i.

A *polynomial equation* is an equation of the form

$$a_n x^n + a_{n-1} x^{n-1} + \cdots + a_1 x + a_0 \;=\; 0$$

which will often be written as $f(x) = 0$, where $f(x) \in \mathbb{F}[x]$. An element $c \in \mathbb{F}$ is called a *root* of the polynomial $f(x)$ if $f(c) = 0$; in other words, a root of the polynomial $f(x)$ is a solution of the polynomial equation $f(x) = 0$.

Let $f(x) = \sum_{i=0}^{n} a_i x^i$ and $g(x) = \sum_{i=0}^{m} b_i x^i$ be two polynomials in $\mathbb{F}[x]$. These polynomials can be added, subtracted and multiplied in the usual way that we deal with algebraic expressions. Their sum is

$$f(x) + g(x) \;=\; \sum_{i=0}^{\max(n,m)} (a_i + b_i) x^i$$

where $a_i = 0$, if $i > n$, and $b_i = 0$, if $i > m$. Their difference is

$$f(x) - g(x) \;=\; \sum_{i=0}^{\max(n,m)} (a_i - b_i) x^i$$

and their product is

$$f(x) \cdot g(x) \;=\; \sum_{i=0}^{m+n} c_i x^i$$

where $c_i = a_0 b_i + a_1 b_{i-1} + \cdots + a_{i-1} b_1 + a_i b_0 = \sum_{j=0}^{i} a_j b_{i-j}$. These are all poly-nomials in $\mathbb{F}[x]$ and, if we denote the degree of $f(x)$ by $\deg f(x)$ then, for nonzero polynomials $f(x)$ and $g(x)$,

$$\deg[f(x) \pm g(x)] \;\leq\; \max\{\deg f(x), \deg g(x)\}$$
$$\deg[f(x) \cdot g(x)] \;=\; \deg f(x) + \deg g(x).$$

Let $f(x) = 2x^2 - x + 4$, $g(x) = x^3 - 3$ and $h(x) = -2x^2 + x - 5$ be polynomials in $\mathbb{Q}[x]$. Then

$$\begin{aligned}
f(x) + g(x) &= x^3 + 2x^2 - x + 1 \\
f(x) + h(x) &= -1 \\
f(x)g(x) &= 2x^5 - x^4 + 4x^3 - 6x^2 + 3x - 12 \\
[f(x)]^2 &= 4x^4 - 4x^3 + 17x^2 - 8x + 16.
\end{aligned}$$

The set of polynomials $\mathbb{F}[x]$ is rather like the integers $\mathbb{Z}$, in that addition, sub-traction and multiplication can be performed in the set, but it is not always possible to divide one element by another nonzero element without leaving a remainder. For example, we can divide $x^2 - 4$ by $x + 2$ and obtain the quotient $x - 2$, because $x^2 - 4 = (x + 2)(x - 2)$. However, we cannot divide $x^2 - 4$ by x and obtain a poly-nomial as a result. (Remember $x - 4x^{-1}$ is not a polynomial, because polynomials do not contain negative powers of x.)

When faced with such a situation in the integers, we used the Division Algorithm to divide one integer by another and we allowed remainders. There is an analogous Division Algorithm for Polynomials. This asserts that the usual long division of poly-nomials can be carried out.

For example, in $\mathbb{Q}[x]$, let us divide the polynomial $f(x) = 3x^4 - 5x^3 - 2x^2 - 1$ by $g(x) = 3x^2 + x - 1$, using long division.

$$
\begin{array}{r}
x^2 - 2x + \frac{1}{3} \\
3x^2 + x - 1 \overline{\smash{\big)}\, 3x^4 - 5x^3 - 2x^2 + 0x - 1} \\
\underline{3x^4 + x^3 - x^2} \\
-6x^3 - x^2 + 0x \\
\underline{-6x^3 - 2x^2 + 2x} \\
x^2 - 2x - 1 \\
\underline{x^2 + \tfrac{1}{3}x - \tfrac{1}{3}} \\
-\tfrac{7}{3}x - \tfrac{2}{3}
\end{array}
$$

Hence when $f(x)$ is divided by $g(x)$ the quotient is $x^2 - 2x + \frac{1}{3}$ with remainder $-\frac{7}{3}x - \frac{2}{3}$. Therefore

$$f(x) = \left(x^2 - 2x + \frac{1}{3}\right)g(x) + \left(-\frac{7}{3}x - \frac{2}{3}\right).$$

Note that the remainder in this case is not a constant, as might be expected. In general the best we can do is to find a remainder whose degree is less than the degree of the divisor.

8.1.1 Division Algorithm for Polynomials.

If $\mathbb{F}$ is a field, and $f(x)$ and $g(x)$ are polynomials in $\mathbb{F}[x]$, where $g(x)$ is not the zero polynomial, then there exist unique polynomials $q(x), r(x) \in \mathbb{F}[x]$ such that

$$f(x) = q(x) \cdot g(x) + r(x) \quad \text{where } \deg r(x) < \deg g(x) \text{ or } r(x) = 0.$$

The polynomial $q(x)$ is called the *quotient* and $r(x)$ is called the *remainder* when $f(x)$ is divided by $g(x)$. If $r(x) = 0$, the zero polynomial, we say that $g(x)$ *divides* $f(x)$ or that $g(x)$ is a *factor* of $f(x)$ and write $g(x)|f(x)$.

Proof.   To prove the existence of $g(x)$ and $r(x)$, we proceed by induction on the degree of $f(x)$. If $f(x)$ is the zero polynomial, the result holds by taking $q(x)$ and $r(x)$ to be the zero polynomial. If $\deg g(x) = 0$, then $g(x)$ is a nonzero constant, say b_0 and

$$f(x) = \frac{f(x)}{b_0} \cdot g(x) + 0$$

so we can take $q(x) = f(x)/b_0$ and $r(x) = 0$.

If $\deg f(x) < \deg g(x)$ then by taking $q(x)$ as the zero polynomial and $r(x)$ as $f(x)$ the assertion is true.

Consider the case when $\deg g(x) = m > 0$. We have just shown that the assertion is true if $f(x) = 0$ or if $\deg f(x) < m$. This provides a basis for the induction to prove the result when $\deg f(x) \geq m$.

Suppose the result is true for all polynomials $f(x)$ of degree less than k, for some $k \geq m$. Let

$$f(x) = a_k x^k + \cdots + a_1 x + a_0$$

be a polynomial of degree k and let

$$g(x) = b_m x^m + \cdots + b_1 x + b_0 \quad \text{where } b_m \neq 0.$$

Now the polynomial $f(x) - \frac{a_k}{b_m} x^{k-m} g(x)$ has degree less than k and, by the induction hypothesis, can be written in the form $q_1(x) \cdot g(x) + r(x)$, where $\deg r(x) < \deg g(x)$ or $r(x) = 0$. Hence

$$f(x) = \left[\frac{a_k}{b_m} x^{k-m} + q_1(x)\right] g(x) + r(x)$$

which shows that the assertion is true for $\deg f(x) = k$ by taking

$$q(x) \;=\; \left[\frac{a_k}{b_m} x^{k-m} + q_1(x)\right].$$

The existence of the quotient $q(x)$ and remainder $r(x)$ for all polynomials $f(x)$ of degree $\geq m$ now follows by induction. The existence of $q(x)$ and $r(x)$ for polynomials $f(x)$ of degree $< m$, and for the special cases, in which $g(x)$ is a constant or $f(x)$ is the zero polynomial, have already been proven.

To show the uniqueness of $q(x)$ and $r(x)$, suppose that

$$f(x) \;=\; q_1(x) \cdot g(x) + r_1(x) \;=\; q_2(x) \cdot g(x) + r_2(x)$$

are two expressions for $f(x)$ satisfying the assertion. Then

$$[q_1(x) - q_2(x)]g(x) \;=\; r_2(x) - r_1(x)$$

where the right hand side is either zero or has degree less than that of $g(x)$. If $q_1(x) \neq q_2(x)$, the left hand side would have degree greater than or equal to that of $g(x)$; this a contradiction. Hence $q_1(x) = q_2(x)$ and also $r_1(x) = r_2(x)$. $\qquad\square$

The quotient and remainder can always be found by long division. For example, if we divide $f(x) = z^4 - iz^3 + 2z^2 - z + 1 - 2i$ by $g(z) = z^2 - i$ in $\mathbb{C}[z]$, we obtain the following.

$$
\begin{array}{r}
z^2 - iz + 2 + i \\
\hline
z^2 + 0z - i \,\big)\; z^4 - iz^3 + 2z^2 - z + 1 - 2i \\
z^4 - iz^2 \\
\hline
- iz^3 + (2 + i)z^2 - z \\
- iz^3 - z \\
\hline
(2 + i)z^2 + 1 - 2i \\
(2 + i)z^2 + 1 - 2i \\
\hline
0
\end{array}
$$

Since the remainder is zero, $g(x)$ divides $f(x)$ and

$$z^4 - iz^3 + 2z^2 - z + 1 - 2i \;=\; (z^2 - iz + 2 + i)(z^2 - i).$$

We can even apply long division to polynomials with coefficients in the finite field $\mathbb{Z}_p$, where p is a prime. Let us denote the elements of $\mathbb{Z}_5$ just by 0, 1, 2, 3 and 4 instead of by [0], [1], [2], [3] and [4]. We shall divide $f(x) = 4x^4 + 4x^3 + 1$ by $g(x) = 2x^2 + 3x + 1$ in $\mathbb{Z}_5[x]$. When carrying out this long division, keep in mind the rather peculiar properties of the field $\mathbb{Z}_5$; for example, $-2 = 3$ because $-2 \equiv 3 \pmod 5$ and 2 divides into 3 exactly 4 times because $3 \equiv 2 \cdot 4 \pmod 5$.

$\boxed{\textit{In } \mathbb{Z}_5}$

$$
\begin{array}{r}
2x^2 + 4x\ + 3 \\
2x^2 + 3x + 1 \ \big/\ \overline{4x^4 + 4x^3 + 0x^2 + 0x + 1} \\
4x^4 +\ \ x^3 + 2x^2 \\
\hline
3x^3 + 3x^2 + 0x \\
3x^3 + 2x^2 + 4x \\
\hline
x^2 +\ \ x + 1 \\
x^2 + 4x + 3 \\
\hline
2x + 3
\end{array}
$$

The quotient is $2x^2 + 4x + 3$ and the remainder is $2x + 3$; hence, in $\mathbb{Z}_5[x]$,

$$4x^4 + 4x^3 + 1 \ = \ (2x^2 + 4x + 3)(2x^2 + 3x + 1) + (2x + 3).$$

The reader will discover, after a little practice, that it is easy, and even fun, to manipulate polynomials over a finite field. One advantage is that, in long division, one never has any ugly fractions to deal with, as is often the case with polynomials over the rational, real and complex fields.

When we divide by a *linear* polynomial, the remainder must be a constant. The value of this constant is given by the following well known theorem.

8.1.2 Remainder Theorem.   The remainder when the polynomial $f(x)$ is divided by $(x - c)$ is $f(c)$.

Proof.   By the Division Algorithm, there exist unique polynomials $q(x)$ and $r(x)$ such that

$$f(x) \ = \ q(x) \cdot (x - c) + r(x)$$

where $\deg r(x) < 1$ or $r(x) = 0$. Therefore the remainder $r(x)$ is a constant that we shall write as r_0. Hence

$$f(x) \ = \ q(x) \cdot (x - c) + r_0.$$

Substituting $x = c$ in this equation, we obtain $f(c) = r_0$, which completes the proof of the theorem. $\square$

8.1.3 Example.   Find the remainder when the complex eighth degree polynomial $f(z) = 5z^8 - 2iz^5 + (1 + i)z^3 - 2z + 1 - i$ is divided by $z + i$.

Solution.   Applying the Remainder Theorem, we see that the remainder is

$$
\begin{aligned}
f(-i) \ &= \ 5(-i)^8 \ - \ 2i(-i)^5 \ + \ (1+i)(-i)^3 \ - \ 2(-i) \ + \ 1 - i \\
&= \ 5 \qquad\quad - \ 2i(-i) \quad + \ (1+i)(i) \qquad + \ 2i \qquad + \ 1 - i \\
&= \ 5 \qquad\quad - \ 2 \qquad\quad + \ i - 1 \qquad\quad + \ 2i \qquad + \ 1 - i \\
&= \ 3 + 2i
\end{aligned}
$$
$\square$

The Remainder Theorem yields an important criterion for a linear polynomial to be a factor of another polynomial.

8.1.4 Factor Theorem. The linear polynomial $(x - c)$ is a factor of the polynomial $f(x)$ if and only if $f(c) = 0$; in other words, if and only if c is a root of the polynomial $f(x)$.

Proof. The polynomial $(x - c)$ is a factor of $f(x)$ if and only if the remainder when $f(x)$ is divided by $(x - c)$ is zero. By the Remainder Theorem 8.1.2, this remainder is $f(c)$. $\square$

8.1.5 Example. Is $x + 1$ a factor of $x^{12} + 1$ or $x^{13} + 1$?

Solution. The polynomial $x + 1$ is a factor if and only if -1 is a root. Now

$$(-1)^{12} + 1 \; = \; 2 \quad \text{and} \quad (-1)^{13} + 1 \; = \; 0.$$

Hence $x + 1$ is a factor of $x^{13} + 1$, but not of $x^{12} + 1$. $\square$

8.1.6 Example. Find a quartic polynomial whose roots are 3, -4, $2 - \sqrt{3}$ and $2 + \sqrt{3}$.

Solution. Such a polynomial must have $(x-3)$, $(x+4)$, $(x-2+\sqrt{3})$ and $(x-2-\sqrt{3})$ as factors. Therefore a suitable polynomial is

$$\begin{aligned} f(x) \; &= \; (x - 3)(x + 4)(x - 2 + \sqrt{3})(x - 2 - \sqrt{3}) \\ &= \; (x^2 + x - 12)(x^2 - 4x + 1) \\ &= \; x^4 - 3x^3 - 15x^2 + 49x - 12. \end{aligned}$$
$\square$

8.1.7 Theorem. A polynomial of degree n over the field $\mathbb{F}$ has at most n distinct roots in $\mathbb{F}$.

Proof. We shall prove this result by induction on the degree. A polynomial of degree 0 is a nonzero constant, and so has no roots; hence the result is true in this case.

Assume, as induction hypothesis, that every polynomial of degree k over $\mathbb{F}$ has at most k distinct roots in $\mathbb{F}$. Let $f(x) \in \mathbb{F}[x]$ have degree $k + 1$. If $f(x)$ has no roots in $\mathbb{F}$, then it certainly has at most $k + 1$ roots in $\mathbb{F}$. Otherwise, if $f(x)$ does have roots, let $c \in \mathbb{F}$ be one such root. By the Factor Theorem 8.1.4

$$f(x) \; = \; q(x) \cdot (x - c)$$

for some $q(x) \in \mathbb{F}[x]$ of degree k. Any root of $f(x)$ must be a root of $q(x)$ or of $x - c$. By the induction hypothesis, $q(x)$ has at most k distinct roots, and $x - c$ has the one root c; hence $f(x)$ has at most $k + 1$ distinct roots in $\mathbb{F}$. $\square$

Any polynomial equation of degree n with rational, real or complex solutions can therefore have at most n different solutions.

When we attempt to factor a polynomial into linear factors in order to find its roots, it may happen that some of the factors occur more than once. A root c is said to have *multiplicity* r if $(x - c)^r$ is the highest power of $(x - c)$ in the polynomial. If $r > 1$, c is called a *multiple root*; if $r = 1$, c is a *simple root*. For example, $x^6 + x^5 - 4x^4 - 2x^3 + 5x^2 + x - 2$ can be factored as $(x - 1)^3(x + 1)^2(x + 2)$, so 1 is a root of multiplicity 3 and -1 is a root of multiplicity 2, while -2 is a simple root.

When factoring the integers, we found that any integer could be written as a product of basic integers, called primes, which could not be factored any further. In an analogous way, a polynomial can be factored, over a given field, into a product of basic polynomials that will factor no further. We call these basic polynomials irreducible.

8.1.8 Definition.   A polynomial in $\mathbb{F}[x]$ of positive degree is called *reducible in* $\mathbb{F}[x]$ if it can be written as the product of two polynomials in $\mathbb{F}[x]$ of positive degree. A polynomial in $\mathbb{F}[x]$ of positive degree is called *irreducible in* $\mathbb{F}[x]$ if it is not reducible; that is, if it cannot be written as a product of two polynomials in $\mathbb{F}[x]$ of positive degree.

For example, $x^2 - 1$ is reducible in $\mathbb{R}[x]$ because it factors as $(x - 1)(x + 1)$. However $x^2 + 1$ is irreducible in $\mathbb{R}[x]$; if $x^2 + 1$ were reducible in $\mathbb{R}[x]$ it would factor into two real linear factors and hence, by the Factor Theorem, would have a real root c such that $c^2 = -1$.

Reducibility depends very much on the given field. For example, $x^2 + 1$ is irreducible in $\mathbb{R}[x]$, but reducible in $\mathbb{C}[x]$ because it factors as $(x + i)(x - i)$.

In the Unique Factorization Theorem for Integers 1.5.5, we showed that the factorization of integers into primes is essentially unique. It is possible to prove in an analogous way, though we shall not do it here, that any nonzero polynomial in $\mathbb{F}[x]$ can be written as a product

$$a \cdot g_1(x) \cdot g_2(x) \cdots g_r(x)$$

where $a \in \mathbb{F}$ and each $g_i(x)$ is a monic irreducible polynomial in $\mathbb{F}[x]$. Furthermore, this expression is unique up to the orders of the factors. (A *monic polynomial* in x is one in which the coefficient of the highest power of x is 1. Any polynomial over a field can be written as a constant times a monic polynomial.)

Reducible polynomials are analogous to composite numbers and irreducible polynomials to prime numbers. While it is relatively straightforward to factor a small integer into primes, it is often very difficult, if not impossible, to factor a given polynomial into irreducible factors.

All polynomials of degree 1 are irreducible, because they cannot be factored as the product of two polynomials of positive degree. It follows from the Factor Theorem that the polynomials of degree 1 are the only irreducible polynomials that have roots in $\mathbb{F}$. Hence any polynomial of degree higher than 1, that has a root in $\mathbb{F}$, must be reducible in $\mathbb{F}[x]$.

The absence of any roots is sufficient to show that a polynomial of degree 2 or 3 is irreducible, but not sufficient to show that polynomials of degree greater than 3 are irreducible.

8.1.9 Proposition.   Let $f(x)$ be a polynomial of degree 2 or 3 in $\mathbb{F}[x]$. Then $f(x)$ is irreducible in $\mathbb{F}[x]$ if and only if $f(x)$ has no roots in the field $\mathbb{F}$.

Proof.   It follows from the Factor Theorem that if $f(x)$ has a root in $\mathbb{F}$, then $f(x)$ is reducible in $\mathbb{F}[x]$.

If a quadratic polynomial is reducible in $\mathbb{F}[x]$, it must factor into two linear factors. If a cubic polynomial is reducible in $\mathbb{F}[x]$, it must factor into three linear factors or one linear factor and one quadratic factor. Hence, a polynomial of degree 2 or 3 which is reducible in $\mathbb{F}[x]$ must contain at least one linear factor and therefore must have a root in the field $\mathbb{F}$.

It follows that a polynomial of degree 2 or 3 that has no roots in $\mathbb{F}$ must be irreducible in $\mathbb{F}[x]$. $\qquad\square$

To show that this result is not true for polynomials of degree 4 or higher, look at $f(x) = x^4 + 2x^2 + 1$ in $\mathbb{R}[x]$. This polynomial $f(x)$ has no real roots because $f(x) \geq 1$ for all $x \in \mathbb{R}$. However, it is reducible in $\mathbb{R}[x]$ because it factors as $f(x) = (x^2 + 1)(x^2 + 1)$.

8.2 EQUATIONS OVER A FINITE FIELD

Let p be a prime number and let $\mathbb{Z}_p = \{0, 1, 2, \ldots, p - 1\}$, the finite field of integers modulo p. Then, any solution to an equation in $\mathbb{Z}_p$ must be one of the elements $0, 1, 2, \ldots, p - 1$. The brute force method for solving such equations is to try each of the values $0, 1, 2, \ldots, p - 1$. If p is small this method is very effective. This is the only general method we mention here, besides those given in Chapter 2 for solving linear equations in $\mathbb{Z}_p$.

8.2.1 Example.   Solve the equation $x^3 + 4x + 1 = 0$ for $x \in \mathbb{Z}_5$.

Solution.   Let $f(x) = x^3 + 4x + 1 \in \mathbb{Z}_5[x]$. We will evaluate $f(x)$ for each element of the finite field $\mathbb{Z}_5$.

In $\mathbb{Z}_5$ x	0	1	2	3	4
x^3	0	1	3	2	4
$x^3 + 4x + 1$	1	1	2	0	1

Hence $f(x) = 0$ if $x = 3$. Therefore the only solution is $x = 3 \in \mathbb{Z}_5$. $\qquad\square$

8.2.2 Example.   Factor the polynomial $f(x) = x^4 + 3x^2 + 5x + 4$ in $\mathbb{Z}_7[x]$.

Solution.   We can find any linear factors of $f(x)$ by looking for the roots of $f(x)$.

In $\mathbb{Z}_7$	x	0	1	2	3	4	5	6
	x^2	0	1	4	2	2	4	1
	x^4	0	1	2	4	4	2	1
$x^4 + 3x^2 + 5x + 4$		4	6	0	1	6	1	3

We see that $x = 2$ is the only root and so $(x - 2)$ must be a factor. Since $-2 = 5$ in $\mathbb{Z}_7$ we can write this factor as $(x + 5)$. Divide $f(x)$ by $(x + 5)$ using long division.

$$
\boxed{In\ \mathbb{Z}_7}
$$

$$
\begin{array}{r}
x^3 + 2x^2 \qquad\quad + 5 \\[2pt]
x + 5\ \overline{\big)\ x^4 + 0x^3 + 3x^2 + 5x + 4} \\[2pt]
\underline{x^4 + 5x^3} \qquad\qquad\qquad\quad \\[2pt]
2x^3 + 3x^2 \qquad\qquad \\[2pt]
\underline{2x^3 + 3x^2} \qquad\qquad \\[2pt]
5x + 4 \\[2pt]
\underline{5x + 4} \\[2pt]
0
\end{array}
$$

Hence $f(x) = (x + 5)(x^3 + 2x^2 + 5)$.

Does $x^3 + 2x^2 + 5$ factor? Any root of $x^3 + 2x^2 + 5$ must also be a root of $f(x)$. Hence 2 is the only element that is possibly a root. When $x = 2$, $x^3 + 2x^2 + 5 = 1 + 1 + 5 = 0$. Therefore $(x - 2) = (x + 5)$ is also a factor of $x^3 + 2x^2 + 5$. Divide $x^3 + 2x^2 + 5$ by $x + 5$ using long division.

$$
\boxed{In\ \mathbb{Z}_7}
$$

$$
\begin{array}{r}
x^2 + 4x + 1 \\[2pt]
x + 5\ \overline{\big)\ x^3 + 2x^2 + 0x + 5} \\[2pt]
\underline{x^3 + 5x^2} \qquad\qquad\qquad \\[2pt]
4x^2 + 0x \qquad\quad \\[2pt]
\underline{4x^2 + 6x} \qquad\quad \\[2pt]
x + 5 \\[2pt]
\underline{x + 5} \\[2pt]
0
\end{array}
$$

Hence $x^3 + 2x^2 + 5 = (x + 5)(x^2 + 4x + 1)$. Again, the only possible root of $x^2 + 4x + 1$ could be 2. When $x = 2$, $x^2 + 4x + 1 = 4 + 1 + 1 = 6 \neq 0$. Therefore $x^2 + 4x + 1$ has no roots and, by Proposition 8.1.9, is irreducible.

The complete factorization of $f(x)$ into irreducible factors in $\mathbb{Z}_7[x]$ is

$$
f(x) \;=\; (x + 5)^2 (x^2 + 4x + 1).
$$

Check. This can be checked to be correct by multiplying out the factors. $\square$

8.2.3 Example. Find all the quadratic irreducible polynomials in $\mathbb{Z}_2[x]$ and determine whether $x^4 + x^2 + 1$ and $x^4 + x + 1$ are irreducible in $\mathbb{Z}_2[x]$.

Solution. Any quadratic polynomial is of the form $a_2 x^2 + a_1 x + a_0$ where $a_2 \neq 0$. In $\mathbb{Z}_2[x]$, the coefficients must either be 0 or 1. Hence there are four quadratic polynomials in $\mathbb{Z}_2[x]$, namely, $x^2 + a_1 x + a_0$, where $a_1, a_0 \in \mathbb{Z}_2 = \{0, 1\}$.

Any irreducible polynomial must have a nonzero constant term, otherwise it would contain a factor x. Therefore let us look at the remaining two quadratics, $x^2 + 1$ and $x^2 + x + 1$.

In $\mathbb{Z}_2$	x	0	1
	x^2	0	1
	$x^2 + 1$	1	0

In $\mathbb{Z}_2$	x	0	1
	x^2	0	1
	$x^2 + x + 1$	1	1

We see that $x^2 + 1$ has 1 as a root and is therefore reducible. In fact, $x^2 + 1 = (x+1)^2$ in $\mathbb{Z}_2[x]$. However $x^2 + x + 1$ has no root and therefore, by Proposition 8.1.9, is irreducible.

Hence the only irreducible quadratic in $\mathbb{Z}_2[x]$ is $x^2 + x + 1$.

Let us now determine whether $x^4 + x^2 + 1$ and $x^4 + x + 1$ have any linear factors in $\mathbb{Z}_2[x]$.

We see that $x^4 + x^2 + 1$ and $x^4 + x + 1$ have no roots and therefore no linear factors. However, as they are of degree 4, we cannot apply Proposition 8.1.9 to conclude that they are irreducible.

In $\mathbb{Z}_2$	x	0	1
	x^2	0	1
	x^4	0	1
	$x^4 + x^2 + 1$	1	1
	$x^4 + x + 1$	1	1

If either quartic factors, it must factor as two irreducible quadratics in $\mathbb{Z}_2[x]$. Since $x^2 + x + 1$ is the only irreducible quadratic, the only possible factorization is as $(x^2 + x + 1)^2$. By multiplication in $\mathbb{Z}_2[x]$, we see that

$$(x^2 + x + 1)^2 = x^4 + x^2 + 1.$$

Hence $x^4 + x^2 + 1$ is reducible, and $x^4 + x + 1$ must be irreducible, in $\mathbb{Z}_2[x]$. $\square$

8.3 RATIONAL ROOTS OF A POLYNOMIAL

We can actually produce an algorithm for finding all the rational roots of a polynomial in $\mathbb{Q}[x]$.

This algorithm will only yield the rational roots, it will not find any irrational roots of a rational polynomial; for example, it will not find the roots $2 \pm \sqrt{3}$ of the polynomial $x^4 - 3x^3 - 15x^2 + 49x - 12$. Neither will the algorithm find rational roots of any real polynomial; it will be useless to find the rational roots of $x^3 - \sqrt{5}x + 4$.

First notice that the roots of a rational polynomial are the same as the solutions of a polynomial equation with *integral* coefficients. If $g(x) \in \mathbb{Q}[x]$, let k be the least common multiple of the denominators of the coefficients of $g(x)$. The roots of $g(x)$ are the same as the solutions to the equation $kg(x) = 0$, which has integral coefficients. The algorithm for finding the rational roots of an equation with integral coefficients is contained in the following theorem.

8.3.1 Rational Roots Theorem.   Let $f(x) = a_n x^n + \cdots + a_0$ be a polynomial with integral coefficients. If p/q is a rational root, in its lowest terms, then $p|a_0$ and $q|a_n$.

Therefore, in order to find the rational roots of $f(x)$, we need only examine a *finite* collection of rational numbers, those whose numerators divide the constant term and whose denominators divide the leading coefficient. Note that the theorem only suggests those rational numbers that *may possibly* be roots. It does not say that all, or even any, of these numbers are in fact roots.

Proof.   If p/q is a rational number in its lowest terms then p and q have no factors in common. If p/q is a root of $f(x)$ then

$$a_n \left(\frac{p}{q}\right)^n + a_{n-1} \left(\frac{p}{q}\right)^{n-1} + \cdots + a_1 \left(\frac{p}{q}\right) + a_0 = 0.$$

Multiplying through by q^n we obtain

$$a_n p^n + a_{n-1} p^{n-1} q + \cdots + a_1 p q^{n-1} + a_0 q^n = 0.$$

and

$$a_n p^n = -q(a_{n-1}p^{n-1} + \cdots + a_1 p q^{n-2} + a_0 q^{n-1}).$$

Since all the symbols in this equation are integers, q divides the right hand side and so $q|a_n p^n$. As p and q have no factors in common, q must divide a_n.

Similarly

$$a_0 q^n = -p(a_n p^{n-1} + a_{n-1}p^{n-1}q + \cdots + a_1 q^{n-1})$$

and it follows that p must divide a_0.   □

8.3.2 Example.   Find all the rational roots of the polynomial

$$g(x) = x^4 + \frac{x^3}{2} - 6x^2 + \frac{3}{2}.$$

Solution. The roots of $g(x)$ are the same as those of the integral equation

$$2x^4 + x^3 - 12x^2 + 3 \; = \; 0$$

If p/q is a rational root, in its lowest terms, then, by the Rational Roots Theorem, $p|3$ and $q|2$. Hence p can be ± 1 or ± 3 and q can be ± 1 or ± 2. Therefore the only rational numbers which can possibly be roots are $\pm 1, \pm 3, \pm 1/2$ or $\pm 3/2$.

Test each of these in turn to see if they are in fact roots

x	-3	$-3/2$	-1	$-1/2$	$1/2$	1	$3/2$	3
$2g(x)$	30	$-69/4$	-8	0	$1/4$	-6	$-21/2$	84

Hence $x = -1/2$ is the only rational root of $g(x)$. $\qquad\square$

8.3.3 Example. Prove that $\sqrt[5]{3}$ is irrational.

Solution. The real number $\sqrt[5]{3}$ is a solution of the equation $x^5 - 3 = 0$. If p/q is a rational solution, in its lowest terms, then by the Rational Roots Theorem, $p|3$ and $q|1$; hence $p/q = \pm 1$ or ± 3.

x	-3	-1	1	3
$x^5 - 3$	-246	-4	-2	240

None of these values are roots of $x^5 - 3$ and so $x^5 - 3 = 0$ has no rational solutions. Therefore $\sqrt[5]{3}$ is irrational. $\qquad\square$

8.3.4 Example. Is $\sqrt{2} + \sqrt{3}$ rational or irrational?

Solution. Put $x = \sqrt{2} + \sqrt{3}$ and let us eliminate the root signs. Squaring we have $x^2 = 2 + 2\sqrt{6} + 3$ and $x^2 - 5 = 2\sqrt{6}$. Squaring again, we have $x^4 - 10x^2 + 25 = 24$ and so x satisfies the equation

$$x^4 - 10x^2 + 1 \; = \; 0.$$

By the Rational Roots Theorem, the only possible rational solutions of this equation are ± 1. Clearly, neither of these is a solution and so $\sqrt{2} + \sqrt{3}$ must be irrational. $\quad\square$

8.3.5 Example. Find all the real solutions to the equation

$$3x^4 + 13x^3 + 16x^2 + 7x + 1 \; = \; 0.$$

Solution. By the Rational Roots Theorem, the only possible rational solutions are ± 1 or $\pm 1/3$. It is clear that if x is positive the left hand side is greater than 1 and so the equation has no real positive solutions. By substitution, we see that both the possible negative rational numbers, -1 and $-1/3$, are solutions. Therefore $x+1$ and $3x+1$ are factors of the left hand side. Divide the left hand side by $(x+1)(3x+1) = 3x^2 + 4x + 1$.

$$\begin{array}{r}
x^2 + 3x + 1 \\
3x^2 + 4x + 1 \overline{\smash{\big)}\ 3x^4 + 13x^3 + 16x^2 + 7x + 1} \\
\underline{3x^4 + 4x^3 + x^2} \\
9x^3 + 15x^2 + 7x \\
\underline{9x^3 + 12x^2 + 3x} \\
3x^2 + 4x + 1 \\
\underline{3x^2 + 4x + 1} \\
0
\end{array}$$

Hence the equation is equivalent to

$$(x + 1)(3x + 1)(x^2 + 3x + 1) = 0$$

and all the real solutions are $x = -1, -3$ and, by the Quadratic Formula, $(-3 \pm \sqrt{5})/2$. The last two, of course, are irrational solutions. $\qquad\Box$

If the leading coefficient and the constant term of an integer polynomial have many factors, then the Rational Roots Theorem will yield a large number of possible rational values to check. For example, if $f(x) = 12x^3 - 5x^2 + 20$, the theorem would tell us that the possible rational roots are p/q where $p|20$ and $q|12$. That is, $p = \pm 1, \pm 2, \pm 4, \pm 5, \pm 10$ or ± 20 and $q = \pm 1, \pm 2, \pm 3, \pm 4, \pm 6$ or ± 12. Hence the possible rational roots p/q are

$$\pm 1, \pm 2, \pm 4, \pm 5, \pm 10, \pm 20, \frac{\pm 1}{2}, \frac{\pm 5}{2}, \frac{\pm 1}{3}, \frac{\pm 2}{3}, \frac{\pm 4}{3}, \frac{\pm 5}{3}, \frac{\pm 10}{3}, \frac{\pm 20}{3}, \frac{\pm 1}{4}, \frac{\pm 5}{4}, \frac{\pm 1}{6}, \frac{\pm 5}{6}, \frac{\pm 1}{12} \text{ or } \frac{\pm 5}{12}$$

a total of 40 possible numbers to be checked! We obviously would like some methods to reduce this list to one of more reasonable proportions. One of the most effective ways to do this is to use the calculus to sketch the graph of the polynomial in order to find the approximate value of the real roots. We discuss this method in Section 8.5. Another method is outlined in Problems 124, 125 and 126 at the end of the chapter.

8.4   COMPLEX ROOTS OF A POLYNOMIAL

The Fundamental Theorem of Algebra guarantees that any polynomial in $\mathbb{C}[x]$ has a root. This, together with the Factor Theorem, shows that any complex polynomial of degree n has n roots in the complex numbers. These n roots may not necessarily be distinct.

8.4.1   Theorem.   Let $f(x) \in \mathbb{C}[x]$ be a polynomial of degree n. Then there are n complex numbers $c_1, c_2, \ldots, c_n$, not necessarily distinct, such that $f(x)$ factors into the product of n linear factors

$$f(x) = a_n(x - c_1)(x - c_2) \cdots (x - c_n)$$

where a_n is the coefficient of x^n in $f(x)$.

Proof.   The proof will be by induction on n, the degree of the polynomial.

When $n = 0$, $f(x) = a_0$ and the result is true.

Suppose that the result is true for all polynomials of degree $n - 1$ and let $f(x) = a_n x^n + \cdots + a_0$ be a polynomial of degree n. By the Fundamental Theorem of Algebra 7.8.1, $f(x)$ has a root, say $c_n \in \mathbb{C}$. Therefore, by the Factor Theorem 8.1.4,

$$f(x) \;=\; g(x)(x - c_n).$$

The degree of the polynomial $g(x)$ must be $n - 1$ and the coefficient of x^{n-1} in $g(x)$ is a_n. By our induction hypothesis we can write

$$g(x) \;=\; a_n(x - c_1)(x - c_2) \cdots (x - c_{n-1})$$

where $c_i \in \mathbb{C}$. Therefore

$$f(x) \;=\; a_n(x - c_1)(x - c_2) \cdots (x - c_{n-1})(x - c_n). \qquad \square$$

8.4.2 Corollary.   Any polynomial of degree n in $\mathbb{C}[x]$ has exactly n roots, where a root of multiplicity k counts as k roots.

Proof.   If $f(x) \in \mathbb{C}[x]$ then, by the above theorem, we can write this as

$$f(x) \;=\; a_n(x - c_1)(x - c_2) \cdots (x - c_n)$$

where $c_1, c_2, \ldots, c_n$ are the n roots of $f(x)$ with a root of multiplicity k counting as k roots. $\qquad \square$

8.4.3 Corollary.   A polynomial is irreducible in $\mathbb{C}[x]$ if and only if it has degree one.

Proof.   By Theorem 8.4.1 any polynomial, of degree 2 or higher, factors into linear factors in $\mathbb{C}[x]$ and so is reducible. The corollary follows because all polynomials of degree 1 are irreducible. $\qquad \square$

There is one important theorem concerning the *complex* roots of a *real* polynomial. For example, consider the real quadratic polynomial $f(x) = x^2 - 4x + 5$. Its complex roots are

$$x \;=\; \frac{4 \pm \sqrt{16 - 20}}{2} \;=\; 2 \pm i.$$

The two roots are complex conjugates of each other. In fact, the non-real complex roots of any real polynomial always occur in conjugate pairs.

8.4.4 Conjugate Roots Theorem.   If $c \in \mathbb{C}$ is a root of a polynomial with real coefficients, then its complex conjugate $\bar{c}$ is also a root.

Proof.   Let $f(x) = a_n x^n + a_{n-1} x^{n-1} + \cdots + a_0 \in \mathbb{R}[x]$.

If c is a complex root of $f(x)$ then

$$
\begin{aligned}
f(c) &= a_n c^n + a_{n-1} c^{n-1} + \cdots + a_0 &= 0 \\
\text{and} \qquad f(\bar{c}) &= a_n \bar{c}^n + a_{n-1} \bar{c}^{n-1} + \cdots + a_0.
\end{aligned}
$$

Since each a_i is real, $a_i = \bar{a}_i$ and, using Proposition 7.3.3, we have

$$
\begin{aligned}
f(\bar{c}) &= \bar{a}_n \bar{c}^n + \bar{a}_{n-1} \bar{c}^{n-1} + \cdots + \bar{a}_0 &= \overline{a_n c^n} + \overline{a_{n-1} c^{n-1}} + \cdots + \overline{a_0} \\
&= \overline{a_n c^n + a_{n-1} c^{n-1} + \cdots + a_0} &= \overline{f(c)} \;=\; \bar{0} \;=\; 0.
\end{aligned}
$$

Hence $\bar{c}$ is also a root of $f(x)$. $\square$

8.4.5 Example.   If $-2 - \sqrt{2}i$ is a root of

$$
f(x) = x^4 + 3x^3 + 4x^2 + 2x + 12
$$

find all its complex roots and factor $f(x)$ as a product of linear factors in $\mathbb{C}[x]$.

Proof.   The polynomial $f(x)$ has real coefficients so, by the Conjugate Roots Theorem, if $-2 - \sqrt{2}i$ is one root, another must be its conjugate, $-2 + \sqrt{2}i$. Hence $(x + 2 + \sqrt{2}i)(x + 2 - \sqrt{2}i) = x^2 + 4x + 6$ is a factor of $f(x)$. Divide $f(x)$ by $x^2 + 4x + 6$ using long division.

$$
\begin{array}{r}
x^2 \;-\; x \;+\; 2 \\
x^2 + 4x + 6 \,\big)\, \overline{x^4 + 3x^3 + 4x^2 + 2x + 12} \\
x^4 + 4x^3 + 6x^2 \\
\hline
-\;x^3 - 2x^2 + 2x \\
-\;x^3 - 4x^2 - 6x \\
\hline
2x^2 + 8x + 12 \\
2x^2 + 8x + 12 \\
\hline
0
\end{array}
$$

Therefore $f(x)$ is indeed divisible by $x^2 + 4x + 6$ and the information given, that $-2 - \sqrt{2}i$ is a root, is correct. Now

$$
f(x) = (x^2 - x + 2)(x^2 + 4x + 6)
$$

and, by the Quadratic Formula, the other two roots are $\frac{1 \pm i\sqrt{7}}{2}$.

The four complex roots of $f(x)$ are $-2 - i\sqrt{2}, -2 + i\sqrt{2}, \frac{1+i\sqrt{7}}{2}$ and $\frac{1-i\sqrt{7}}{2}$ and $f(x)$ factors into linear factors in $\mathbb{C}[x]$ as

$$
f(x) = \left(x + 2 + i\sqrt{2}\right)\left(x + 2 - i\sqrt{2}\right)\left(x - \tfrac{1}{2} - i\tfrac{\sqrt{7}}{2}\right)\left(x - \tfrac{1}{2} + i\tfrac{\sqrt{7}}{2}\right). \quad \square
$$

8.5 APPROXIMATING REAL ROOTS

There is no algorithm, analogous to that for rational polynomials, for finding the real roots of an arbitrary polynomial with real coefficients. The best we can do is to sketch the graph of the polynomial and try to find the *number* of real roots by determining the number of times the graph intersects the horizontal axis. We can then find the *approximate* values of the real roots to any required degree of accuracy.

Of course, if the real polynomial we are interested in has rational coefficients, we can first apply the Rational Roots Theorem to find all the rational roots. We can then factor out the corresponding linear factors to simplify the polynomial. A prior estimate of the approximate values of all the roots is very useful in eliminating most of the candidates for rational roots.

Any real polynomial $f(x) \in \mathbb{R}[x]$ defines a polynomial function $f : \mathbb{R} \to \mathbb{R}$. It can be shown that the graph of any such function is always continuous; this means that the graph contains no holes or breaks in it. It seems intuitively obvious that if the values of a continuous function change sign in an interval, then the graph must cross the horizontal axis, at least once, in that interval. This fact, known as the Intermediate Value Theorem, will be very useful in approximating real roots. We just state the theorem we need here without proof, as the proof relies on the deeper properties of the real number system.

8.5.1 Intermediate Value Theorem. If $f(x) \in \mathbb{R}[x]$ and $f(a)$ and $f(b)$ are of opposite sign, then $f(x)$ has at least one root between a and b.

One way to draw the graph of a polynomial function, in order to find its roots, is to plot a large number of points of the graph. However, by using a little calculus, it is possible to reduce this work considerably and at the same time obtain more precise information on the number of real roots. If

$$f(x) \quad = \quad a_n x^n + a_{n-1} x^{n-1} + \cdots + a_2 x^2 + a_1 x + a_0$$

is a polynomial of degree n, its *derivative*

$$f'(x) \quad = \quad n a_n x^{n-1} + (n-1) a_{n-1} x^{n-2} + \cdots + 2a_2 x + a_1$$

is a polynomial of degree $n - 1$ whose value at any point x is the slope of the graph of $f(x)$ at the point x. The roots of the derivative $f'(x)$ yield all the stationary value of the function $f(x)$. A stationary value or turning point is either a *local maximum*, a *local minimum* or a *point of inflection*.

A knowledge of all the turning points and of the behaviour of the graph for large positive and negative values of the variable will enable us to find the number of real roots and their approximate values.

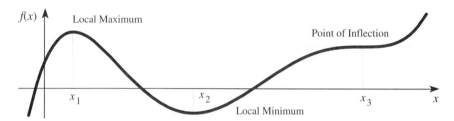

Since any polynomial has only a finite number of roots, its graph must remain on one side of the horizontal axis for sufficiently large positive (and negative) values of the variable. In other words, the sign of the polynomial must remain unchanged for sufficiently large positive (or negative) values of the variable. We show in Proposition 8.5.5 that the sign of the polynomial $f(x) = a_n x^n + \cdots + a_1 x + a_0$ will be the same as the sign of its leading term, $a_n x^n$, whenever $|x|$ is sufficiently large. For example, if $f(x) = -4x^3 + x^2 - x - 5$, then $f(x)$ is negative for large positive values of x and $f(x)$ is positive for large negative values of x.

8.5.2 Example.   Determine the rational roots of

$$f(x) = x^4 - x^3 + x^2 - 12$$

and find the number of real roots.

Solution.   Differentiating

$$f(x) = x^4 - x^3 + x^2 - 12$$

we obtain its derivative

$$f'(x) = 4x^3 - 3x^2 + 2x = (4x^2 - 3x + 2)x.$$

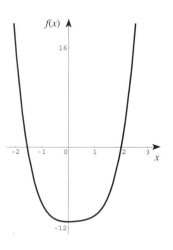

This derivative is zero only when $x = 0$, because the quadratic $4x^2 - 3x + 2$ has no real roots. Hence the only turning point of the graph of $f(x)$ occurs at $x = 0$ when $f(x) = -12$. When x is very large, positive or negative, the value of $f(x)$ is the same as its leading term x^4. Hence, when x is large, positive or negative, $f(x)$ is positive. Therefore it follows from the graph, that $f(x)$ has one positive root and one negative root.

By the Rational Roots Theorem, the possible values of rational roots are $\pm 1, \pm 2, \pm 3, \pm 4, \pm 6$ and ± 12.

x	-12	-6	-3	-2	-1	0	1	2	3	4	6	12
$f(x)$				16	-9	-12	-11	0				

The values in the previous table are the only ones we need to calculate. We can see that $x = 2$ is the positive root. As $f(-2)$ and $f(-1)$ have different signs, it follows from the Intermediate Value Theorem that the negative root must lie between -2 and -1; hence it cannot be rational because none of the possible values of the rational roots lie in that range.

Summing up, we see that $f(x)$ has one rational root, namely $x = 2$ and one other real root, an irrational root lying between -2 and -1. ☐

8.5.3 Example. Find the number of real solutions of the equation

$$12x^3 - 5x^2 + 20 = 0$$

and determine whether any of these solutions are rational.

Solution. Let $f(x) = 12x^3 - 5x^2 + 20$.
Differentiating we have

$$f'(x) = 36x^2 - 10x = 2x(18x - 5).$$

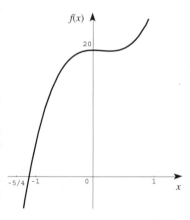

Therefore the slope of the graph of $f(x)$ is zero when $x = 0$ and $x = 5/18$. When $x = 0, f(x) = 20$ and when $x = 5/18, f(x)$ is still positive. For large values of x, $f(x)$ is dominated by $12x^3$. Hence for large positive values of x, $f(x)$ is positive and for large negative values of x, $f(x)$ is negative. The graph therefore has the form indicated and we see that $f(x)$ has only one real root, which is negative.

As mentioned at the end of Section 8.3, the possible rational roots of $f(x)$ are

$$\pm 1, \pm 2, \pm 4, \pm 5, \pm 10, \pm 20, \frac{\pm 1}{2}, \frac{\pm 5}{2}, \frac{\pm 1}{3}, \frac{\pm 2}{3}, \frac{\pm 4}{3}, \frac{\pm 5}{3}, \frac{\pm 10}{3}, \frac{\pm 20}{3}, \frac{\pm 1}{4}, \frac{\pm 5}{4}, \frac{\pm 1}{6}, \frac{\pm 5}{6}, \frac{\pm 1}{12}, \frac{\pm 5}{12}.$$

x	$-5/4$	-1
$f(x)$	$-45/4$	3

Calculating $f(-1)$ we see that it is positive; hence the real root is less than -1. The next possible rational root below -1 is $-5/4$ and $f(-5/4)$ is negative. Hence the only real solution to the equation $f(x) = 0$ lies between -1 and -1.25 and, since there are no other possible rational roots in this range, the solution must be irrational. ☐

In the above example, we have located an irrational root lying between -1 and -1.25. We can find the value of this root to any degree of accuracy by successive approximations using the Intermediate Value Theorem. The following example shows one general method.

8.5.4 Example.   Find the real solution to the equation in the previous example,

$$12x^3 - 5x^2 + 20 \;=\; 0$$

correct to 2 decimal places.

Proof.   We know that the root of $f(x) = 12x^3 - 5x^2 + 20$ lies between -1 and -1.25. Let us now look at the value of $f(-1.1)$. By using the Binomial Theorem, we obtain the approximation $f(-1.1) \approx -12[1+3(.1)+3(.001)] - 5[1.21] + 20 \approx -2.0$.

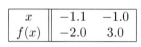

x	-1.1	-1.0
$f(x)$	-2.0	3.0

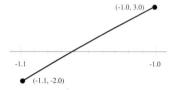

The root therefore lies between -1.0 and -1.1.

We now wish to approximate the root further to find the value of the second decimal place. By looking at the sketch of the graph between -1.0 and -1.1 it would appear that a second approximation would be -1.06. Again, using the Binomial Theorem, we obtain the following approximations.

$$
\begin{aligned}
f(-1.06) &\approx -12[1 + 3(.06) + 3(.0036)] - 5[1 + 2(.06)] + 20 \\
&\approx -14.28 - 5.60 + 20 = +0.12 \\
f(-1.07) &\approx -12[1 + 3(.07) + 3(.0049)] - 5[1 + 2(.07)] + 20 \\
&\approx -14.64 - 5.70 + 20 = -0.34 \\
f(-1.065) &\approx -12[1 + 3(.065) + 3(.004)] - 5[1 + 2(.065)] + 20 \\
&\approx -14.484 - 5.65 + 20 = -0.134
\end{aligned}
$$

x	-1.07	-1.065	-1.06
$f(x)$	-0.34	-0.134	$+0.12$

Therefore the solution lies between -1.06 and -1.065 and is -1.06 correct to 2 decimal places. $\square$

One crude general result follows immediately from the continuity of the polynomial functions.

8.5.5 Proposition.   If $f(x) \in \mathbb{R}[x]$ is a polynomial of odd degree then $f(x)$ has at least one real root.

Proof.   Let

$$
\begin{aligned}
f(x) &= a_n x^n + a_{n-1} x^{n-1} + \cdots + a_1 x + a_0 \\
&= x^n \left(a_n + \frac{a_{n-1}}{x} + \cdots + \frac{a_1}{x^{n-1}} + \frac{a_0}{x^n} \right).
\end{aligned}
$$

Let M be the larger of $(|a_{n-1}| + |a_{n-2}| + \cdots + |a_1| + |a_0|)/|a_n|$ and 1. Then, if $|x| > M$

$$\left| \frac{a_{n-1}}{x} + \cdots + \frac{a_1}{x^{n-1}} + \frac{a_0}{x^n} \right| \leq \left| \frac{a_{n-1}}{x} \right| + \cdots + \left| \frac{a_1}{x^{n-1}} \right| + \left| \frac{a_0}{x^n} \right|$$

$$\leq \left| \frac{a_{n-1}}{x} \right| + \cdots + \left| \frac{a_1}{x} \right| + \left| \frac{a_0}{x} \right| \leq \frac{M|a_n|}{|x|}$$

$$< |a_n|.$$

Therefore when $|x| > M$ the function $f(x)$ is dominated by its highest term and the sign of $f(x)$ is the same as that of $a_n x^n$.

If n is odd, then $f(x)$ has different signs when $x > M$ and $x < -M$. Therefore, by the Intermediate Value Theorem, $f(x)$ has a real root between $-M$ and $+M$. $\square$

The linear factorization of complex polynomials together with the Conjugate Roots Theorem allows us to determine all the irreducible polynomials in $\mathbb{R}[x]$.

8.5.6 Theorem. Let $f(x)$ be a polynomial of degree n in $\mathbb{R}[x]$. Then $f(x)$ can be factored in $\mathbb{R}[x]$ into irreducible factors as

$$f(x) = a_n(x - c_1)(x - c_2) \cdots (x - c_r)q_1(x)q_2(x) \cdots q_s(x)$$

where a_n is the coefficient of x^n in $f(x)$, $q_i(x) = x^2 + k_i x + \ell_i$ with $k_i^2 - 4\ell_i < 0$ and $r + 2s = n$.

Proof. By Theorem 8.4.1, $f(x)$ has n roots in $\mathbb{C}$, counting multiplicities. Let c_1, $c_2, \ldots, c_r$ be all the real roots, including multiplicities. By the Conjugate Roots Theorem 8.4.4, the other roots occur as complex conjugate pairs, say $d_1, \overline{d}_1, d_2, \overline{d}_2, \ldots, d_s,$ $\overline{d}_s$ where $r + 2s = n$. Now

$$(x - d_i)(x - \overline{d}_i) = x^2 - (d_i + \overline{d}_i)x + d_i\overline{d}_i = x^2 + k_i x + \ell_i$$

where $k_i = -(d_i + \overline{d}_i)$ and $\ell_i = d_i\overline{d}_i$. By Proposition 7.3.3, k_i and ℓ_i are real. The quadratic $x^2 + k_i x + \ell_i$ has no real roots; therefore it is irreducible in $\mathbb{R}[x]$ and $k_i^2 - 4\ell_i < 0$.

Hence, if the coefficient of x^n in $f(x)$ is a_n,

$$f(x) = a_n(x - c_1)(x - c_2) \cdots (x - c_r)(x - d_1)(x - \overline{d}_1) \cdots (x - d_s)(x - \overline{d}_s)$$
$$= a_n(x - c_1)(x - c_2) \cdots (x - c_r)q_1(x) \cdots q_s(x)$$

where $q_i(x) = x^2 + k_i x + \ell_i$. $\square$

8.5.7 Corollary. A polynomial is irreducible in $\mathbb{R}[x]$ if and only if it is linear or it is quadratic of the form $ax^2 + bx + c$ where $b^2 - 4ac < 0$.

Proof. This follows directly from the previous theorem. $\square$

There is an analogous theorem to the Conjugate Roots Theorem for *certain irrational* roots of *rational* polynomials.

8.5.8 Theorem.   Let $f(x) \in \mathbb{Q}[x]$. If $a + b\sqrt{c}$ is a real root of $f(x)$ where $a, b, c \in \mathbb{Q}$ and $\sqrt{c}$ is irrational then $a - b\sqrt{c}$ is also a real root.

Proof.   This theorem can be proved in a similar way to the Conjugate Roots Theorem 8.4.4 by defining the notion of conjugates for each fixed c, in the set of numbers $\{a + b\sqrt{c} \mid a, b \in \mathbb{Q}\}$, by

$$\overline{a + b\sqrt{c}} \;=\; a - b\sqrt{c}$$

and establishing the analogue of Proposition 7.3.3(i) and (ii). $\qquad\qquad\square$

8.5.9 Example.   It is given that $1 - \sqrt{2}$ and $2 + 3i$ are roots of the polynomial

$$f(x) \;=\; x^6 - 6x^5 + 15x^4 - 16x^3 + 7x^2 - 10x - 7.$$

Find all the roots and factor $f(x)$ into irreducible polynomials in $\mathbb{C}[x]$, $\mathbb{R}[x]$ and $\mathbb{Q}[x]$.

Solution.   Since $f(x)$ has rational coefficients and $1 - \sqrt{2}$ and $2 + 3i$ are roots, it follows from Theorem 8.5.8 and the Conjugate Roots Theorem that $1 + \sqrt{2}$ and $2 - 3i$ are also roots. Therefore a factor of $f(x)$ is

$$(x - 1 + \sqrt{2})(x - 1 - \sqrt{2})(x - 2 - 3i)(x - 2 + 3i)$$
$$= (x^2 - 2x - 1)(x^2 - 4x + 7)$$
$$= x^4 - 6x^3 + 14x^2 - 10x - 7.$$

Divide $f(x)$ by this polynomial.

$$
\begin{array}{r}
x^2 \qquad\qquad + \;\; 1 \\
x^4 - 6x^3 + 14x^2 - 10x - 7 \enclose{longdiv}{x^6 - 6x^5 + 15x^4 - 16x^3 + 7x^2 - 10x - 7} \\
\underline{x^6 - 6x^5 + 14x^4 - 10x^3 - 7x^2} \\
x^4 - 6x^3 + 14x^2 - 10x - 7 \\
\underline{x^4 - 6x^3 + 14x^2 - 10x - 7} \\
0
\end{array}
$$

The quotient and other factor of $f(x)$ is $x^2 + 1$. Hence the roots of $f(x)$ are $1 \pm \sqrt{2}, \pm i$, and $2 \pm 3i$. In $\mathbb{C}[x]$, the polynomial factors into linear factors as

$$f(x) \;=\; (x - 1 + \sqrt{2})(x - 1 - \sqrt{2})(x - i)(x + i)(x - 2 - 3i)(x - 2 + 3i).$$

To factor the polynomial in $\mathbb{R}[x]$, we combine the pairs of factors corresponding to the pairs of complex conjugate roots to obtain

$$f(x) \;=\; (x - 1 + \sqrt{2})(x - 1 - \sqrt{2})(x^2 + 1)(x^2 - 4x + 7).$$

To factor the polynomial in $\mathbb{Q}[x]$ we combine the pair of factors containing square roots to obtain

$$f(x) \;\;=\;\; (x^2 - 2x - 1)(x^2 + 1)(x^2 - 4x + 7). \qquad \square$$

8.6 POLYNOMIAL INEQUALITIES

Now that we have many methods at our disposal for finding real roots of real polynomials, we shall take a look at solving polynomial inequalities.

There are two basic methods that we can use to solve inequalities of the form $f(x) > 0$ or $f(x) \geq 0$, where $f(x) \in \mathbb{R}[x]$. One method is to sketch the graph of $f(x)$ and determine its roots. The solution to the inequality can then be read off from the graph. The other method is to factor $f(x)$ into irreducible factors in $\mathbb{R}[x]$ as in Theorem 8.5.6. The solution to the inequality can be found by looking at the signs of all the factors. An irreducible quadratic factor will have the same sign for all $x \in \mathbb{R}$, because it has no real roots.

8.6.1 Example.   Factor the polynomial

$$f(x) \;\;=\;\; 3x^3 - 4x^2 - 2x + 1$$

into irreducible real factors and solve the inequality $f(x) > 0$.

Solution.   Let us first determine whether $f(x)$ has any rational roots. If p/q is a rational root, in its lowest terms, the $p|1$ and $q|3$. Hence the possible rational roots are ± 1 and $\pm 1/3$.

x	-1	$-1/3$	$1/3$	1
$f(x)$	-4	$8/9$	0	-2

Therefore $1/3$ is a root and $(3x - 1)$ is a factor of $f(x)$. Divide $f(x)$ by $(3x - 1)$.

$$
\begin{array}{r}
x^2 \;-\; x \;-\; 1 \\
3x - 1 \,\overline{\big)\; 3x^3 \;-\; 4x^2 \;-\; 2x \;+\; 1} \\
\underline{3x^3 \;-\; x^2} \\
-3x^2 \;-\; 2x \\
\underline{-3x^2 \;+\; x} \\
-3x \;+\; 1 \\
\underline{-3x \;+\; 1} \\
0
\end{array}
$$

Hence

$$f(x) = (3x - 1)(x^2 - x - 1)$$
$$= (3x - 1)\left(x - \frac{1}{2} - \frac{\sqrt{5}}{2}\right)\left(x - \frac{1}{2} + \frac{\sqrt{5}}{2}\right).$$

To solve the inequality $f(x) > 0$, consider the following table.

	Sign of			
Range	$3x - 1$	$x - \frac{1}{2} - \frac{\sqrt{5}}{2}$	$x - \frac{1}{2} + \frac{\sqrt{5}}{2}$	$f(x)$
$x < (1 - \sqrt{5})/2$	$-$	$-$	$-$	$-$
$(1 - \sqrt{5})/2 < x < 1/3$	$-$	$-$	$+$	$+$
$1/3 < x < (1 + \sqrt{5})/2$	$+$	$-$	$+$	$-$
$(1 + \sqrt{5})/2 < x$	$+$	$+$	$+$	$+$

The solution set to $f(x) > 0$ is

$$\{x \in \mathbb{R} \mid (1 - \sqrt{5})/2 < x < 1/3 \quad \text{or} \quad (1 + \sqrt{5})/2 < x\}$$

which is the union of the open intervals

$$\left(\frac{1 - \sqrt{5}}{2}, \frac{1}{3}\right) \cup \left(\frac{1 + \sqrt{5}}{2}, \infty\right). \qquad \square$$

8.6.2 Example.   Solve the inequality $x^6 + 5x^2 - 6 \leq 0$.

Solution.   We shall sketch the graph of $f(x) = x^6 + 5x^2 - 6$. Differentiating, we have $f'(x) = 6x^5 + 10x = 2x(3x^4 + 5)$. Hence the slope of the graph of $f(x)$ is zero only when $x = 0$, in which case $f(x) = -6$.

As $f(x)$ is positive for large positive or negative values of x, it follows from the graph that $f(x)$ has two real roots. The possible rational roots are $\pm 1, \pm 2, \pm 3$ and ± 6. It is easily seen that $f(1) = 0$ and $f(-1) = 0$, so 1 and -1 are the only real roots.

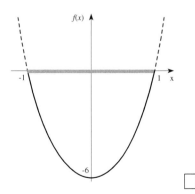

The solution set to $f(x) \leq 0$ is therefore

$$\{x \in \mathbb{R} \mid -1 \leq x \leq 1\}$$

which is the closed interval $[-1, 1]$. $\qquad \square$

8.7 MULTIPLE ROOTS

If a polynomial contains a multiple root, there is an algorithm that will find the repeated factors. This algorithm involves the derivative of the polynomial and the concept of the greatest common divisor of polynomials. We define the greatest common divisor in exactly the same way as we did for integers in Definition 1.2.1.

8.7.1 Definition. Let $f(x), g(x) \in \mathbb{F}[x]$, where $\mathbb{F}$ is some field. The polynomial $d(x) \in \mathbb{F}[x]$ is a *greatest common divisor* of $f(x)$ and $g(x)$ if

(i) $d(x)$ divides both $f(x)$ and $g(x)$

(ii) any divisor of both $f(x)$ and $g(x)$ also divides $d(x)$.

If this is the case, we write $d(x) = \text{GCD}(f(x), g(x))$.

Most of the results concerning greatest common divisor of integers carry over to give results about the greatest common divisor of polynomials. The greatest common divisor of two polynomials can be obtained from the factorization of the polynomials into irreducible factors (corresponding to the prime factorization of integers). For example, if $f(x) = (x-2)^2(x+1)^3(x+\sqrt{2})(x-\sqrt{2})$ and $g(x) = (x-2)^3(x+\sqrt{2})$ are two polynomials in $\mathbb{R}[x]$ then $\text{GCD}(f(x), g(x)) = (x-2)^2(x+\sqrt{2})$. There is even a Euclidean Algorithm for Polynomials that can be used to find greatest common divisors. The statement of the result is identical to the Euclidean Algorithm for Integers except that the integers are replaced by polynomials in $\mathbb{F}[x]$.

The algorithm for finding the multiple factors of a polynomial $f(x)$ consists of finding the greatest common divisor of $f(x)$ and its derivative $f'(x)$.

8.7.2 Multiple Roots Theorem. If $f(x) \in \mathbb{F}[x]$, the multiple roots of $f(x)$ are precisely the roots of $\text{GCD}(f(x), f'(x))$.

Proof. Suppose that $r \in \mathbb{F}$ is a multiple root of $f(x)$ so that $(x-r)^2$ is a factor of $f(x)$ and we can write

$$f(x) = (x-r)^2 q(x), \quad \text{where } q(x) \in \mathbb{F}[x].$$

By the rule for differentiating a product, we have

$$f'(x) = 2(x-r)q(x) + (x-r)^2 q'(x)$$

and $f'(r) = 0$. Hence $(x-r)$ is a factor of both $f(x)$ and $f'(x)$ and will be a factor of $\text{GCD}(f(x), f'(x))$.

Now suppose that $c \in \mathbb{F}$ is a root of $f(x)$ but is not a multiple root, so that

$$f(x) = (x-c)p(x), \quad \text{where } p(c) \neq 0.$$

Differentiating, we have

$$f'(x) \quad = \quad p(x) + (x - c)p'(x)$$

and $f'(c) = p(c) \neq 0$. Hence $(x - c)$ is not a factor of $f'(x)$ or of $\mathrm{GCD}(f(x), f'(x))$.

Therefore the only roots of $f(x)$ that are roots of $\mathrm{GCD}(f(x), f'(x))$ are the multiple roots.

On the other hand, $\mathrm{GCD}(f(x), f'(x))$ is a factor of both $f(x)$ and $f'(x)$, so any root of the greatest common divisor must be a root of $f(x)$ and $f'(x)$ and, by what we have shown, must be a multiple root of $f(x)$. $\qquad\square$

8.7.3 Example.   It is known that the polynomial

$$f(x) \quad = \quad 3x^3 - 5\sqrt{2}x^2 + 2x + 2\sqrt{2}$$

has a multiple root. Find all its roots.

Solution.   Differentiating $f(x)$, we have

$$f'(x) \quad = \quad 9x^2 - 10\sqrt{2}x + 2.$$

We shall not find $\mathrm{GCD}(f(x), f'(x))$ directly, but will check to see which roots of $f'(x)$ are also roots of $f(x)$. By the Quadratic Formula, the roots of $f'(x)$ are

$$x \quad = \quad \frac{10\sqrt{2} \pm \sqrt{200 - 72}}{18} = \frac{5\sqrt{2} \pm \sqrt{32}}{9} = \frac{5\sqrt{2} \pm 4\sqrt{2}}{9} = \sqrt{2} \quad \text{or} \quad \frac{\sqrt{2}}{9}.$$

Now $f(\sqrt{2}) = 6\sqrt{2} - 10\sqrt{2} + 2\sqrt{2} + 2\sqrt{2} = 0$ and so by the previous theorem, $\sqrt{2}$ must be a multiple root of $f(x)$. As $f(x)$ is only a cubic it cannot have two different multiple roots; hence $\sqrt{2}/9$ is not a multiple root.

The polynomial $(x - \sqrt{2})^2 = x^2 - 2\sqrt{2}x + 2$ must be a factor of $f(x)$ and we can use long division to find the remaining factor.

$$
\begin{array}{r}
3x + \sqrt{2} \\
x^2 - 2\sqrt{2}x + 2 \enclose{longdiv}{3x^3 - 5\sqrt{2}x^2 + 2x + 2\sqrt{2}} \\
3x^3 - 6\sqrt{2}x^2 + 6x \\
\hline
\sqrt{2}x^2 - 4x + 2\sqrt{2} \\
\sqrt{2}x^2 - 4x + 2\sqrt{2} \\
\hline
0
\end{array}
$$

Therefore $f(x) = (x - \sqrt{2})^2(3x + \sqrt{2})$ and its roots are $\sqrt{2}$, $\sqrt{2}$ and $-\sqrt{2}/3$. $\qquad\square$

8.8 PARTIAL FRACTIONS

A quotient $f(x)/g(x)$ of two polynomials $f(x)$ and $g(x)$ is called a *rational function* of x. Such rational functions can be manipulated in a similar way to rational numbers. For example,

$$\frac{1}{x-3} - \frac{1}{x+2} = \frac{(x+2)-(x-3)}{(x-3)(x+2)} = \frac{5}{x^2-x-6}.$$

It is useful in the Integral Calculus and in the Theory of Differential Equations, to be able to express a rational function $f(x)/g(x)$ as a sum of fractional forms, called *partial fractions*, whose denominators are simpler than $g(x)$. Taking the above numerical example, we see that $5/(x^2-x-6)$ can be written in terms of the simpler fractions $1/(x-3)$ and $1/(x+2)$.

If the degree of $f(x)$ is less than the degree of $g(x)$ then $f(x)/g(x)$ is called a *proper fraction*. Just as in rational numbers, any rational function can be expressed as a whole polynomial plus a proper fraction. Let $f(x)/g(x)$ be any rational function and, using the Division Algorithm, write

$$f(x) = q(x)g(x) + r(x) \quad \text{where } r(x) = 0 \text{ or } \deg r(x) < \deg g(x).$$

Then

$$\frac{f(x)}{g(x)} = q(x) + \frac{r(x)}{g(x)} \quad \text{where } \frac{r(x)}{g(x)} \text{ is a proper fraction.}$$

Recall that any real polynomial can be factored into linear and irreducible quadratic factors in $\mathbb{R}[x]$. This allows us to decompose any fraction into partial fractions as follows.

8.8.1 Partial Fraction Decomposition. Any real fraction $f(x)/g(x)$ can be written as a sum of a real polynomial and real partial fractions of the following types.

(i) For each nonrepeating linear factor $(ax+b)$ of $g(x)$, the partial fraction decomposition contains a term of the form

$$\frac{A}{ax+b} \quad \text{where } A \in \mathbb{R}.$$

(ii) For each repeating linear factor $(ax+b)^r$ of $g(x)$, the decomposition contains a term of the form

$$\frac{A_1}{ax+b} + \frac{A_2}{(ax+b)^2} + \cdots + \frac{A_r}{(ax+b)^r} \quad \text{where each } a_i \in \mathbb{R}.$$

(iii) For each nonrepeating quadratic factor (ax^2+bx+c) of $g(x)$, the decomposition contains a term of the form

$$\frac{Ax + B}{ax^2 + bx + c} \quad \text{where } A, B \in \mathbb{R}.$$

(iv) For each repeating quadratic factor $(ax^2 + bx + c)^r$ of $g(x)$, the decomposition contains a term of the form

$$\frac{A_1 x + B_1}{ax^2 + bx + c} + \frac{A_2 x + B_2}{(ax^2 + bx + c)^2} + \cdots + \frac{A_r x + B_r}{(ax^2 + bx + c)^r}$$

where each a_i and $b_i \in \mathbb{R}$.

Before we prove this result, we give various examples to show how the constants in the partial fraction decomposition can be found.

8.8.2 Example.   Decompose $\dfrac{7x + 8}{2x^2 - x - 1}$ into partial fractions.

Solution.   By the above result, we can write

$$\frac{7x + 8}{2x^2 - x - 1} \;=\; \frac{7x + 8}{(x - 1)(2x + 1)} \;=\; \frac{A}{x - 1} + \frac{B}{2x + 1} \quad \text{where } A, B \in \mathbb{R}.$$

Multiply each side by $(x - 1)(2x + 1)$ to obtain

$$\begin{aligned}
7x + 8 &= A(2x + 1) + B(x - 1) \\
&= (2A + B)x + (A - B).
\end{aligned}$$

The polynomial $7x + 8$ must be identical to the polynomial $(2A + B)x + (A - B)$. Hence they must have the same coefficients, and $7 = 2A + B$ and $8 = A - B$.

Solving these two equations, we obtain $A = 5$ and $B = -3$. Hence

$$\frac{7x + 8}{2x^2 - x - 1} \;=\; \frac{5}{x - 1} - \frac{3}{2x + 1}.$$

Alternative Method.   Start from the relation

$$\frac{7x + 8}{2x^2 - x - 1} \;=\; \frac{A}{x - 1} + \frac{B}{2x + 1} \quad \text{where } A, B \in \mathbb{R}.$$

Multiply both sides by $(x - 1)$ to obtain

$$\frac{7x + 8}{2x + 1} \;=\; A + \frac{B(x - 1)}{2x + 1}.$$

The rational functions on each side must be identical. Therefore the equality holds for all values of x (except when $2x + 1 = 0$). In particular, when $x = 1$, $A = 5$. Similarly, by multiplying the partial fraction decomposition by $(2x + 1)$ and then putting $x = -1/2$, we obtain $B = -3$. □

8.8.3 Example. Decompose $\dfrac{x^2 - 10x + 7}{x^3 - 3x^2 + 4}$ into partial fractions.

Solution. We first have to factor the denominator $g(x) = x^3 - 3x^2 + 4$. The possible rational roots of $g(x)$ are $\pm 1, \pm 2$ and ± 4. It is seen that $g(-1) = 0$ and $g(2) = 0$. Hence $(x + 1)(x - 2) = x^2 - x - 2$ is a factor of $g(x)$.

$$
\begin{array}{r}
x \quad - \quad 2 \\
x^2 - x - 2 \,\big/\, \overline{x^3 - 3x^2 + 0x + 4} \\
x^3 - x^2 - 2x \\
\hline
-2x^2 + 2x + 4 \\
-2x^2 + 2x + 4 \\
\hline
0
\end{array}
$$

Therefore $g(x) = (x - 2)^2 (x + 1)$ and we can write

$$
\frac{x^2 - 10x + 7}{(x - 2)^2 (x + 1)} = \frac{A}{x - 2} + \frac{B}{(x - 2)^2} + \frac{C}{x + 1}.
$$

Multiplying each side by $(x + 1)$ and then putting $x = -1$ we obtain

$$
\frac{1 + 10 + 7}{(-1 - 2)^2} = C \quad \text{and so} \quad C = 2.
$$

Multiplying each side by $(x - 2)^2$ and then putting $x = 2$ we obtain

$$
\frac{4 - 20 + 7}{3} = B \quad \text{and so} \quad B = -3.
$$

We cannot obtain A by a similar trick. We could find A by multiplying each side by $(x - 2)^2 (x + 1)$ and then comparing coefficients. A simpler way is to put $x = 0$ in the expressions as they stand to obtain

$$
\frac{7}{4} = \frac{A}{-2} + \frac{B}{4} + C = \frac{A}{-2} - \frac{3}{4} + 2
$$

and so $A = -1$.

The partial fraction decomposition is therefore

$$
\frac{x^2 - 10x + 7}{x^3 - 3x^2 + 4} = \frac{2}{x + 1} - \frac{1}{x - 2} - \frac{3}{(x - 2)^2}.
$$

□

The following lemmas will help us to prove the existence of the Partial Fraction Decomposition.

8.8.4 Lemma.   If $\mathrm{GCD}(g(x), h(x)) = 1$ then, for any real polynomial $f(x)$, there exist real polynomials $s(x)$ and $t(x)$ such that

$$\frac{f(x)}{g(x)h(x)} = \frac{s(x)}{g(x)} + \frac{t(x)}{h(x)}.$$

Proof.   The Euclidean Algorithm for Polynomials allows us to construct real polynomials $p(x)$ and $q(x)$ such that

$$p(x)g(x) + q(x)h(x) = \mathrm{GCD}(g(x), h(x)) = 1.$$

Multiplying this equation by $f(x)$ and dividing by $g(x)h(x)$ we obtain

$$\frac{f(x)p(x)}{h(x)} + \frac{f(x)q(x)}{g(x)} = \frac{f(x)}{g(x)h(x)}.$$

The result now follows with $s(x) = f(x)q(x)$ and $t(x) = f(x)p(x)$.   □

8.8.5 Lemma.   If $f(x)$ and $g(x)$ are real polynomials then, for each integer r, there exist real polynomials $p_0(x), p_1(x), \ldots, p_r(x)$ such that

$$\frac{f(x)}{[g(x)]^r} = p_0(x) + \frac{p_1(x)}{g(x)} + \frac{p_2(x)}{[g(x)]^2} + \cdots + \frac{p_r(x)}{[g(x)]^r}.$$

where $p_1(x), p_2(x), \ldots, p_r(x)$ are zero or have degrees that are all less than the degree of $g(x)$.

Proof.   Dividing $f(x)$ by $g(x)$, using the Division Algorithm, we obtain real polynomials $q_r(x)$ and $p_r(x)$ such that

$$f(x) = q_r(x)g(x) + p_r(x) \qquad \text{where } \deg p_r(x) < \deg g(x) \text{ or } p_r(x) = 0.$$

By repeated use of the Division Algorithm, we obtain

$$q_r(x) = q_{r-1}(x)g(x) + p_{r-1}(x)$$
$$q_{r-1}(x) = q_{r-2}(x)g(x) + p_{r-2}(x)$$
$$\vdots$$
$$q_2(x) = q_1(x)g(x) + p_1(x)$$

where, for each $k = r - 1, r - 2, \ldots, 1$, either $\deg p_k(x) < \deg g(x)$ or $p_k(x) = 0$. Putting $q_1(x) = p_0(x)$ and combining the above equations we obtain

$$f(x) = p_0(x)[g(x)]^r + p_1(x)[g(x)]^{r-1} + \cdots + p_{r-1}(x)g(x) + p_r(x).$$

We obtain the required result on dividing by $[g(x)]^r$. $\qquad\square$

Proof of the Partial Fraction Decomposition 8.8.1. By Theorem 8.5.6, the real polynomial $g(x)$ can be factored into irreducible linear quadratic factors in $\mathbb{R}[x]$. By grouping together all the multiple factors, and repeatedly using Lemma 8.8.4 and then Lemma 8.8.5 we obtain the result. $\qquad\square$

Exercise Set 8

1 - 8. Find the sum, difference and product of each of the following pairs of polynomials with coefficients in the indicated field.

1. $2x^3 + x^2 - 7x + 1$ and $x^2 - 2x - 1$ in $\mathbb{Q}[x]$

2. $x^2 + \frac{1}{2}x + \frac{1}{4}$ and $x^2 - \frac{1}{2}x + 1$ in $\mathbb{Q}[x]$

3. $x^2 - \sqrt{2}x + 1$ and $x^2 + \sqrt{2}x + 1$ in $\mathbb{R}[x]$

4. $ix^3 + (1 + 2i)x - 3$ and $x^2 - ix + 1 - i$ in $\mathbb{C}[x]$

5. $x^3 + 2x + 2$ and $x^4 + x^2 + x + 1$ in $\mathbb{Z}_3[x]$

6. $x^2 + x + 1$ and $x^3 + x^2 + x + 1$ in $\mathbb{Z}_2[x]$

7. $2x^2 + x + 4$ and $3x^2 + 2x + 1$ in $\mathbb{Z}_5[x]$

8. $x^5 + 2x + 4$ and $x^7 + 5x^3 + 4$ in $\mathbb{Z}_7[x]$

9. Do all polynomials of degree 1 with integral coefficients have an integral root? Do all polynomials of degree 1 with rational coefficients have a rational root?

10. Do all polynomials of degree 1 with coefficients in $\mathbb{Z}_5$ have a root in $\mathbb{Z}_5$? Do all polynomials of degree 2 with coefficients in $\mathbb{Z}_5$ have a root in $\mathbb{Z}_5$?

11. List all the polynomials of degree 3 with coefficients in $\mathbb{Z}_2$.

12. Find a polynomial in $\mathbb{Z}_2[x]$ that has no roots in $\mathbb{Z}_2$.

13 - 16. *Find all the roots, with their multiplicities, for the following polynomials in* $\mathbb{C}[x]$.

13. $(x-1)(x+2)(3x-5)$ **14.** $(x+1)^2(4x+1)^4(x-i)$
15. $(x^2-1)(2x^2+x-5)$ **16.** $x^2+2ix-1$

17 - 26. *Find the quotient and remainder when* $f(x)$ *is divided by* $g(x)$.

17. $f(x)=x^3+x^2+2x-1$ and $g(x)=x^2-2x+1$ in $\mathbb{Q}[x]$
18. $f(x)=x^2-2x+1$ and $g(x)=x^3+x^2+2x-1$ in $\mathbb{R}[x]$
19. $f(x)=x^4+\frac{5}{2}x^3+\frac{5}{2}x^2+\frac{3}{2}x+\frac{1}{2}$ and $g(x)=x^2+2x+1$ in $\mathbb{Q}[x]$
20. $f(x)=x^8+1$ and $g(x)=x-1$ in $\mathbb{C}[x]$
21. $f(x)=x^3+ix^2+(1+i)x+1$ and $g(x)=x+i$ in $\mathbb{C}[x]$
22. $f(x)=x^4+x+1$ and $g(x)=ix^2+x-2$ in $\mathbb{C}[x]$
23. $f(x)=x^3+2x^2+2$ and $g(x)=2x^2+x+1$ in $\mathbb{Z}_3[x]$
24. $f(x)=3x^5+3x^4+4x^2+4x+3$ and $g(x)=5x^3+2x^2+6x+3$ in $\mathbb{Z}_7[x]$
25. $f(x)=x^{10}+x^8+x+1$ and $g(x)=x^3+x+1$ in $\mathbb{Z}_2[x]$
26. $f(x)=10x^5+4x^3+x+3$ and $g(x)=3x^5+4$ in $\mathbb{Z}_{11}[x]$

27. Let $f(x)$ divide $g(x)$. If c is a root of $f(x)$, show that c is a root of $g(x)$. Does the converse hold?

28 - 33. *Find the remainder when* $f(x)$ *is divided by* $g(x)$.

28. $f(x)=4x^5+x^4-3x^3+x+5$ and $g(x)=x-1$ in $\mathbb{Q}[x]$
29. $f(x)=x^7+10x^5-4x^3+x^2$ and $g(x)=x+2$ in $\mathbb{Q}[x]$
30. $f(x)=ix^6+(1-2i)x^5+5ix^4-x+4$ and $g(x)=x+i$ in $\mathbb{C}[x]$
31. $f(x)=x^3+3x+1$ and $g(x)=x-1+4i$ in $\mathbb{C}[x]$
32. $f(x)=x^{72}+2x^{31}-1$ and $g(x)=x+\frac{1}{2}+\frac{\sqrt{3}i}{2}$ in $\mathbb{C}[x]$
33. $f(x)=x^5+2x+1$ and $g(x)=3x-4$ in $\mathbb{Q}[x]$

34. Factor the polynomials x^2-5x+5, x^2-5x+6 and x^2-5x+7 into irreducible factors in $\mathbb{C}[x]$, $\mathbb{R}[x]$ and $\mathbb{Q}[x]$.

35. Is x^3+x^2+1 an irreducible polynomial in $\mathbb{Z}_2[x]$?

36. When is x^3+px+q exactly divisible by x^2+mx-1?

37. When is x^4+px+q exactly divisible by x^2+mx+1?

38 - 41. *Solve the following polynomial equations over the indicated finite field, stating the multiplicity of any repeated solutions.*

38. $x^3+2x+2=0$ in $\mathbb{Z}_5$ **39.** $x^6+x^5+x+1=0$ in $\mathbb{Z}_2$
40. $x^5+x^4+x^3+2x^2+2x+2=0$ in $\mathbb{Z}_3$
41. $x^4+2x=4$ in $\mathbb{Z}_7$

42 - 46. *Find all the rational roots of each of the following rational polynomials.*

42. $x^3 + \frac{x^2}{2} + \frac{x}{2} - \frac{1}{2}$　　　　　　　　**43.** $x^4 + x + 1$

44. $x^4 + \frac{5}{6}x^3 - \frac{5x^2}{18} + \frac{1}{9}$　　　　　**45.** $x^3 - 6x^2 + 15x - 14$

46. $x^{17} - 2x^{14} + 1$

47. If p is a prime and n is an integer greater than 1, prove that $\sqrt[n]{p}$ is irrational.

48. Factor $2x^4 + x^3 + x^2 + 2x - 6$ in $\mathbb{Q}[x]$ and in $\mathbb{C}[x]$.

49. Find a rational polynomial with $\sqrt{2} + \sqrt{5}$ as a root, and then show that $\sqrt{2} + \sqrt{5}$ is irrational.

50 - 53. *Find all the real solutions to each of the following equations.*

50. $x^3 + 7x^2 + 8x - 10 = 0$

51. $2x^5 + x^4 - 8x^3 - 4x^2 + 8x + 4 = 0$

52. $4x^4 + x^2 + 3x + 1 = 0$　　　　　　**53.** $x^3 + \frac{23}{6}x^2 + \frac{29}{6}x + 2 = 0$

54. By means of the substitution $x = iy$, solve the equation $x^3 - 3ix^2 - x - 2i = 0$ in $\mathbb{C}$.

55 - 56. *Find all the complex roots of the following polynomials.*

55. $z^5 + 4z$　　　　　　　　　　**56.** $z^4 + iz^2 + 2$

57. Solve the equation $x^4 - 8x^3 + 18x^2 - 8x + 1 = 0$ given that $2 - \sqrt{3}$ is one solution.

58. If $1+i$ and $\sqrt{8}-1$ are roots of $f(x) = 2x^6 - 3x^5 - 17x^4 + 63x^3 - 91x^2 + 60x - 14$ find all its roots and factor $f(x)$ into irreducible polynomials in $\mathbb{C}[x]$, $\mathbb{R}[x]$ and $\mathbb{Q}[x]$.

59. Find a polynomial of lowest degree with integer coefficients that has $4 - \sqrt{2}$ and $3 - \sqrt{2}$ as roots.

60. Find a polynomial of degree 5 in $\mathbb{Q}[x]$ that has $2 - i$ and $\sqrt{2}i$ as roots.

61 - 64. *Find all the complex roots of each of the following real polynomials. In each case one root $x = c$ is given.*

61. $x^4 + 2x^3 + 2x^2 + 6x - 3$;　$c = -1 - \sqrt{2}$

62. $x^4 - 2x^3 - 2x^2 + 10x - 15$;　$c = 1 + \sqrt{2}i$

63. $x^4 - 10x^3 + 23x^2 + 30x - 78$;　$c = 5 - i$

64. $x^4 - (2 + 2\sqrt{2})x^3 + (2 + 4\sqrt{2})x^2 + (2\sqrt{2} - 6)x - 3$;　$c = \sqrt{2} + i$

65. Let $f(x) = x^2 - 5 \in \mathbb{Q}[x]$. Is $f(x)$ irreducible in $\mathbb{Q}[x]$ or in $\mathbb{R}[x]$?

66 - 69. *In each of the following equations, find the rational solutions, the number of real solutions and, for each irrational solution, c, find the integer a for which $a < c < a + 1$.*

66. $x^3 + x - 5 = 0$ **67.** $x^4 - 5x^3 - 6x^2 + 20x + 20 = 0$
68. $2x^4 + x^3 + 2x^2 + 3x + 1 = 0$ **69.** $x^5 + 4x - 7 = 0$

70 - 73. *Find all the rational solutions and the real solutions, to one decimal place, for each of the following equations.*

70. $x^4 - 4x^3 + 23 = 0$ **71.** $4x^3 - 9x^2 - 5x + 3 = 0$
72. $2x^5 + 12x^4 + x^2 + 11x + 30 = 0$ **73.** $3x^3 - 2x^2 + 5x + 1 = 0$

74 - 77. *Solve the following inequalities for $x \in \mathbb{R}$.*

74. $(x - 1)(3x + 2)(x + 6) \le 0$ **75.** $(x - 1)^2(x + 4)(x - 7) < 0$
76. $x^3 - 6x - 4 > 0$ **77.** $4x^4 - 13x^2 - 4x + 5 > 0$

78. Solve the inequality $x^3 - 27x + 5 > 0$, for $x \in \mathbb{R}$, to within one decimal place.

79 - 82. *By solving the equation $f'(x) = 0$, find the multiple roots, with their multiplicities, of each of the following polynomials.*

79. $f(x) = 27x^3 - 54x^2 + 36x - 8$ **80.** $f(x) = x^3 + 2x - 4$
81. $f(x) = x^4 - 4x^3 + 2x^2 + 4x + 1$
82. $f(x) = \sqrt{3}x^4 - 8x^3 + 6\sqrt{3}x^2 - 3\sqrt{3}$

83. Find a and b if $ax^{n+1} + bx^n + 1$ is divisible by $(x - 1)^2$.

84 - 86. *Find the greatest common divisor of each of the following pairs of polynomials.*

84. $f(x) = x^3 + x^2 + x + 1$ and $g(x) = x^2 + 4x + 3$ in $\mathbb{R}[x]$
85. $f(x) = x^3 - x^2 + ix - i$ and $g(x) = x^2 + i$ in $\mathbb{C}[x]$
86. $f(x) = x^5 + x^4 + x^2 + x$ and $g(x) = x^3 + x^2 + x + 1$ in $\mathbb{Z}_2[x]$

87 - 94. *Decompose the following into real partial fractions.*

87. $\dfrac{3}{4x^2 - x}$ **88.** $\dfrac{2x^2 + 1}{x^3 + x^2}$

89. $\dfrac{11x + 1}{4x^2 + 3x - 1}$ **90.** $\dfrac{1}{x^2 + 8x + 15}$

91. $\dfrac{(x + 3)(x - 3)}{(x + 1)^2(x + 5)}$ **92.** $\dfrac{x}{x^2 - 2}$

93. $\dfrac{2x^2 + x - 3}{x^3 - 1}$ **94.** $\dfrac{x^2 + 1}{x^3 - x + 6}$

95 - 96. *Find the roots of each polynomial in the fields,* $\mathbb{Q}$, $\mathbb{R}$, $\mathbb{C}$, *and* $\mathbb{Z}_7$.

95. $x^3 + 15x^2 + 15x + 14$ **96.** $2x^3 - 7x^2 + 16x - 15$

97 - 100. *Factor each polynomial into irreducible factors in the fields,* $\mathbb{Q}[x]$, $\mathbb{R}[x]$, $\mathbb{C}[x]$, *and* $\mathbb{Z}_p[x]$, *for the given p.*

97. $2x^3 + 2x^2 - 11x - 2$; $p = 3$ **98.** $3x^3 - x^2 + x + 2$; $p = 2$
99. $2x^4 + 5x^3 + 6x^2 + 4x + 1$; $p = 5$ **100.** $6x^4 + x^3 + 2x^2 - 4x + 1$; $p = 3$

Problem Set 8

101. Let $f(x)$ and $g(x)$ be two polynomials with coefficients in a field $\mathbb{F}$. If $f(x)$ divides $g(x)$, and $g(x)$ divides $f(x)$, show that $f(x) = cg(x)$ for some $c \in \mathbb{F}$.

102. Use the Factor Theorem to factor $x^3 + y^3 + z^3 - 3xyz$.

103. Let $\zeta = \text{cis}(2\pi/n)$. Show that 1, ζ, $\zeta^2, \ldots, \zeta^{n-1}$ are distinct solutions of $z^n = 1$ and show that

$$1 + \zeta + \zeta^2 + \cdots + \zeta^{n-1} = 0.$$

104. Prove that $x^{4n} + x^{3n} + x^{2n} + x^n + 1$ is divisible by $x^4 + x^3 + x^2 + x + 1$ whenever n is a positive integer, that is not a multiple of 5.

105. *(Wilson's Theorem)* If p is a prime, factor $x^{p-1} - 1$ in $\mathbb{Z}_p[x]$ and prove that $(p - 1)! \equiv -1 \pmod{p}$.

106. If α and β are roots of $x^2 + bx + c$, show that $\alpha + \beta = -b$ and $\alpha\beta = c$.

107. If α, β and γ are roots of $x^3 + bx^2 + cx + d$, show that $\alpha + \beta + \gamma = -b$, $\alpha\beta + \beta\gamma + \gamma\alpha = c$ and $\alpha\beta\gamma = -d$.

108. If α and β are roots of $x^2 - 10x + 2$, find a quadratic with 3α and 3β as roots.

109. If α and β are roots of $x^2 - 10x + 2$, find a quadratic with α^2 and β^2 as roots.

110. If α, β and γ are roots of $x^3 + 2x^2 - 3x + 5$, find $\alpha^3 + \beta^3 + \gamma^3$.

111. If α, β and γ are roots of $x^3 + 2x^2 - 3x + 5$, find a cubic with α^2, β^2 and γ^2 as roots.

112. If $f(x)$ and $g(x)$ are two polynomials of degree n, which give the same value for $n + 1$ different values of x, show that they have the same coefficients.

113. Let $\mathbb{F}$ be a field. When is the following theorem true? "If two polynomials in $\mathbb{F}[x]$ take the same values for all $x \in \mathbb{F}$, then they have the same coefficients."

114 - 118. *If $f : \mathbb{N} \to \mathbb{R}$ is a function from the nonnegative integers, $\mathbb{N}$, to the real numbers, define a new function*

$$\triangle f : \mathbb{N} \longrightarrow \mathbb{R} \quad by \quad \triangle f(n) = f(n+1) - f(n)$$

and inductively define $\triangle^{r+1} f = \triangle(\triangle^r f)$. The function $f : \mathbb{N} \to \mathbb{R}$ is called a polynomial function of degree r if

$$f(n) \;=\; a_r n^r + \cdots + a_1 n + a_0 \quad \text{for all } n \in \mathbb{N}$$

where $a_1, a_1, \ldots, a_r \in \mathbb{R}$ and $a_r \neq 0$.

114. If $f(n) = n^2 - 3n + 5$, calculate $\triangle f(n), \triangle^2 f(n)$ and $\triangle^3 f(n)$ for $n = 0, 1, 2, 3, 4$ and 5.

115. If $f : \mathbb{N} \to \mathbb{R}$ is any polynomial function of degree r, show that $\triangle^{r+1} f$ is the zero function, while $\triangle^r f$ is not the zero function.

116. Certain values of a polynomial function f are given in the following table.

n	12	13	14	15	16
$f(n)$	60	64	67	72	82

What is the smallest possible degree of f? If f does have this smallest degree, calculate $f(17)$ and $f(18)$.

117. (i) Calculate $\triangle f$ when $f(n) = \binom{n}{r}$.
  (ii) Show that, for any polynomial function of degree r,

$$f(n) \;=\; c_r \binom{n}{r} + c_{r-1} \binom{n}{r-1} + \cdots + c_0$$

  where $c_i = \triangle^i f(0)$.
  (iii) If a function f satisfies $\triangle^{r+1} f = 0, \triangle^r f \neq 0$, show that f is a polynomial function of degree r.

118. (i) Show that $\quad f(n+1) - f(0) \;=\; \triangle f(0) + \triangle f(1) + \cdots + \triangle f(n).$
  (ii) Calculate $\quad 1 + 2 + \cdots + n$
  $$1^2 + 2^2 + \cdots + n^2$$
  $$1^3 + 2^3 + \cdots + n^3$$

  using Problems 117(iii) and 118(i).

119. Find all irreducible polynomials of degree ≤ 4 in $\mathbb{Z}_2[x]$.

120. Find one irreducible quadratic and one irreducible cubic in $\mathbb{Z}_3[x]$.

121. (i) Show that $f_n(x) = x^n + x + 1 \in \mathbb{Z}_2[x]$ has no roots in $\mathbb{Z}_2$.

(ii) For each degree $n \geq 2$, find polynomials in $\mathbb{Z}_2[x]$ of degree n which have both elements of $\mathbb{Z}_2$ as roots.

122. Check that $x^3 + 5x \in \mathbb{Z}_6[x]$ has roots 0, 1, 2, 3, 4 and 5 in $\mathbb{Z}_6$. Does this contradict Theorem 8.1.7?

123. Is $\sqrt{3} + \sqrt[3]{3}$ rational or irrational?

124. If p/q is a rational root, in its lowest terms, of a polynomial $f(x)$ with integral coefficients, then show that

$$f(x) \;=\; (qx - p)g(x)$$

for some polynomial $g(x)$ with *integral* coefficients.

125. Let $f(x)$ be a polynomial with integral coefficients. Show that the rational number p/q, in its lowest terms, cannot be a root of $f(x)$ unless $|q - p|$ divides $|f(1)|$. This result can be used to shorten the list of possible rational roots of an integral polynomial.

126. Let $f(x)$ be a polynomial with integral coefficients. For each integer m, generalize the result of the previous problem by finding a necessary condition for p/q to be a rational root of $f(x)$, in terms of the divisibility of $f(m)$.

127 - 130. Find all the rational roots of the following equations.

127. $x^3 + 20x - 144 = 0$ **128.** $8x^3 + 20x^2 + 14x - 93 = 0$

129. $9x^4 - 2x^2 - 2x + 24 = 0$

130. $20x^5 + 8x^4 + 15x^3 + x^2 - 27x - 10 = 0$

131. Show that an even degree polynomial with odd integer coefficients contains no rational roots.

132. Prove that there is no polynomial of positive degree with integer coefficients that takes prime values for all positive integers.

133. (i) Use De Moivre's Theorem and the Binomial Theorem to prove that, for each integer r, $\cos(\frac{2r\pi}{5})$ is a solution to the equation

$$16x^5 - 20x^3 + 5x - 1 \;=\; 0.$$

(ii) Factor $16x^5 - 20x^3 + 5x - 1$ into irreducible factors in $\mathbb{R}[x]$ and find the value of $\cos(\frac{2\pi}{5})$.

134. (i) Write $\cos 4\theta$ in terms of $\cos \theta$ and find the values of $\cos \theta$ for which

$$\cos 4\theta = \cos \theta.$$

(ii) Which values of θ satisfy the equation $\cos 4\theta = \cos \theta$?

135. If the rational polynomial $x^3 + bx^2 + cx + d$ has a rational root, r, and if $c + r^2 = 0$, show that all of the roots are rational.

136. Prove Theorem 8.5.8 by dividing $f(x)$ by the quadratic

$$(x - a - b\sqrt{c})(x - a + b\sqrt{c}).$$

137. (i) Let $f(x)$ be a real polynomial that changes sign between a and b. By factoring $f(x)$ into irreducible real factors, prove that $f(x)$ has a real root between a and b.

(ii) Hence prove that an odd degree real polynomial always has at least one real root. (These proofs of the Intermediate Value Theorem 8.5.1 and Proposition 8.5.5 appear to avoid the use of continuity. However, continuity is needed in the proof of the Fundamental Theorem of Algebra, which is used in Theorem 8.5.6 for the factorization of real polynomials.)

138. The polynomial $f(x) = x^7 - 8x^6 + 17x^5 + 5x^4 - 22x^3 - 37x^2 - 26x + 10$ is known to have $3 - i$ and $2 + \sqrt{3}$ as roots. Find all its roots and factor it into irreducible factors in $\mathbb{C}[x]$, $\mathbb{R}[x]$ and $\mathbb{Q}[x]$.

139. Let

$$f_n(x) = 1 + x + \frac{x^2}{2!} + \cdots + \frac{x^n}{n!}.$$

Show that $f_n(x)$ has no real roots if n is even, and one real root if n is odd.

***140 - 143.** Solve the following inequalities for $x \in \mathbb{R}$, giving your answer, if necessary, to one decimal place.*

140. $\dfrac{x}{2x^2 + x - 1} \geq 4$

141. $\dfrac{1}{(x - 2)(x - 3)} > \dfrac{1}{(x - 1)(x - 4)}$

142. $\dfrac{4}{x} \geq x^2 + 3x - 1$

143. $|x^3 - 3x - 1| < 2x$

144. If a cubic polynomial with rational coefficients has a double root, show that all its roots are rational.

145. Show that the remainder, when the real polynomial $f(x)$ is divided by $(x - c)^2$, is $f'(c)(x - c) + f(c)$, where $f'(x)$ is the derivative of $f(x)$.

146. Generalize the previous problem and find the remainder when the real polynomial $f(x)$ is divided by $(x - c)^r$.

147. If $f(x)$ and $g(x)$ are irreducible polynomials in $\mathbb{F}[x]$, with $f(x) \neq kg(x)$ for any $k \in \mathbb{F}$, show that $\mathrm{GCD}(f(x), g(x)) = 1$.

148. Find the repeated root of the polynomial $x^4 - 6x^3 + 10x^2 - 6x + 9$.

149. By looking at $f(x) + f'(x)$, show that the polynomial

$$f(x) \;=\; x^6 - 6x^5 + 32x^4 - 128x^3 + 388x^2 - 776x + 777$$

has no repeated roots.

150. Show that $f(x) = x^3 + px + q$ has a double root if and only if $\dfrac{4p^3}{27} + q^2 = 0$.

151. Find polynomials $s(x), t(x) \in \mathbb{Z}_3[x]$ such that

$$s(x)(x^4 + 2x^2 + 1) + t(x)(x^4 + x^3 + 2x^2 + x + 1) \;=\; x^2 + 1 \quad \text{in } \mathbb{Z}_3[x].$$

*152 - 153. For each polynomial $f(x)$, find all the values of the rational number m for which $f(x)$ has a rational root. For each of these values of m that are **integers**, factor $f(x)$ into irreducible factors in $\mathbb{Q}[x]$, $\mathbb{R}[x]$, and $\mathbb{C}[x]$.*

152. $f(x) = x^3 + 3x^2 + mx + 5$ **153.** $f(x) = x^3 + mx^2 - 5x - 3$

154. (a) Let $f(x) = x^5 + 3x^4 + 2x^3 + 2x^2 + x - 1$. It is known that i is a root of $f(x)$. Factor $f(x)$ completely over the fields $\mathbb{Q}$, $\mathbb{R}$, $\mathbb{C}$, and $\mathbb{Z}_5$.

    (b) Let $g(x) = x^4 + x^3 - 2x^2 + 3x - 1$ in $\mathbb{Q}[x]$. Find $\mathrm{GCD}(f(x), g(x))$ where $f(x) \in \mathbb{Q}[x]$ is the polynomial in part (a).

155. (a) Let $f(x) = x^4 - 6x^3 + 14x^2 - 16x + 8$. Find a repeated root of $f(x)$ in $\mathbb{Q}$, or prove that one does not exist.

    (b) Factor $f(x)$ into a product of irreducible polynomials in $\mathbb{Q}[x]$, $\mathbb{R}[x]$, $\mathbb{C}[x]$, and $\mathbb{Z}_5[x]$.

156. Find $\mathrm{GCD}(f(x), f(x+1))$ when $f(x) = x^4 - 5x^2 + 4$.

157. If a, b and c are distinct integers, prove that there is no polynomial $p(x)$, with integral coefficients, for which $p(a) = b$, $p(b) = c$ and $p(c) = a$.

158. If $p(x) = 4x^5 + 8x^4 + 15x^3 + 30x^2 - 4x - 8$ then $p(2i) = 0$. Find all the real roots of $p(x)$, and hence factor $p(x)$ into irreducible factors in $\mathbb{Q}[x]$, $\mathbb{R}[x]$, $\mathbb{C}[x]$, and $\mathbb{Z}_7[x]$.

159. The polynomial $f(x) = x^5 + 2x^4 - 3x^2 - 4x - 2$ has $\sqrt{2}$ as one of its roots. Factor $f(x)$ into irreducible polynomials over the rational numbers, the real numbers, and the complex numbers.

160. The polynomial $f(x) = 3x^5 - 2x^4 + x^3 + 24x^2 - 16x + 8$ has $1 + \sqrt{3}i$ as a root. Find the irreducible factors of $f(x)$ over $\mathbb{Q}[x]$, $\mathbb{R}[x]$, and $\mathbb{C}[x]$.

Appendix

TRIGONOMETRY

We always measure angles in *radians*. One revolution or 360° is equal to 2π radians. An angle is therefore just a real number (modulo 2π).

The values of the trigonometric functions *sine* and *cosine* are illustrated in the following diagram. Consider the unit circle in the coordinate plane and a radius vector making an angle θ with the positive x-axis. A positive angle is measured in a counter-clockwise direction. The sine of θ, $\sin \theta$, is the projection of the radius vector onto the y-axis and the cosine of θ, $\cos \theta$, is the projection on the x-axis.

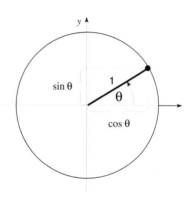

The sine and cosine are real valued functions whose domain is the set of all real numbers, $\mathbb{R}$, and whose image is the set of real numbers from -1 to 1.

All trigonometric functions are periodic of period 2π so, for example,

$$\sin(\theta + 2k\pi) \;=\; \sin \theta \quad \text{for all } \theta \in \mathbb{R} \text{ and all } k \in \mathbb{Z}.$$

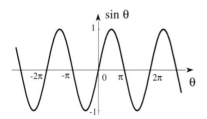

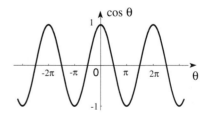

241

Four other trigonometric functions can be defined in terms of sine and cosine.

The *tangent* of θ, $\tan\theta = \sin\theta/\cos\theta$.

The *secant* of θ, $\sec\theta = 1/\cos\theta$.

The *cosecant* of θ, $\operatorname{cosec}\theta = 1/\sin\theta$.

The *cotangent* of θ, $\cot\theta = 1/\tan\theta$.

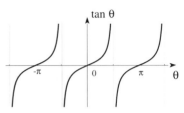

For example, $\tan\theta$ defines a function whose domain is all the real numbers, except $(2k+1)\pi/2$ where $k \in \mathbb{Z}$, and whose image is $\mathbb{R}$.

The trigonometric functions of the angles $\pi/4$, $\pi/6$ and $\pi/3$ should be remembered by means of the following right angled triangles.

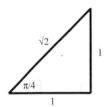
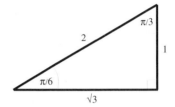

Using the above triangles and the relations

$$\begin{aligned} \sin(-\theta) &= -\sin\theta, & \cos(-\theta) &= \cos\theta \\ \sin(\pi-\theta) &= \sin\theta & \cos(\pi-\theta) &= -\cos\theta \end{aligned}$$

we obtain the following table of values of the trigonometric functions.

θ		$\sin\theta$			$\cos\theta$			$\tan\theta$		
Radians	*Degrees*									
0	0°	0	=	0.0	1	=	1.0	0	=	0.0
$\pi/6$	30°	$1/2$	=	0.5	$\sqrt{3}/2$	$\approx$	0.886	$1/\sqrt{3}$	$\approx$	0.577
$\pi/4$	45°	$1/\sqrt{2}$	$\approx$	0.707	$1/\sqrt{2}$	$\approx$	0.707	1	=	1.0
$\pi/3$	60°	$\sqrt{3}/2$	$\approx$	0.866	$1/2$	=	0.5	$\sqrt{3}$	$\approx$	1.732
$\pi/2$	90°	1	=	1.0	0	=	0.0	∞	=	∞
$2\pi/3$	120°	$\sqrt{3}/2$	$\approx$	0.866	$-1/2$	=	−0.5	$-\sqrt{3}$	$\approx$	−1.732
$3\pi/4$	135°	$1/\sqrt{2}$	$\approx$	0.707	$-1/\sqrt{2}$	$\approx$	−0.707	-1	=	−1.0
$5\pi/6$	150°	$1/2$	=	0.5	$-\sqrt{3}/2$	$\approx$	−0.866	$-1/\sqrt{3}$	$\approx$	−0.577
π	180°	0	=	0.0	-1	=	−1.0	0	=	0.0
$7\pi/6$	210°	$-1/2$	=	−0.5	$-\sqrt{3}/2$	$\approx$	−0.866	$1/\sqrt{3}$	$\approx$	0.577
$5\pi/4$	225°	$-1/\sqrt{2}$	$\approx$	−0.707	$-1/\sqrt{2}$	$\approx$	−0.707	1	=	1.0
$4\pi/3$	240°	$-\sqrt{3}/2$	$\approx$	−0.866	$-1/2$	=	−0.5	$\sqrt{3}$	$\approx$	1.732
$3\pi/2$	270°	-1	=	−1.0	0	=	0.0	∞	=	∞
$5\pi/3$	300°	$-\sqrt{3}/2$	$\approx$	−0.866	$1/2$	=	0.5	$-\sqrt{3}$	$\approx$	−1.732
$7\pi/4$	315°	$-1/\sqrt{2}$	$\approx$	−0.707	$1/\sqrt{2}$	$\approx$	0.707	-1	=	−1.0
$11\pi/6$	330°	$-1/2$	=	−0.5	$\sqrt{3}/2$	$\approx$	0.866	$-1/\sqrt{3}$	$\approx$	−0.577
2π	360°	0	=	0.0	1	=	1.0	0	=	0.0

Standard Trigonometric Formulas.

$$\sin^2 \theta + \cos^2 \theta = 1$$
$$\sin\left(\tfrac{\pi}{2} - \theta\right) = \cos\theta$$
$$\cos\left(\tfrac{\pi}{2} - \theta\right) = \sin\theta$$
$$\sin(\theta + \phi) = \sin\theta\cos\phi + \cos\theta\sin\phi$$
$$\sin(\theta - \phi) = \sin\theta\cos\phi - \cos\theta\sin\phi$$
$$\cos(\theta + \phi) = \cos\theta\cos\phi - \sin\theta\sin\phi$$
$$\cos(\theta - \phi) = \cos\theta\cos\phi + \sin\theta\sin\phi$$
$$\sin 2\theta = 2\sin\theta\cos\theta$$
$$\cos 2\theta = \cos^2\theta - \sin^2\theta$$
$$= 2\cos^2\theta - 1 = 1 - 2\sin^2\theta$$
$$\sin\theta + \sin\phi = 2\sin\left(\frac{\theta + \phi}{2}\right)\cos\left(\frac{\theta - \phi}{2}\right)$$
$$\sin\theta - \sin\phi = 2\cos\left(\frac{\theta + \phi}{2}\right)\sin\left(\frac{\theta - \phi}{2}\right)$$
$$\cos\theta + \cos\phi = 2\cos\left(\frac{\theta + \phi}{2}\right)\cos\left(\frac{\theta - \phi}{2}\right)$$
$$\cos\theta - \cos\phi = -2\sin\left(\frac{\theta + \phi}{2}\right)\sin\left(\frac{\theta - \phi}{2}\right)$$

INEQUALITIES

It is not always possible to reduce a mathematical problem to an exact equation, though it may be possible to obtain an inequality instead. Any inequality of the form $a > b$ may be rewritten as $a - b > 0$; in other words, an inequality can be reduced to the question of whether a certain expression is positive or not. We state some basic assumptions about the positive real numbers from which the properties of inequalities can be derived.

The *positive real numbers*, $\mathbb{R}_{>0}$, satisfy the following properties.

(i) If x and y are positive, then $x + y$ and xy are positive.

(ii) For each $x \in \mathbb{R}$, exactly one of the following three relations hold: x is positive, $-x$ is positive, or $x = 0$.

The relation *greater than* may be defined in terms of the positive numbers by:

$$a > b \text{ if and only if } a - b \text{ is positive.}$$

By '$a \geq b$', we mean $a > b$ or $a = b$. We say that a is *negative* if $-a$ is positive.

For example, $6 > 4$, $-2 > -3$, $7 \geq 4$ and $7 \geq 7$.

Properties of Inequalities.

   (i) If $a > b$ and $b > c$ then $a > c$. *(Transitive Property)*

   (ii) If $a > b$ and $c > d$ then $a + c > b + d$.

   (iii) If $a > b$ and $c > 0$ then $ac > bc$.

   (iv) If $a > b$ and $c < 0$ then $ac < bc$.

   (v) If $a > b$ then $-a < -b$.

   (vi) If $ab > 0$ then either a and b are both positive, or a and b are both negative.

   (vii) If $ab < 0$ then either a is positive and b negative, or a is negative and b positive.

   (viii) If $a \neq 0$ then a^2 is positive.

Property (ii) shows that we may freely add inequalities, but Properties (v) and (iv) show that we have to be more careful when subtracting inequalities or multiplying both sides of an inequality by any expression. If we multiply both sides by a positive number then the inequality sign remains the same, but if we multiply by a negative number then the inequality sign is reversed.

The problem of solving an inequality can be reduced to the problem of solving the corresponding equality. If the graph of the function f is known then the values of x for which $f(x) > 0$ or $f(x) \geq 0$ can be read off. The crucial parts of the graph are the points in which it crosses the x-axis. These are the values of x for which $f(x) = 0$. Therefore the solution of an inequality depends on the solution of the corresponding equality.

Even if the graph is not known exactly, it is helpful to check a solution to an inequality by making a rough sketch of the graph.

Example. Solve the inequality $x^2 - 3x - 4 > 0$.

Solution. The quadratic $x^2 - 3x - 4$ can be factored and the inequality becomes

$$(x - 4)(x + 1) > 0.$$

By Property (vi), either (i) $x - 4 > 0$ and $x + 1 > 0$, or (ii) $x - 4 < 0$ and $x + 1 < 0$. That is, either (i) $x > 4$ and $x > -1$, or (ii) $x < 4$ and $x < -1$. Hence either (i) $x > 4$, or (ii) $x < -1$.

The solution to the inequality is therefore $x > 4$ or $x < -1$. The solution set can be written as $\{x \in \mathbb{R} \mid x > 4 \text{ or } x < -1\}$, which is the union of the open intervals $(-\infty, -1) \cup (4, \infty)$.

Check. The graph of $f(x) = x^2 - 3x - 4$ is a parabola that crosses the x-axis at $x = -1$ and $x = 4$. From the graph we see that the solution to $f(x) > 0$ is $x > 4$ or $x < -1$.

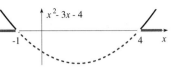

Example. Solve the inequality $\dfrac{x-1}{x+1} \geq 3$.

Solution. Notice that x cannot be -1 because the left hand side is not defined there. Rewriting the inequality, we have

$$\frac{x-1-3x-3}{x+1} \geq 0 \qquad \text{and so} \qquad \frac{2(x+2)}{x+1} \leq 0.$$

Since $(x+1) \neq 0$, we can multiply both sides of the inequality by the positive quantity $(x+1)^2$ to obtain

$$2(x+2)(x+1) \leq 0.$$

Therefore either (i) $x + 2 \geq 0$ and $x + 1 < 0$, or (ii) $x + 2 \leq 0$ and $x + 1 > 0$. In case (i), $x \geq -2$ and $x < -1$ and we see that $-2 \leq x < -1$.

Case (i)   Case (ii)

In case (ii), $x \leq -2$ and $x > -1$, which is impossible.

The solution set to the original inequality is therefore $\{x \in \mathbb{R} \mid -2 \leq x < -1\}$, which is the half-open interval $[-2, -1)$.

Check. If we sketch the function

$$f(x) = \frac{x-1}{x+1}$$

we obtain a hyperbola and we see that $f(x) \geq 3$ when $-2 \leq x < -1$.

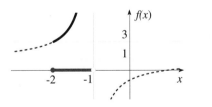

Example. Solve the inequality $|x + 2| > 3x$.

Solution. Recall that the absolute value $|x + 2|$ is defined as $x + 2$ if $x + 2 \geq 0$ and as $-(x + 2)$ is $x + 2 < 0$. Therefore, whenever an inequality contains an absolute value, we must consider the different ranges of x separately.

Case (i). Let $x \geq -2$. The inequality now becomes

$$x + 2 > 3x$$

or $2 > 2x$. Hence $x < 1$ which, together with condition $x \geq -2$, implies that the inequality is satisfied when $-2 \leq x < 1$.

Case (ii). Let $x < -2$. The inequality, in this range, becomes $-x - 2 > 3x$ or $-2 > 4x$. Hence $x < -1/2$ which, together with the condition $x < -2$, implies that the inequality is satisfied when $x < -2$.

The complete solution set to the original inequality is therefore

$$\{x \in \mathbb{R} \mid x < -2 \text{ or } -2 \leq x < 1\} = \{x \in \mathbb{R} \mid x < 1\}$$

which is the open interval $(-\infty, 1)$.

Check. If we sketch the graphs of $f(x) = |x+2|$ and $g(x) = 3x$ we see that

$$f(x) > g(x)$$

whenever $x < 1$.

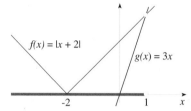

One of the most important inequalities in many variables is the connection between the arithmetic and geometric means. Let $a_1, a_2, \ldots, a_n$ be n positive real numbers. Their *arithmetic mean* is the number

$$\mathrm{AM}(a_1, a_2, \ldots, a_n) = \frac{a_1 + a_2 + \cdots + a_n}{n}$$

that is, the ordinary 'average' of the numbers. Their *geometric mean* is the number

$$\mathrm{GM}(a_1, a_2, \ldots, a_n) = \sqrt[n]{a_1 \cdot a_2 \cdots a_n}.$$

Theorem of the Means.

If a_1 and a_2 are positive real numbers then

$$\mathrm{AM}(a_1, a_2) \geq \mathrm{GM}(a_1, a_2)$$

with equality holding if and only if $a_1 = a_2$.

Proof. Consider the difference between the two means

$$\begin{aligned}
\mathrm{AM}(a_1, a_2) - \mathrm{GM}(a_1, a_2) &= \frac{a_1 + a_2}{2} - \sqrt{a_1 a_2} \\
&= \frac{a_1 - 2\sqrt{a_1}\sqrt{a_2} + a_2}{2} \\
&= \frac{(\sqrt{a_1} - \sqrt{a_2})^2}{2} \geq 0
\end{aligned}$$

equality holding if and only if $\sqrt{a_1} = \sqrt{a_2}$; that is, if and only if $a_1 = a_2$.

Hence $\dfrac{a_1 + a_2}{2} \geq \sqrt{a_1 a_2}$, equality holding if and only if $a_1 = a_2$.

Answers

to the odd numbered Exercises and Problems

EXERCISE SET 0, page 16

1. True statement

3. Not a statement

5. Not a statement

7.

P	NOT(NOT P)
T	T
F	F

9.

P	Q	R	$P \Longrightarrow$ $(Q$ OR $R)$
T	T	T	T
T	T	F	T
T	F	T	T
T	F	F	F
F	T	T	T
F	T	F	T
F	F	T	T
F	F	F	T

11.

P	Q	R	$(P$ OR NOT $Q)$ $\Longrightarrow R$
T	T	T	T
T	T	F	F
T	F	T	T
T	F	F	F
F	T	T	T
F	T	F	T
F	F	T	T
F	F	F	F

15.

P	Q	P NOR Q
T	T	F
T	F	F
F	T	F
F	F	T

17. $Q \Longrightarrow P$

19. $P \Longrightarrow Q$

21. $P \Longleftrightarrow Q$

25. $P \Longrightarrow Q$

27. Q AND NOT P

29. If I have broken my leg then I cannot walk.

31. If I take the bus then I have broken my leg or I cannot walk.

33. $\exists x \ \forall y \quad x \leq y$; integers

35. $\exists x \ \forall y \ \forall z \quad x > yz$; integers

37. $\exists x \ ($ NOT $P(x)$ AND NOT $Q(x))$

39. $\forall x \ (P(x)$ AND NOT $Q(x))$

41. Every real number is as large as any real number. False
43. There is a smallest real number. False
45. Equivalent   **47.** Not equivalent
49. $\exists x \, ((x \in A) \text{ AND } (x \in B) \text{ AND } (x \notin C))$
51. $\exists \epsilon > 0 \; \forall \delta > 0 \; \exists x \quad (0 < |x - a| < \delta \text{ AND } |f(x) - L| \geq \epsilon)$
57. If $x^2 \leq 9$ then $x \leq 3$.
59. If a number is prime then it is not divisible by 2.

EXERCISE SET 1, page 42

1. $q = 4, r = 1$ **3.** $q = 1, r = 0$
5. $q = -3, r = 0$ **7.** $q = -23, r = 7$
13. 11   **15.** 1
17. 16
19. $11 = 14 \cdot 484 + (-15)451$ is one form
21. $1 = (-7)17 + 8 \cdot 15$ is one form
23. $5 = (-1)100 + (-3)(-35)$ is one form
25. $17 = 0 \cdot 51 + 1 \cdot 17$ is one form   **29.** 195/782
31. $x = 2, y = -1$ is one solution   **33.** $x = 9, y = 0$ is one solution
35. No solutions
37. $x = 4 - 9n, y = 7n - 3$, where $n \in \mathbb{Z}$, is one way to write all the solutions
39. $x = 8n - 1, y = 5n - 1$, where $n \in \mathbb{Z}$, is one way to write all the solutions
41. No solutions
43. $(x, y) = (2, 108), (11, 94), (20, 80), (29, 66), (38, 52), (47, 38), (56, 24)$,
or $(65, 10)$
45. No nonnegative solutions
47. Yes; $1000 = 847 + 153 = 660 + 340 = 473 + 527 = 286 + 714 = 99 + 901$
49. Yes; $120 = 84 + 36$ **51.** Yes, in two ways
53. 311   **55.** 16033
57. $(1628)_9$ **59.** $(1010)_3$
61. $(BAX)_{60}$ where $B = 11$, $A = 10$ and $X = 39$
63. $(3233)_4$ and $(1001110)_4$ **67.** 6
71. $2^5 \cdot 3 \cdot 5 \cdot 11$, $2^3 \cdot 5^2 \cdot 17^2$, GCD = 40, LCM = 7629600

PROBLEM SET 1, page 45

75. No; for example, $a = b = 1, c = 3$
77. $c = 13, 18, 21, 23, 26, 67, 70, 72, 75, 80$ and all c in the range $28 \leq c \leq 65$
except 30,32,35,40,53,58,61,63.
79. 18 small and 10 large trucks, or 1 small and 24 large trucks.
81. No

85. Solve $ax + \text{GCD}(b, c) \cdot t = e$ and $by' + cz' = \text{GCD}(b, c)$ and take $y = ty'$, $z = tz'$.

87. One solution is $x = 10$, $y = -125$, $z = 25$.

91. Base 4 below 1000 and base 5 or 6 below 10^6

95. Look at the powers of 2 in the numerator and denominator.

99. True   **101.** True

105. $\phi(7) = 6$, $\phi(12) = 4$, $\phi(16) = 8$, $\phi(25) = 20$, $\phi(27) = 18$

EXERCISE SET 2, page 70

1. $-12, -4$ and 0; $-11, 1$ and 5; $-6, 2$ and 10; $-9, -1, 3$ and 7.

3. 1   **5.** 6

9. $k = 16$ **11.** $k = 28$

13. The sum of the digits is divisible by 3 and the last two digits are divisible by 4.

15. The sum of the digits is divisible by 7.

17. 2, 4, 5, 8 and 10   **19.** 2, 3, 4, 6 and 11

21. The calculation is incorrect.

23. Reflexive and transitive   **25.** Reflexive and symmetric

27.

+	[0]	[1]
[0]	[0]	[1]
[1]	[1]	[0]

·	[0]	[1]
[0]	[0]	[0]
[1]	[0]	[1]

$[1]^{-1} = [1]$

29.

+	[0]	[1]	[2]	[3]	[4]	[5]	[6]
[0]	[0]	[1]	[2]	[3]	[4]	[5]	[6]
[1]	[1]	[2]	[3]	[4]	[5]	[6]	[0]
[2]	[2]	[3]	[4]	[5]	[6]	[0]	[1]
[3]	[3]	[4]	[5]	[6]	[0]	[1]	[2]
[4]	[4]	[5]	[6]	[0]	[1]	[2]	[3]
[5]	[5]	[6]	[0]	[1]	[2]	[3]	[4]
[6]	[6]	[0]	[1]	[2]	[3]	[4]	[5]

·	[0]	[1]	[2]	[3]	[4]	[5]	[6]
[0]	[0]	[0]	[0]	[0]	[0]	[0]	[0]
[1]	[0]	[1]	[2]	[3]	[4]	[5]	[6]
[2]	[0]	[2]	[4]	[6]	[1]	[3]	[5]
[3]	[0]	[3]	[6]	[2]	[5]	[1]	[4]
[4]	[0]	[4]	[1]	[5]	[2]	[6]	[3]
[5]	[0]	[5]	[3]	[1]	[6]	[4]	[2]
[6]	[0]	[6]	[5]	[4]	[3]	[2]	[1]

$[1]^{-1} = [1]$, $[2]^{-1} = [4]$, $[3]^{-1} = [5]$, $[4]^{-1} = [2]$, $[5]^{-1} = [3]$, $[6]^{-1} = [6]$

33. $x \equiv 5$ or $12 \pmod{14}$ **35.** $x \equiv 103 \pmod{128}$

37. No solution   **39.** $x \equiv 1$ or $5 \pmod 8$

41. $x \equiv 1 \pmod 2$ **43.** $[21]$

45. $x = [5]$ **47.** $x = [0], [2], [3]$ or $[5]$

49. $x \equiv 19 \pmod{20}$ **51.** $x \equiv 17 \pmod{42}$

53. $x \equiv 65 \pmod{161}$ **55.** $x = 124$ or 299

PROBLEM SET 2, page 72

59. Yes   **61.** $2^{91} \not\equiv 2 \pmod{91}$

63. $k = 1$ only

65. Prove $2^{32} \equiv -1 \pmod{641}$ using $5^5 \cdot 2^3 \equiv 1$ and $5 \cdot 2^7 \equiv -1 \pmod{641}$

67. (b) $-\pi$ and π, $11\pi/6$ and $23\pi/6$.

71. $x = [1], y = [6]$

73. Yes   **75.** 4

79. If $a \not\equiv 0 \pmod{p}$ there exists b such that $ab \equiv 1 \pmod{p}$. Hence the nonzero congruence classes in $\mathbb{Z}_p$ can be paired off, $[a]$ with $[b]$, where $[a][b] = [1]$; $[1]$ and $[p-1]$ being paired with themselves. These facts can be used to prove Wilson's Theorem.

81. $x \equiv 25, 51$ or $77 \pmod{78}$ or equivalently $x \equiv 25 \pmod{26}$

83. 144 days and 720 days   **85.** No solution

89. 119   **91.** $x \equiv 55a_1 + 45a_2 \pmod{99}$

EXERCISE SET 3, page 91

1. 10   **3.** 70

7. $n = 7$ **9.** $\sum_{r=3}^{n}(r^2 - 1)$

21. True   **23.** True

33. (e) Multiplication is defined by $n \cdot 1 = n$ and $n \cdot (m^\dagger) = (n \cdot m) + n$.

35. $a^5 - 5a^4 + 10a^3 - 10a^2 + 5a - 1$

37. $256x^8 - 768x^6y^3 + 864x^4y^6 - 432x^2y^9 + 81y^{12}$

39. 79.925   **41.** $26400000x^{22}$

PROBLEM SET 3, page 94

55. Move the smallest disc to peg B, if n is odd, or to peg C, if n is even.

59. 1, 1, 2, 3, 5, 8, 13, 21, 34, 55, 89, 144, 233, 377, 610

61. The remainders are the previous terms in the sequence.

69. Imagine that a cuckolded husband has horns on his head that can be seen by all the other men, but cannot be seen or felt by himself. Then use as induction hypothesis, "If n wives committed adultery then their husbands would know about it by the morning of the nth day".

71. $(n^2 + n + 2)/2$ **79.** $x_n x_{n-1} \cdots x_2 x_1$

81. $x_1 - 2x_2 + 4x_3 + \cdots + (-2)^{n-1}x_n$

83. $e(0) = 1; e(n) = e(n-1) + \frac{1}{n!}$ for $n > 0$

EXERCISE SET 4, page 109

9. a, c, e

11. $f/2, f/2.8, f/4, f/5.7, f/8, f/11.3, f/16$

13. 16

17. $\sqrt{6}$

21. $3a^{13/4} - a^{3/2}$

25. .175 or .174$\dot{9}$

29. 19/45

15. 27

19. 4

23. .08$\dot{3}$

27. 421/200

31. 487/3700

PROBLEM SET 4, page 111

33. $\mathbb{Z}$ is the quotient set of $\mathbb{P} \times \mathbb{P}$ under the equivalence relation $\sim$, defined by $(a, b) \sim (c, d)$ if and only if $a + d = b + c$.

35. (a) $\sqrt{2}$ and $1 - \sqrt{2}$ (b) $\sqrt{2}$ and $\sqrt{2}$ (c) Yes; consider $x = \sqrt{2}^{\sqrt{2}}$. If x is rational this provides an example. If x is irrational, then $x^{\sqrt{2}} = (\sqrt{2}^{\sqrt{2}})^{\sqrt{2}} = (\sqrt{2})^2 = 2$ provides an example.

39. $3\sqrt[3]{9} + 3\sqrt[3]{6} + 4\sqrt[3]{4}$

43. $(.13)_6$

47. $(.\dot{0}1\dot{1}\dot{0})_3$

41. (b) Yes (c) See Problem 42

45. .2453$\dot{7}\dot{0}$

49. 1315/504

EXERCISE SET 5, page 138

1. Not a function

5. $X = \mathbb{R}$
$Y = \{y \mid y \geq -1\}$
$f : X \to Y$ has no inverse

7. $X = \mathbb{R} - \{-1, 0\}$
$Y = \mathbb{R} - \{0, 1\}$
$f : X \to Y$ has an inverse
$f^{-1}(x) = \frac{1-x}{x}$

9. $X = \mathbb{R}$
$Y = [-1, 1]$
$f : X \to$ has no inverse

11. $X = \{x \mid x < 3\}$
$Y = \mathbb{R}$
$f : X \to Y$ has an inverse
$f^{-1}(x) = 3 - 10^x$

13. $X = \bigcup_{k \in \mathbb{Z}} [2k\pi, (2k+1)\pi]$
$Y = [0, 1]$
$f : X \to Y$ has no inverse

3. Not a function

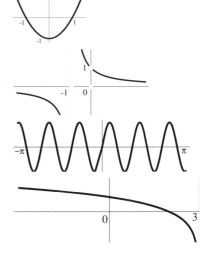

15.

fog   *gof*

17.

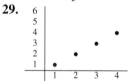   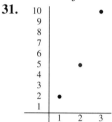

goh   *fo(goh)*   *(fog)oh*

19. $X = \{x \mid x \leq 3\}$, $Y = \{y \mid y \geq 0\}$, $f^{-1}(x) = 3 - x^2$

21. $X = Y = \mathbb{R} - \{1/2\}$, $f^{-1}(x) = f(x)$

23. $X = \{x \mid x \geq 0\}$, $Y = \{y \mid y \geq 1\}$, $f^{-1}(x) = (\log_3 x)^2$

25. Not an injection   **27.** Not an injection

29.   **31.**

33. $f \circ g(x) = x^2 - 2x$, $g \circ f(x) = x^2 - 2$, $f \circ f(x) = x^4 - 2x^2$, $g \circ f \circ g(x) = x^2 - 2x - 1$

35. $f^{-1}(n) = f(n)$ **39.** Bijective, $f^{-1}(x) = \sqrt[3]{x} + 2$

41. Injective only   **43.** Neither need be bijective

49. Domain $= (-\infty, -1] \cup [1, \infty)$ and the Image $= [-\pi, -\pi/2] \cup [0, \pi/2)$ or $[0, \pi/2) \cup (\pi/2, \pi]$; $y = \text{Sec}^{-1}$ if $x = \sec y$.

51. $x = 1$ **53.** $\text{Sin}^{-1} x + \text{Cos}^{-1} x = \pi/2$

55.   **57.**

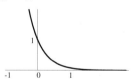   

59. $x = 256$ **61.** $x = \log_e \sqrt{2} = (\log_e 2)/2$

63. $x = 1/\sqrt[3]{5}$ **65.** $e^{x \log_e x}$

67. About 13%   **69.** 18 radians or about 3 turns

71. (i) 0, (ii) $f(-x) = -f(x)$, (iii) na, (iv) na, (v) ra

73. $f(x) = 2^x$ **75.** $f(x) = 0$

79. $\begin{pmatrix} 1 & 2 & 3 & 4 \\ 3 & 2 & 1 & 4 \end{pmatrix}$ **81.** $\begin{pmatrix} 1 & 2 & 3 & 4 \\ 3 & 4 & 2 & 1 \end{pmatrix}$

83. $\begin{pmatrix} 1 & 2 & 3 & 4 \\ 4 & 2 & 1 & 3 \end{pmatrix}$ **85.** $\begin{pmatrix} 1 & 2 & 3 & 4 \\ 3 & 1 & 2 & 4 \end{pmatrix}$

PROBLEM SET 5, page 143

87. $ad - bc \neq 0$ and $a = -d$ or $a = d, b = c = 0$

89. $(2, 1), (3, 2), (3, 1), (4, 3), (4, 2), (4, 1)$

91.

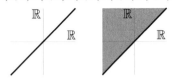

93. Call the number and see who answers. Then check this name in the telephone directory to see if it corresponds to the given number.

95. f does have an inverse; f can be shown to be monotone increasing by either using the calculus, or directly. It is difficult to find an equation for the inverse function.

97. $n!/(n - r)!$

107. \$57.04

111. 2.7183

113. (ij)

115. One form is $(13) \circ (12)$.

119. When $\text{GCD}(a, b) = 1$

EXERCISE SET 6, page 161

3. $(25, 323), (265, 323)$

5. $(5, 10379), (8141, 10379)$

7. $(4493, 7663)$

9. $(621, 47083)$

13. 71 and 97

15. 1291 and 2131

17. 115

19. 3884

21. 2

23. 4218

25. 833

27. 2469

29. 2210

31. 23

33. 19

35. 143

37. 65018

39. About 2.5 minutes

PROBLEM SET 6, page 163

47. (ii) 7

51. 1 and 106 (mod 133)

EXERCISE SET 7, page 193

1. 2

3. $3 + 11i$

5. 3

7. $13 + i$

9. $2 + 6i$

11. $(2 - i)/5$

13. $1 - i$

15. i

17. 0

19. $2 - 11i$

21. $i/5$

23. 4 and -7

25. -3 and 0

27. $3 + 2i$ and $\sqrt{13}$

29. i and 1

31. $2 - \frac{i}{\sqrt{2}}$ and $\frac{3\sqrt{2}}{2}$

33.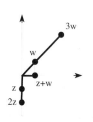

35.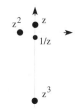

37.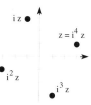

39. $(\sqrt{2}, 7\pi/4)$

41. $(2, 4\pi/3)$

43. $(-\sqrt{6}/2, \sqrt{6}/2)$

45. $(-1/2, -\sqrt{3}/2)$

47. $8(\cos \pi + i \sin \pi)$

49. $2(\cos \frac{3\pi}{2} + i \sin \frac{3\pi}{2})$

51. $\frac{\sqrt{6}}{3}(\cos \frac{\pi}{4} + i \sin \frac{\pi}{4})$

53. 4

55. $-\sqrt{2} - \sqrt{2}i$

57. 3 and $\frac{3\pi}{2}$

59. 2^{15} and $\frac{3\pi}{2}$

61. $0, 1$ or $(-1 \pm \sqrt{3}i)/2$

63. $(\sqrt{3} + i)/2$

65. $(-1 + \sqrt{3}i)/2048$

67. $-7/9$

71. $\pm 1, \pm i$

73. $\frac{\pm 1 \pm i}{\sqrt{2}}$

75. $\pm \frac{\sqrt[4]{2}}{2}(1 + \sqrt{3}i)$
$\pm \frac{\sqrt[4]{2}}{2}(\sqrt{3} - i)$

77. $\pm \frac{(1+i)}{\sqrt{2}}$

79. $\frac{1 \pm \sqrt{111}i}{14}$

81. $\frac{-i \pm \sqrt{15}}{8}$

83. $\frac{1+i}{\sqrt[3]{2}}$
$\frac{-1 - i \pm \sqrt{3}(1 - i)}{2\sqrt[3]{2}}$

89.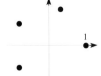

91.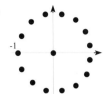

93.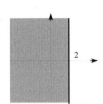

95.

97.

99.

101.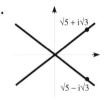

103.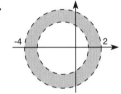

105. $e^{(\log_e 2 + 3i\pi/2)}$

107. $e^{\log_e 3}$

PROBLEM SET 7, page 197

109. $(-\sqrt{3} - 3i)/2\sqrt{2}$

111. The sum of the squares of the diagonals of a parallelogram equals the sum of the squares of its sides.

113.

115.

119. 0 and $\operatorname{cis}(2k\pi/n)$ for $k = 0, 1, 2, \ldots, n - 1$ and $\mathbb{R}$, if $n = 2$

127. $\pm 4 \pm i$

129. $\pm(1 - i), \pm(1 + i)/\sqrt{2}$

131. $U = \frac{e^{ax}}{a^2+b^2}(a\cos bx + b\sin bx) + C, \quad V = \frac{e^{ax}}{a^2+b^2}(a\sin bx - b\cos bx) + C$

135.

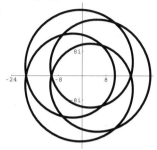

137. $(\sqrt{5}-1)/4$

EXERCISE SET 8, page 231

1. $2x^3 + 2x^2 - 9x, 2x^3 - 5x + 2, 2x^5 - 3x^4 - 11x^3 + 14x^2 + 5x - 1$

3. $2x^2 + 2, -2\sqrt{2}x, x^4 + 1$

5. $x^4 + x^3 + x^2, x^4 + 2x^3 + x^2 + 2x + 2, x^7 + x^2 + x + 2$

7. $3x, 4x^2 + 4x + 3, x^4 + 2x^3 + x^2 + 4x + 4$

9. No; yes

11. $x^3, x^3 + 1, x^3 + x, x^3 + x + 1, x^3 + x^2, x^3 + x^2 + 1, x^3 + x^2 + x, x^3 + x^2 + x + 1$

13. $1, -2, 5/3$

15. $1, -1, (-1 + \sqrt{41})/4, (-1 - \sqrt{41})/4$

17. $x + 3$ and $7x - 4$ **19.** $x^2 + \frac{1}{2}x + \frac{1}{2}$ and 0

21. $x^2 + 1 + i$ and $2 - i$ **23.** $2x$ and $x + 2$

25. $x^7 + x^4 + x^2 + x + 1$ and x **27.** No

29. -412 **31.** $-43 + 40i$

33. $1915/243$ **35.** Yes

37. $p = m^3 - 2m, q = m^2 - 1$ **39.** $1, 1$

41. No solutions   **43.** No solutions

45. 2 **49.** $x^4 - 14x^2 + 9$

51. $-1/2, \sqrt{2}, \sqrt{2}, -\sqrt{2}, -\sqrt{2}$ **53.** $-1, -4/3, -3/2$

55. $0, 1 + i, 1 - i, -1 + i, -1 - i$ **57.** $2 - \sqrt{3}, 2 - \sqrt{3}, 2 + \sqrt{3}, 2 + \sqrt{3}$

59. $x^4 - 14x^3 + 69x^2 - 140x + 98$ **61.** $-1 - \sqrt{2}, -1 + \sqrt{2}, \sqrt{3}i, -\sqrt{3}i$

63. $5 + i, 5 - i, \sqrt{3}, -\sqrt{3}$ **65.** In $\mathbb{Q}[x]$ only

67. Four real solutions; the rational solution -1 and three irrational solutions, one between -2 and -1, one between 3 and 4 and one between 5 and 6

69. One irrational solution between 1 and 2

71. $3/4, (3 - \sqrt{5})/2 \approx .4$ and $(3 + \sqrt{5})/2 \approx 2.6$

73. $-.2$ **75.** $-4 < x < 1$ and $1 < x < 7$

77. $x < (1 - \sqrt{41})/4, -1 < x < 1/2$ and $(1 + \sqrt{41})/4 < x$

79. $2/3$ with multiplicity 3 **81.** $1 \pm \sqrt{2}$, each of multiplicity 2

83. $a = n, b = -n - 1$

85. $x^2 + i$

87. $\frac{12}{4x-1} - \frac{3}{x}$

89. $\frac{3}{4x-1} + \frac{2}{x+1}$

91. $\frac{1}{x+5} - \frac{2}{(x+1)^2}$

93. $\frac{2x+3}{x^2+x+1}$

95. -14 in $\mathbb{Q}$ and $\mathbb{R}$; $-14, (-1 \pm \sqrt{3}i)/2$ in $\mathbb{C}$; $0, 2, 4$ in $\mathbb{Z}_7$

97. $(x - 2)(2x^2 + 6x + 1)$ in $\mathbb{Q}[x]$; $2(x - 2)\left(x + \frac{3-\sqrt{7}}{2}\right)\left(x + \frac{3+\sqrt{7}}{2}\right)$ in $\mathbb{R}[x]$ and $\mathbb{C}[x]$; $2(x + 1)^2(x + 2)$ in $\mathbb{Z}_3[x]$

99. $(x+1)(2x+1)\left(x + \frac{1+\sqrt{3}i}{2}\right)\left(x + \frac{1-\sqrt{3}i}{2}\right)$ in $\mathbb{C}[x]$; $(x+1)(2x+1)(x^2+x+1)$ in $\mathbb{Q}[x]$ and $\mathbb{R}[x]$; $2(x + 1)(x + 3)(x^2 + x + 1)$ in $\mathbb{Z}_3[x]$

PROBLEM SET 8, page 235

109. $x^2 - 96x + 4$

111. $x^3 - 10x^2 - 11x - 25$

113. When $\mathbb{F}$ is infinite

117. (i) $\triangle f(n) = \binom{n}{r-1}$

119. $x, x + 1, x^2 + x + 1, x^3 + x + 1, x^3 + x^2 + 1, x^4 + x + 1, x^4 + x^3 + 1,$ $x^4 + x^3 + x^2 + x + 1$

121. $x^n + x$

123. Irrational

127. 4

129. No rational roots

133. $\cos \frac{2\pi}{5} = \frac{\sqrt{5}-1}{4}$

139. Prove the result by induction, using the facts that $f'_n(x) = f_{n-1}(x)$ and that $f_{2r}(x) = x^{2r}/(2r)! > 0$ whenever $f'_{2r}(x) = 0$.

141. $1 < x < 2$ and $3 < x < 4$

143. $1.3 < x < 2.3$

151. $s(x) = 1 + x, t(x) = -x$

153. $m = -1, 7, 5/3$; if $m = -1$, then $f(x) = (x + 1)^2(x - 3)$ in $\mathbb{Q}[x]$, $\mathbb{R}[x]$ and $\mathbb{C}[x]$; if $m = 7$, then $f(x) = (x - 1)(x^2 + 8x + 3)$ in $\mathbb{Q}[x]$ and $f(x) = (x - 1)(x + 4 - \sqrt{13})(x + 4 + \sqrt{13})$ in $\mathbb{R}[x]$ and $\mathbb{C}[x]$

155. (b) $(x - 2)^2(x^2 - 2x + 2)$ in $\mathbb{Q}[x]$ and $\mathbb{R}[x]$; $(x - 2)^2(x - 1 + i)(x - 1 - i)$ in $\mathbb{C}[x]$; $(x + 1)(x + 2)(x + 3)^2$ in $\mathbb{Z}_5[x]$

159. $(x+1)(x^2-2)(x^2+x+1)$ over the rationals; $(x+1)(x-\sqrt{2})(x+\sqrt{2})(x^2+x+1)$ over the reals and $(x + 1)(x - \sqrt{2})(x + \sqrt{2})\left(x + \frac{1+\sqrt{3}i}{2}\right)\left(x + \frac{1-\sqrt{3}i}{2}\right)$ over the complex numbers

Glossary of Symbols

Symbol	Meaning	Page
$\forall$	for all	8
$\mathbb{C}$	Complex numbers	167
$C(n, r)$	n choose r	86
$_nC_r$	n choose r	86
cis θ	$\cos \theta + i \sin \theta$	179
$\cos^{-1} x$	inverse cosine of x	131
$\deg f(x)$	degree of $f(x)$	203
e	base of natural logarithms ≈ 2.71828	136
$e^{i\theta}$	$\cos \theta + i \sin \theta$	183
$\exists$	there exists	9
$\mathbb{F}$	Field such as $\mathbb{Q}$, $\mathbb{R}$, $\mathbb{C}$, or $\mathbb{Z}_p$, for p prime	201
$\mathbb{F}[x]$	set of polynomials in x with coefficients from $\mathbb{F}$	202
$\text{GCD}(a, b)$	Greatest Common Divisor of a and b	22
$\text{GCD}(f(x), g(x))$	Greatest Common Divisor of $f(x)$ and $g(x)$	225
i	complex number $(0, 1)$ that satisfies $i^2 = -1$	167
iff	if and only if	5
$\text{LCM}(a, b)$	Least Common Multiple of a and b	45
$\log_b x$	logarithmic function	135
$\mathbb{N}$	Nonnegative integers	236
$\emptyset$	empty set	8
$\mathbb{P}$	Positive integers or natural numbers	7
$\mathbb{P}_n$	first n positive integers $\{1, 2, 3, \ldots, n\}$	125
$\mathcal{P}(X)$	set of all subsets of X	141
$\mathbb{Q}$	rational numbers	100
$\mathbb{R}$	Real numbers	7, 102
$\mathbb{R}_{>0}$	positive real numbers	134
$\mathbb{R}_{\geq 0}$	nonnegative real numbers	118
$\mathcal{S}_n$	set of permutations of $\{1, 2, \ldots, n\}$	137
$\sin^{-1} x$	inverse sine of x	130
$\tan^{-1} x$	inverse tangent of x	131
$\mathbb{Z}$	integers	7
$\mathbb{Z}_m$	integers modulo m	56

$\prod$	product	92
$\sum$	sum	80
$\phi(n)$	Euler ϕ-function	48
$\in$	belongs to	7
$\notin$	does not belong to	7
$\subseteq$	is contained in	8
$\supseteq$	contains	8
$\cap$	intersection	8
$\cup$	union	8
$\approx$	approximately equal to	136, 157
$\Longrightarrow$	implies	5, 7
$\Longleftrightarrow$	if and only if	5, 7
$\#X$	number of elements or cardinality of the set X	125
$g \circ f$	composition of functions	118
$a\|b$	a divides b	19
$a \equiv b \pmod{m}$	a is congruent to b modulo m	49
aRb	a is related to b	54
S/R	quotient set of S by R	56
$\binom{n}{r}$	n choose r	86
$\begin{pmatrix} 1 & 2 & \dots & n \\ \sigma_1 & \sigma_2 & \dots & \sigma_n \end{pmatrix}$	permutation of $1, 2, \dots, n$	137
$n!$	factorial n	78
$f : X \to Y$	function f with domain X and codomain Y	113
$x \mapsto y$	x maps to y	117
b^x	exponential function	132
a^{-1}	inverse of a	58
$\sqrt[n]{a}$	nth root of a	103
$a^{m/n}$	nth root of a^m	103
f^{-1}	inverse of the function f	120
$f(x)$	image of x under f	113
$f(X)$	image of the set X under f	113
$X \times Y$	Cartesian product of the sets X and Y	115, 8
$\overline{z}$	conjugate of z	171
$|z|$	modulus or absolute value of z	116, 171
$\lfloor x \rfloor$	greatest integer less than or equal to x	47, 96, 140
$[a]$	equivalence class or congruence class containing a	54
$\{x\}$	set containing x	7
$(r_n \dots r_1 r_0)_b$	base b expansion	36
$b.\dot{a}_1\dot{a}_2$	recurrent decimal	106
(x, y)	Cartesian coordinates	177
(r, θ)	polar coordinates	177
$\square$	end of a proof or example (Q.E.D.)	6

Index